LIVING TODAY

LEAVING CERTIFICATE
HOME ECONOMICS

MARGARET P. KINSELLA &

MARGUERITE O'BRIEN

GILL & MACMILLAN

Gill & Macmillan
Hume Avenue
Park West
Dublin 12
www.gillmacmillan.ie

© Margaret P. Kinsella and Marguerite O'Brien, 2009

978 07171 4566 9

Design and typesetting by Anú Design, Tara
Artwork by RR Info Tech Ltd and Peter Bull
Index compiled by Cover to Cover

The paper used in this book is made from the wood pulp of managed forests. For every tree felled, at least one tree is planted, thereby renewing natural resources.

Higher Level Material

A green vertical bar line is placed on the left side of any material that is relevant to Higher Level students only (e.g. *Essential amino acids and non-essential amino acids* on page 5).

Contents

Food Science and Nutrition ● ● ●

1.	Food Choices	2
2.	Protein	5
3.	Carbohydrates	16
4.	Lipids	27
5.	Vitamins	36
6.	Minerals	45
7.	Water	52

Diet and Health ● ● ●

8.	Energy	54
9.	Dietary Guidelines	57
10.	Dietary and Food Requirements	60

Food Commodities ● ● ●

11.	Meat	76
12.	Poultry	82
13.	Fish	84
14.	Eggs	90
15.	Milk	99
16.	Butter	106
17.	Cream	108
18.	Yoghurt	110
19.	Cheese	112

20.	Alternative Protein Foods	115
21.	Fruit	118
22.	Vegetables	121
23.	Nuts and Legumes	127
24.	Cereals	129
25.	Fats and Oils	135
26.	Meal Management and Planning	140
27.	Food Preparation and Cooking Processes	141
28.	Food Preparation and Cooking Equipment	159
29.	Recipe Modification	160
30.	Aesthetic Awareness of Food	161
31.	Sensory Analysis	163
32.	The Irish Diet	167
33.	The Irish Food Industry	170

Food Processing and Packaging ● ● ●

34.	Food Processing	176
35.	Food Packaging	180
36.	Food Labelling	184
37.	Food Additives	186
38.	Microbiology	193
39.	Food Spoilage	206
40.	Food Preservation	212
41.	Food Hygiene and Safety	224
42.	National Food Safety Agencies	229
43.	Food Laws	231

Family Resource Management ● ● ●

44.	Family Resource Management	234
45.	Managing Household Financial Resources	241
46.	Housing Finance	256
47.	Household Technology	262

48.   Textiles   273

49.   Consumer Studies   279

The Family in Society ● ● ●

50.   Introducing Sociological Concepts   298

51.   The Family   300

52.   Marriage   307

53.   The Family as a Caring Unit   313

54.   Family Law   320

Elective 1
Home Design and Management ● ● ●

1.   Housing   324

2.   Designing the House Interior   343

3.   The Energy-Efficient Home   371

4.   Systems and Services   382

Elective 2
Social Studies ● ● ●

1.   Social Change and the Family   408

2.   Education   412

3.   Work   427

4.   Unemployment   440

5.   Leisure   443

6.   Poverty   449

Recipes

459

Index

479

eTest.ie – what is it?

A revolutionary new website-based testing platform that facilitates a social learning environment for Irish schools. Both students and teachers can use it, either independently or together, to make the whole area of testing easier, more engaging and more productive for all.

Students – do you want to know how well you are doing? Then take an eTest!

At eTest.ie, you can access tests put together by the author of this textbook. You get instant results, so they're a brilliant way to quickly check just how your study or revision is going.

Since each eTest is based on your textbook, if you don't know an answer, you'll find it in your book.

Register now and you can save all of your eTest results to use as a handy revision aid or to simply compare with your friends' results!

Teachers – eTest.ie will engage your students and help them with their revision, while making the jobs of reviewing their progress and homework easier and more convenient for all of you.

Register now to avail of these exciting features:

- Create tests easily using our pre-set questions OR you can create your own questions
- Develop your own online learning centre for each class that you teach
- Keep track of your students' performances

eTest.ie has a wide choice of question types for you to choose from, most of which can be graded automatically, like multiple-choice, jumbled-sentence, matching, ordering and gap-fill exercises. This free resource allows you to create class groups, delivering all the functionality of a VLE (Virtual Learning Environment) with the ease of communication that is brought by social networking.

Section

FOOD SCIENCE AND NUTRITION

1 Food Choices

2 Protein

3 Carbohydrates

4 Lipids

5 Vitamins

6 Minerals

7 Water

1 Food Choices

Factors Affecting Food Choices

Many factors affect our choice of foods. These include: culture, availability, nutritional awareness, sensory aspects, a person's eating patterns, marketing and advertising, cost and health status.

CAN SAM Cook Healthy?

Learning Links Learning Links Learning Links

Culture:

* Different countries have their own food culture and eat certain types of food, e.g. Italian, Chinese and French.
* Religious beliefs have an influence on food choices, e.g. Hindus are often vegetarians; Muslims don't eat pork.
* Due to immigration and travel, world cuisine restaurants have opened up. This has also been influenced by television programmes.

Availability:

* Different foods are more available at different times of the year, e.g. Brussels sprouts at Christmas.
* The importation of food, including canned and frozen food, makes food available all year around.
* People living in rural areas may not have access to all available foods and may have a limited choice.

Nutritional awareness:

* People today tend to be more health conscious.
* People read food labels and eat foods that are healthy.
* Subjects like Home Economics and SPHE, as well as television programmes, make people more nutritionally aware.
* People are becoming aware of the importance of having a healthy diet.

Sensory aspects:

* The saying 'we eat with our eyes' is very true, as the way something looks can affect whether or not we'll eat it.
* Other factors, like smell and taste, influence our food choices.

Fig 1.1: A Hindu family having a meal.

A person's eating patterns:

* Busy lifestyles in families affect what food we choose to eat.
* There has been a huge increase in fast food and convenience food.

Fig 1.2: Healthy food.

* The type of work someone does and the hours they work also influences meal times and their choice of food.
* Other influencing factors include a person's leisure pursuits, their moral beliefs, etc.

Marketing and advertising:

* The ways in which food products are marketed and advertised have been shown to influence what we choose to buy.
* Advertising campaigns aim to increase awareness of a product with a specific target market in mind.

* The different advertising media used include television, radio, billboards and magazines.
* Marketing strategies influence our food choices with clever supermarket layouts, e.g. luxuries at eye level, special promotions and tasting sessions in supermarkets.

Cost:

* People's budgets have always been a huge influence on what foods they choose.
* Families from lower socio-economic backgrounds will have less money available for luxury food items.
* People with a greater disposable income often tend to spend money eating out and travelling abroad, both of which enable people to widen their preference of different foods.

Health status:

* A person's state of health will influence what foods they eat.
* Special dietary needs must be taken into consideration when choosing foods, e.g. individuals with high cholesterol will choose low-fat products.
* Other examples include people with coeliac disease, who have to restrict their gluten intake.
* Pregnant women, the elderly and people recovering from illness all have to be aware of their particular health status when choosing food.

➡ NUTRITIONAL TERMS

Term	Explanation
Macronutrients	• These nutrients are required by the body in large amounts. • They include protein, fat and carbohydrates.
Micronutrients	• These nutrients are required by the body in small amounts. • They include vitamins and minerals.
Elemental composition	• The elements that a nutrient is composed of, e.g. lipid is made up of carbon, hydrogen and oxygen.

Term	Explanation
Chemical formula	• The formula or equation that explains how a nutrient is formed, e.g. the formula for glucose is $C_6H_{12}O_6$.
Composition	• The percentage of the nutrient found in the food.
Biological function	• The role of the nutrient specific to the body.
Deficiency diseases	• These occur when the body lacks a particular nutrient. The symptoms vary according to the nutrient.
Classification	• Nutrients can be categorised or grouped according to a number of similarities.
Property	• Each nutrient has specific properties which are the distinguishing feature of the nutrient.
Dietetic value	• This indicates the value of a particular food to an individual's diet.
Malnutrition	• This is referred to as an imbalance of nutrients. It generally occurs when an individual lacks a particular nutrient.
Undernutrition	• This occurs when there is a total lack of nutrients. • It is common in underdeveloped countries where starvation can be widespread.
Metabolism	• This is the sum of the chemical reactions that occur within the body. • There are two forms of metabolism: anabolism and catabolism. • Anabolism is a reaction which requires energy to synthesise new materials, e.g. hormones. • Catabolism provides energy when food is broken down.
Metabolic rate	• This is the rate at which an individual uses energy. • Basal metabolic rate (BMR) is the minimum amount of energy required to live, i.e. for breathing. • BMR is measured when a person is completely at rest twelve hours after eating.
Enzymes	• These are biological catalysts which speed up or slow down chemical reactions that occur within the body without themselves changing. • Each enzyme has a specific function. • An enzyme requires a specific environment in order to function correctly, e.g. correct temperature and pH.

Protein 2

Protein Composition

The **elemental composition** of a protein:

✳ Carbon.
✳ Hydrogen.
✳ Oxygen.
✳ Nitrogen.
✳ With trace amounts of sulphur, iron and phosphorus.

The **chemical composition** of a protein:

✳ Protein is composed of amino acids.
✳ Amino acids are held together by peptide links.
✳ Each amino acid contains hydrogen, carbon, variable, an amino group and a carboxyl group.
✳ **R** denotes the variable group and this changes for each amino acid.

Amino Acids

Basic structure of an amino acid:

H = Hydrogen
C = Carbon
R = Variable
NH₂ = Amino group
COOH = Carboxyl group

$$R - \underset{\underset{NH_2}{|}}{\overset{\overset{H}{|}}{C}} - COOH \qquad H - \underset{\underset{NH_2}{|}}{\overset{\overset{H}{|}}{C}} - COOH$$

Fig 2.1: Basic structure of an amino acid.

Example of an amino acid: glycine.

Essential amino acids and non–essential amino acids:

✳ There are over twenty amino acids found in food.
✳ Amino acids are divided into two groups: essential amino acids and non-essential amino acids.
✳ An essential amino acid is an amino acid that is not manufactured in the body and that therefore should be taken in through food.
✳ There are ten essential amino acids. These are:
  ● Valine.
  ● Lysine.
  ● Leucine.
  ● Isoleucine.
  ● Methionine.   adults   children
  ● Threonine.
  ● Tryptophan.
  ● Phenylalanine.
  ● Arginine.
  ● Histidine.

Adults only need the first eight of these essential amino acids, but **children** need all ten.

Valerie **L**arkin **L**oves **I**mitating **M**ichael **T**homas **T**elling **P**eople **A**bout **H**istory

Learning Links Learning Links Learning Links

* A non-essential amino acid is an amino acid that is manufactured in the body and is therefore not obtained from food.
* There are ten non-essential amino acids. These are:
  * Alanine.
  * Aspargine.
  * Aspartic acid.
  * Cysteine.
  * Glutamic acid.
  * Glycine.
  * Ornithine.
  * Proline.
  * Serine.
  * Tyrosine.

Peptide links:

* A peptide link is formed when two amino acids are joined together.
* The OH from the carboxyl group of one amino acid joins with the H from the amino group of a second amino acid.
* The H and the OH combine to form a molecule of water.

* This loss of water is known as a condensation reaction.
* The opposite of a condensation reaction is hydrolysis, whereby water is added to separate amino acids (occurs during digestion).
* Two amino acids joined together is known as a dipeptide.
* A chain of amino acids joined together is known as a polypeptide chain.

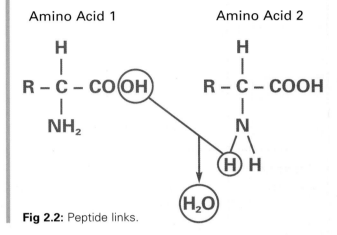

Fig 2.2: Peptide links.

Protein Structures

There are three distinct protein structures. They are the primary, secondary and tertiary structures.

Primary Structure	• This is a sequence of amino acids held together by peptide links. • Insulin is an example of a primary structure of protein. 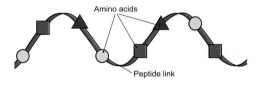 **Fig 2.3:** Primary structure of protein.
Secondary Structure	• This occurs when there is folding of the primary structure. • This results in definite shape and structure. • In this structure there are cross-links. The two main types of cross-links are disulphide links and hydrogen bonds. ➡ **Disulphide Link**: • When two sulphur molecules are joined together, a disulphide link is formed. ➡ **Hydrogen bonds**: • A molecule of hydrogen from the amino group is attracted to oxygen from the carboxyl group. A hydrogen bond is formed, e.g. collagen.

Secondary Structure	• The amino acid cysteine contains sulphur and when two cysteine amino acids join together a disulphide link is formed. • This can occur on the same polypeptide chain or between two polypeptide chains. 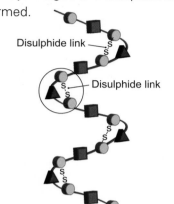 **Fig 2.4:** Disulphide link. 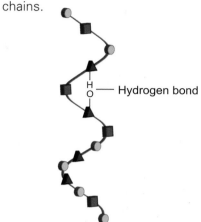 **Fig 2.5:** Hydrogen bonds.
Tertiary Structure	• This is the excessive folding of a secondary structure. • It is generally three-dimensional. • Tertiary structures can be either fibrous or globular. • **Fibrous** is straight, coiled or zigzag in shape. • **Fibrous** structure is insoluble in water. Examples include gluten in wheat and elastin in meat. • **Globular** is spherical in shape. • **Globular** structure is soluble in water. Examples include myoglobin in meat and haemoglobin in blood. 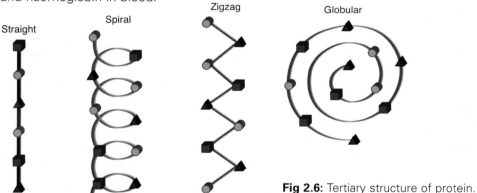 **Fig 2.6:** Tertiary structure of protein.

Classification of Proteins

Proteins are classified as follows.

✱ **Simple proteins**:
These occur in both plants and animals.

✱ **Conjugated proteins**:
These are globular proteins which are joined with non–protein molecules.

✱ **Derived proteins**:
These are proteins that are formed due to chemical or enzymatic action on the protein itself. An example of this is when the protein caseinogen is digested, the enzyme rennin works on this protein to produce a derived protein, casein.

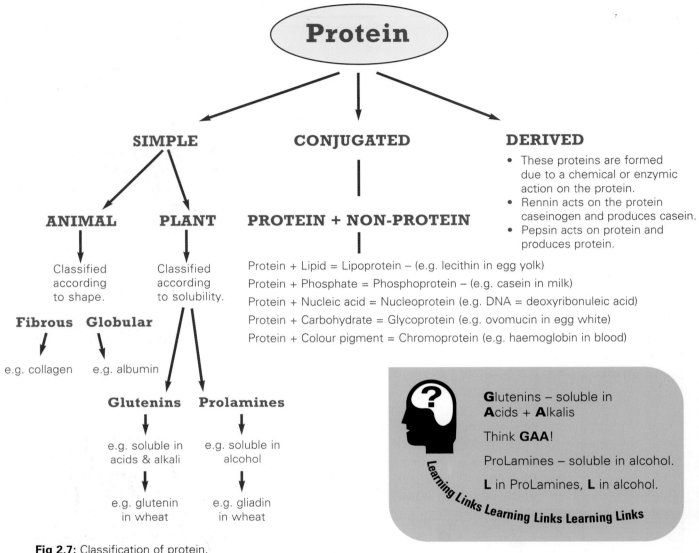

Protein

SIMPLE

ANIMAL
Classified according to shape.

Fibrous
↓
e.g. collagen

Globular
↓
e.g. albumin

PLANT
Classified according to solubility.

Glutenins
↓
e.g. soluble in acids & alkali
↓
e.g. glutenin in wheat

Prolamines
↓
e.g. soluble in alcohol
↓
e.g. gliadin in wheat

CONJUGATED

PROTEIN + NON-PROTEIN

Protein + Lipid = Lipoprotein – (e.g. lecithin in egg yolk)

Protein + Phosphate = Phosphoprotein – (e.g. casein in milk)

Protein + Nucleic acid = Nucleoprotein (e.g. DNA = deoxyribonuleic acid)

Protein + Carbohydrate = Glycoprotein (e.g. ovomucin in egg white)

Protein + Colour pigment = Chromoprotein (e.g. haemoglobin in blood)

DERIVED

- These proteins are formed due to a chemical or enzymic action on the protein.
- Rennin acts on the protein caseinogen and produces casein.
- Pepsin acts on protein and produces protein.

Learning Links Learning Links Learning Links

Glutenins – soluble in **A**cids + **A**lkalis

Think **GAA**!

ProLamines – soluble in alcohol.

L in ProLamines, **L** in alcohol.

Fig 2.7: Classification of protein.

Sources of Protein

Protein is found in both animal and plant sources.

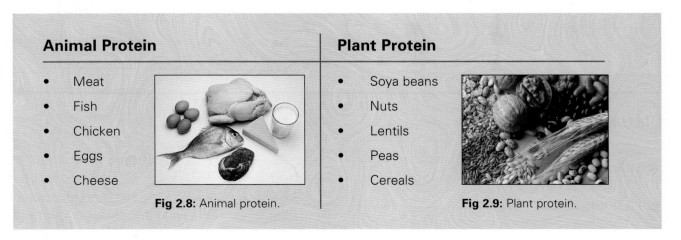

Animal Protein

- Meat
- Fish
- Chicken
- Eggs
- Cheese

Fig 2.8: Animal protein.

Plant Protein

- Soya beans
- Nuts
- Lentils
- Peas
- Cereals

Fig 2.9: Plant protein.

Some common proteins found in food are given below.

Food	Protein
• Cheese	• Caseinogen
• Milk	• Lactalbumin, caseinogen, lactoglobulin
• Eggs	• Ovalbumin, livetin, vitellin
• Fish	• Myosin, collagen, actin
• Meat fibres	• Myosin, actin, globulin
• Meat connective tissue	• Collagen. elastin
• Wheat	• Gluten

Biological Value of Protein

✱ Biological value is a measure of the quality of the protein.

✱ It is measured as a percentage (%).

✱ The biological value is established by the number of essential amino acids that are present in the protein.

There are two types: high biological value protein (HBV) and low biological value protein (LBV).

HBV Protein	LBV Protein
• HBV proteins contain **all** the essential amino acids.	• LBV protein **lacks one or more** of the essential amino acids.
• These are also called **complete** proteins.	• These are also called **incomplete** proteins.
• HBV proteins generally come from **animal sources**.	• LBV proteins generally come from **plant sources**.
• Soya beans are an exception (they are of plant origin but are a source of HBV protein).	• Gelatine is an exception (it is an animal protein but is a source of LBV protein).

HBV and LBV Foods

HBV Foods	LBV Foods
• Eggs = 100%	• Rice = 67%
• Milk = 95%	• Wheat = 53%
• Meat and fish = 80–90%	• Maize = 40%
• Soya beans = 74%	• Gelatine = 0%

Supplementary/Complementary Value

✱ When two low biological protein foods are combined together they are said to give all the essential amino acids.

✱ This is known as supplementary/complementary value, e.g. beans on toast.

	high		**low**
Beans	= ↑ lysine	Beans	= ↓ methionine
	low		**high**
Toast	= ↓ lysine	Toast	= ↑ methionine

Properties of Protein

Denaturation:

✱ Denaturation is a change in the nature of the protein.

✱ The protein chain unfolds, causing a change to the structure.

✱ Denaturation is caused by heat, chemicals and agitation.

✱ It is often an irreversible process.

Heat:

✱ Most proteins coagulate/set when heated.

✱ E.g. egg white coagulates at 60°C; egg yolk coagulates at 68°C.

Chemicals:

✱ Acids, alkali, alcohol and enzymes cause changes to the protein structure.

✱ E.g. lemon juice added to milk causes the milk protein caseinogen to curdle.

✱ E.g. enzyme rennin coagulates milk protein caseinogen in the stomach.

Agitation:

✱ This is also known as mechanical action.

✱ It involves whipping or whisking the protein.

✱ This results in the protein chain unfolding and partial coagulation.

Solubility:

✱ Proteins are generally insoluble in water.

✱ There are two exceptions – egg white in cold water and connective tissue, which is converted to gelatine in hot water.

Maillard reaction:

✱ Maillard reaction is also known as non-enzymic browning. It occurs when food is roasted, baked or grilled.

> **Amino Acid + Carbohydrate + Dry Heat = Brown Colour**

✱ Examples include roast potatoes, toast.

Elasticity:

✱ Certain proteins have an elastic property, e.g. gluten, the protein found in flour, enables bread to rise during cooking.

Foam formation:

✱ When egg white is whisked, air bubbles are formed as the protein chains unravel.

✱ Whisking also produces heat, which slightly sets the egg white.

✱ This foam will collapse after a while, unless it is subjected to heat.

✱ This property is used to make meringues.

Gel formation:

✱ Collagen, when heated, forms gelatine.

✱ Gelatine can absorb large amounts of water and, when heated, forms a sol.

✱ On cooling, this sol becomes solid and a gel is formed.

✱ A gel is a semi-solid viscous solution.

✱ All gels have a three-dimensional network whereby water becomes trapped.

✱ This property is used in making cheesecakes and soufflés.

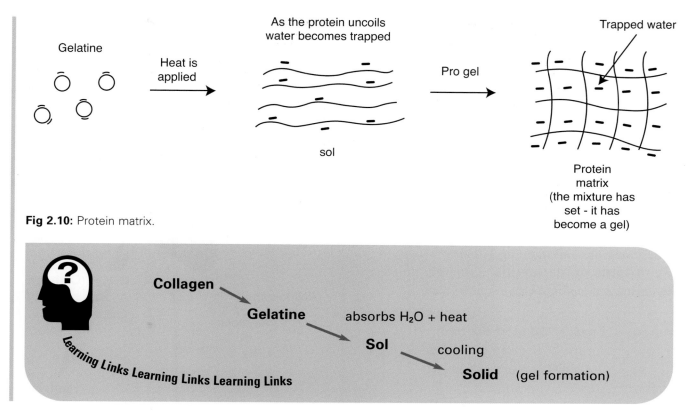

Fig 2.10: Protein matrix.

Collagen → Gelatine absorbs H₂O + heat → Sol cooling → Solid (gel formation)

Learning Links Learning Links Learning Links

Heat and Protein

The effects of dry and moist heat on protein are shown below.

Dry Heat	Moist Heat
• Maillard reaction • Coagulation • Colour change • Overcooking causes protein to be indigestible.	• Tenderising meat; collagen changes to gelatine • Coagulation • Colour change • Overcooking causes protein to be indigestible.

Functions of Protein

There are three functions of protein: structural, physiologically active and nutrient.

Structural	Physiologically active	Nutrient
• These are used for growth and repair, e.g. the production of cells, skin and muscle.	• These are used for the production of enzymes, hormones, antibodies, nucleoproteins and blood proteins.	• These provide the body with essential amino acids. • Excess protein is used for energy.

Deficiencies of Protein

There are five main consequences when protein is absent from a diet.

* Retarded growth.
* Delayed healing of wounds.
* Susceptibility to illness and infection.
* Kwashiorkor and marasmus.
* Lack of energy.

Kwashiorkor and marasmus are diseases found mainly in developing countries.

Symptoms of kwashiorkor: Retarded growth, skin conditions and thinning of hair.

Symptoms of marasmus: Extremely thin legs and arms, retarded growth, a sunken face.

> **Energy Value of Protein:**
> 1 gram of protein provides
> 4kcal/17kJ of energy.

RDA of Protein

Protein requirement is based on:

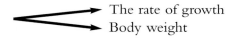

The rate of growth
Body weight

* Child 30–50g/day.
* Adolescent 60–80g/day.
* Adult 50–75g/day.
* Pregnant woman 70–85g/day.

Protein is essential for all those growing, in particular children and adolescents, and for pregnant women, lactating women and convalescents.

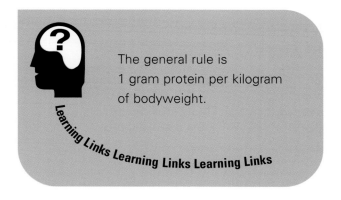

The general rule is 1 gram protein per kilogram of bodyweight.

Learning Links Learning Links Learning Links

Deamination

Deamination occurs when excess amino acids are broken down by the liver.

* The amino group (NH_2) is converted to ammonia which, in turn, is converted to urea.
* Urea is excreted by the body in urine.
* The carboxyl group (COOH) is oxidised to provide heat and energy.

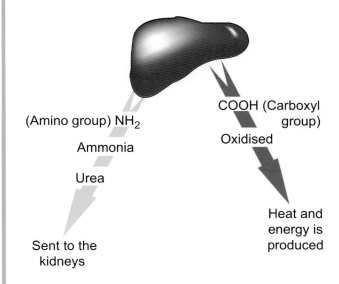

(Amino group) NH_2

Ammonia

Urea

Sent to the kidneys

COOH (Carboxyl group)

Oxidised

Heat and energy is produced

Fig 2.11: Deamination.

Digestion of Protein

The digestion of protein occurs in two main areas: **the stomach and small intestine**.

* The stomach contains two enzymes: pepsin and rennin.
* Pepsin acts on protein to form peptones (shorter chains of protein).
* Rennin acts on caseinogen to produce casein.
* Hydrochloric acid (HCl) present in the stomach denatures the protein.
* Further digestion of protein occurs in the duodenum, where the enzyme trypsin (a pancreatic enzyme) acts on protein to form peptides.
* Finally, the digestion of protein takes place in the ileum, where the enzyme peptidase acts on peptides and breaks them down into amino acids.

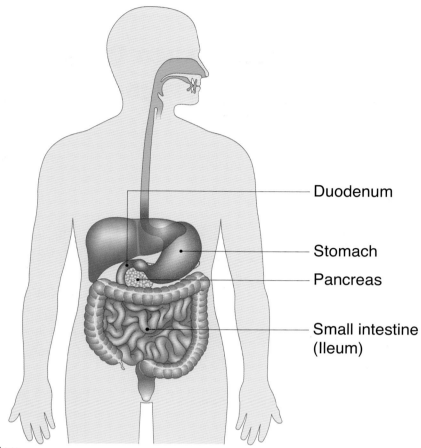

Fig 2.12: The human digestive system.

Organ/Gland	Secretion	Enzymes	Substrate	Product
• Stomach	• Gastric juice	• Pepsin • Rennin	• Protein • Caseinogen	• Peptones • Casein
• Pancreas	• Pancreatic juice	• Trypsin	• Peptones	• Peptides
• Ileum (part of small intestine)	• Intestinal juice	• Peptidase	• Peptides	• Amino acids

Absorption and Utilisation of Protein

✱ Amino acids pass into the blood capillaries of the villi in the small intestine.

✱ From here, they are carried to the liver via the portal vein.

✱ When the amino acids reach the liver, they are used in a number of different ways, including:

- To maintain and repair liver cells.
- To form new cells and repair tissues.
- Any excess proteins are deaminated in the liver.

Part Exam Question
2006 Higher Level

Questions

1. Name two proteins present in meat. (6)
2. Explain:
   (a) High biological protein.
   (b) Essential amino acid. (12)
3. Describe:
   (a) The primary structure of protein.
   (b) The secondary structure of protein. (24)

Answers

1. Name two proteins present in meat. (6)

   2 proteins @ 3 marks each = 6.

   • Myosin, actin, globulin – present in meat fibre.
   • Elastin, collagen – present in connective tissue of meat.

2. Explain:
   (a) High biological protein.
   (b) Essential amino acid. (12)

   (3 points @ 2 marks each) x 2 = 6 x 2 = 12.

   High biological value:
   • Biological value is a measure of the quality of the protein. Biological value is measured as a percentage (%).
   • The biological value is established by the number of essential amino acids that are present in the protein.
   • There are two types of biological value: high biological value and low biological value.

   • HBV protein contains all the essential amino acids.
   • These are generally found in animal sources.
   • They are also known as complete proteins.
   • Examples include meat, fish, eggs.
   • One exception is the soya bean, which is of 74% HBV.
   HBV foods:
   Eggs = 100%
   Milk = 95%
   Meat and fish = 80–90%

   Essential amino acid:
   An essential amino acid is an amino acid which is not manufactured in the body and therefore should be taken in through food. There are ten essential amino acids, including:
   • Valine.
   • Lysine.
   • Leucine.
   • Isoleucine.

3. Describe:
   (a) The primary structure of protein.
   (b) The secondary structure of protein. (24)

   (3 points @ 2 marks each) x 2 = 6 x 2 = 12.

   The primary structure of protein:
   • This is a sequence of amino acids held together by peptide links. Insulin is an example of a primary structure of protein.

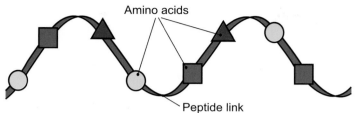

Amino acids

Peptide link

Fig 2.3: Structure of protein.

The secondary structure of protein:
This occurs when there is folding of the primary structure.

- This results in definite shape and structure.

- In the secondary structure there are cross-links. The two main types of cross-links are disulphide links and hydrogen bonds.

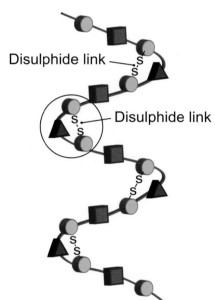

Disulphide link — S:S

Disulphide link — S:S

Fig 2.4: Disulphide links.

- When two sulphur molecules are joined together a disulphide link is formed.
- The amino acid cysteine contains sulphur and when two cysteine amino acids are joined together a disulphide link is formed.

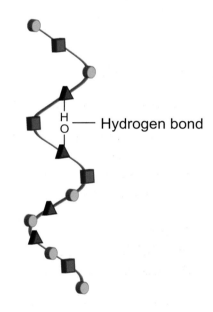

Hydrogen bond — H O

Fig 2.5: Hydrogen bonds.

- A molecule of hydrogen from the amino group is attracted to oxygen from the carboxyl group.
- A hydrogen bond is formed.
- An example is collagen.
- This can occur on the same polypeptide chain or between two polypeptide chains.

3 Carbohydrates

The Formation of Carbohydrates in Plants

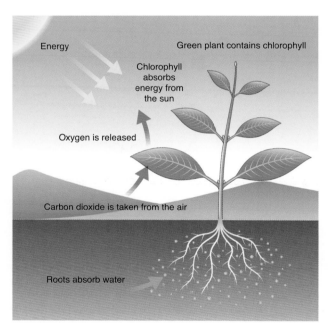

Energy

Green plant contains chlorophyll

Chlorophyll absorbs energy from the sun

Oxygen is released

Carbon dioxide is taken from the air

Roots absorb water

Fig 3.1: The process of photosynthesis.

Carbohydrates are formed in plants through the following process, which is known as **photosynthesis**.
* The roots absorb water from the soil.
* The leaves absorb carbon dioxide from the air.
* Chlorophyll (green pigment) in leaves absorbs energy from the sun.
* Sugar is made. The energy is used to create glucose from carbon dioxide and water.
* Oxygen is released into the air.

Carbon dioxide + Water + Chlorophyll $\rightarrow$ Glucose + Oxygen
energy

$$6CO_2 + 6H_2O + \text{Chlorophyll} \rightarrow C_6H_2O_6 + 6O_2 \text{ energy}$$

Fig 3.2: The equation for photosynthesis.

Elemental Composition

The elements that make up carbohydrates are:
* Carbon.
* Hydrogen.
* Oxygen.

Chemical Structure of Carbohydrates

There are three types of carbohydrates: monosaccharides, disaccharides and polysaccharides.

Monosaccharides:

* A monosaccharide contains one sugar unit.
* $C_6H_{12}O_6$ is the chemical formula of a mono-saccharide.
* Glucose, fructose and galactose are the three monosaccharides.

How to draw a monosaccharide:

Step One
Begin with the hexagon.

Step Two
At the top right corner insert oxygen.

Step Three
At the remaining corners of the hexagon insert carbon (C).

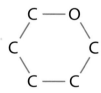

Step Four
From these carbons draw a line up and down.

Step Five
Carbons one, two and four are the same with H on top of C and OH underneath.

Step Six
Carbon three has OH on top and H on the bottom.

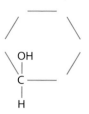

Step Seven
The last carbon has CH_2OH on top and H on the bottom. The diagram is now complete.

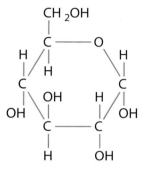

Fig 3.3: Chemical structure of a monosaccharide (glucose $C_6H_{12}O_6$).

Disaccharides:

* These are formed when two monosaccharides join together with the elimination of water (condensation reaction).
* There are three disaccharides: maltose, sucrose and lactose.
* The chemical formula of a disaccharide is $C_{12}H_{12}O_{11}$.

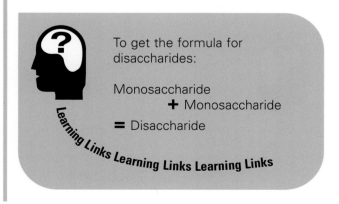

To get the formula for disaccharides:

Monosaccharide
+ Monosaccharide
= Disaccharide

Learning Links Learning Links Learning Links

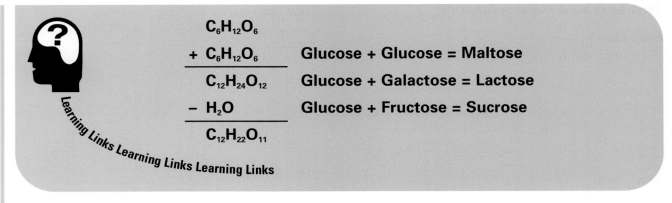
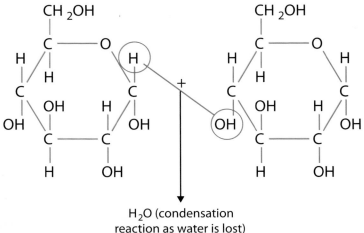

H_2O (condensation reaction as water is lost)

Fig 3.4: Chemical structure of a disaccharide.

Polysaccharides:

These are formed when three or more monosaccharides join together with the loss of a water molecule each time. They may be straight or branched chains.

Examples of polysaccharides are:

✱ Starch, pectin, cellulose, gums and glycogen.

✱ Pectin, cellulose and gums are also known as non-starch polysaccharides.

✱ Starch is made up of glucose units.

✱ Straight chains are known as amylose.

✱ Branched chains are known as amylopectin.

$C_6H_{12}O_6$

$- H_2O$

$(C_6H_{10}O_5)^n$

Fig 3.5: Chemical structure of a polysaccharide.

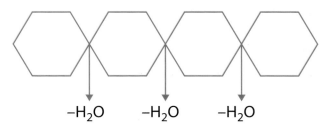

$-H_2O$ $-H_2O$ $-H_2O$

Fig 3.6: A polysaccharide.

Non-starch polysaccharides:

* These are also known as NSPs, dietary fibre and roughage.
* NSPs cannot be digested in the body and absorb large amounts of water.
* They aid in the removal of waste from the body, by a process known as peristalsis.
* Peristalsis is the muscular movement of food along the gut.
* Sources of NSPs include wholemeal bread, brown rice and wholemeal pasta.
* Refined foods contain few if any NSPs.

Classification of Carbohydrates

The smallest part of a carbohydrate is a sugar unit.

Type	No. of Sugar Units	Formula	Diagram	Examples Source	Food
Monosaccharides	One sugar unit	$C_6H_{12}O_6$		• Glucose • Fructose • Galactose	• Fruit • Honey • Digested milk
Disaccharides	Two sugar units	$C_{12}H_{22}O_{11}$		• Lactose • Maltose • Sucrose	• Milk • Barley • Table sugar
Polysaccharides	Three or more sugar units	$(C_6H_{10}O_5)_n$		• Starch • Cellulose • Pectin • Glycogen	• Potatoes • Skins of fruit and vegetables • Fruits • Stored animal starch

Sources of Carbohydrates

There are three main sources of carbohydrates: sugar, starch and cellulose.

Sugar:

Sugar is found in jam, biscuits, cakes, sweets, honey and fruit.

Starch:

Starch is found in potatoes, rice, pasta, bread and breakfast cereals.

Cellulose:

Cellulose is found in wholemeal bread, wholemeal pasta and rice, wholegrain breakfast cereals and the skin of fruit and vegetables

Properties of Carbohydrates

Sugar:

Fig 3.7: Foods containing sugar.

Shauna **A**nd **C**iara **M**ade **S**weet **H**omemade **I**ced **C**ookies
(Higher Level)

MASS *(Ordinary Level)*

Learning Links Learning Links Learning Links

Solubility:

* Sugars are white crystalline compounds that are soluble in water.
* Solubility is increased by heating the water.
* A syrup is formed when sugar is heated.

Assists aeration:

* Sugar denatures egg protein, enabling aeration to occur, e.g. in the making of sponge cakes.

Caramelisation:

* When sugars are heated, they produce a range of brown substances known as a caramel.
* There are ten gradual changes in sugar between melting and caramelisation.
* These stages occur between 104°C and 177°C.
* Eventually, the heat will cause carbonisation (burning).

Maillard reaction:

* Sugar (Carbohydrate) + Amino Acids + Dry Heat = Browning of foods, e.g. roast potatoes.

Sweetness:

* Sugar has varying degrees of sweetness based on a point scale using the tasting method.
* Sucrose has a relative sweetness of 100.
* Fructose has a relative sweetness of 170.
* Lactose has a relative sweetness of 15.

Hydrolysis:

* Hydrolysis is the chemical breakdown of a molecule by adding water to produce smaller molecules.
* This occurs when water is added to a disaccharide to produce two monosaccharides.
* Hydrolysis is the reverse of the condensation reaction.

Inversion:

* The hydrolysis of sucrose is also known as the inversion of sucrose (mixture of glucose and fructose), known as 'invert sugar'.
* Inversion may be brought about by either: (a) heating sucrose with an acid; or (b) adding the enzyme invertase, or sucrose.
* Invert sugar is used in the production of jam.

Crystallisation:

* This occurs if more sugar is added than can be absorbed by a liquid.
* Crystal particles are formed when the mixture cools.
* Crystallisation is used in the confectionery and sweet industry.

Starch:

Fig 3.8: Foods containing starch.

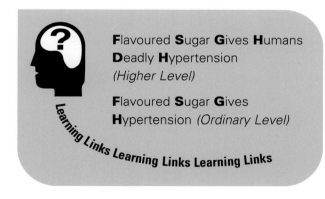

Flavoured Sugar Gives Humans Deadly Hypertension *(Higher Level)*

Flavoured Sugar Gives Hypertension *(Ordinary Level)*

Learning Links Learning Links Learning Links

Flavour:

* Starch (a white powder) is not sweet in flavour.

Solubility:

* Starch is insoluble in cold water.

Gelatinisation:

* Gelatinisation is based on the principle that when starch is heated in the presence of water, starch grains swell, burst and absorb the liquid, resulting in the thickening of the liquid.

* As the temperature rises, this mixture becomes even more viscous, forming a sol. (A sol contains particles that do not fully dissolve but are evenly dispersed throughout the liquid.)
* On cooling, this becomes a gel.
* An example of gelatinisation is using flour to thicken soups and sauces.

Hygroscopic:

* This property relates to how starch absorbs moisture from the air, e.g. biscuits soften if they are not kept airtight.

Dextrinisation:

* Dextrins are shorter chains of starch.
* On heating, dextrins form longer chains and become brown-coloured substances called pyrodextrins.
* An example of dextrinisation is toasting bread.

Hydrolysis:

* Hydrolysis is a chemical breakdown of a molecule by adding water to produce smaller molecules.
* Disaccharides become monosaccharides partly due to hydrolysis.

Non-Starch Polysaccharides (NSPs):

Cellulose:

* Can absorb large amounts of water.
* Cannot be digested, however adds bulk to the diet (gives a feeling of fullness).
* Aids the removal of waste from the body.
* Is insoluble in water.

Fig 3.9: Foods containing cellulose.

All **NSPs** are **insoluble** in **water**.

Learning Links Learning Links Learning Links

Pectin:

Pectin extraction:

✳ Pectin is a polysaccharide found in fruit and vegetables.

✳ It is involved in the setting of jams and jellies.

✳ The following shows the pectin change in the ripening of fruit:

Under-Ripe to Ripe to Over-Ripe

↓   ↓   ↓

Protopectin to Pectin to Pectic Acid (Pectose)

✳ For pectin extraction:
  - Use of fruit rich in pectin, e.g. blackcurrants and apples.
  - Heat needs to be applied to the fruit.
  - The addition of acid, e.g. lemon juice, changes protopectin to pectin.

Gel formation:

✳ When pectin is heated in the presence of acid and sugar, water becomes trapped.

✳ The long chains of polysaccharides cool to form a gel.

✳ An example of this is in making jam.

The Effects of Heat on Carbohydrates

There are two types of heat that can affect carbohydrates: dry heat and moist heat.

Dry Heat	Moist Heat
• Carbohydrate food browns due to the presence of dextrins, e.g. toast. • Sugar caramelises, e.g. caramel slices. • Maillard reaction occurs because of the interaction between sugar and amino acids, e.g. roast potatoes.	• Cellulose softens, e.g. cooked vegetables. • Starch grains swell, burst and absorb liquid, e.g. flour used to thicken sauces. • Pectin is extracted by heating fruit in water with sugar and acid, e.g. jam making. • Sugar dissolves in warm liquid, e.g. making syrups.

Biological Functions of Carbohydrates

Carbohydrates have four main biological functions.

✳ They are needed for heat and energy.

✳ They spare protein for the job of heat and energy.

✳ Excess carbohydrates are:
  - converted into glycogen and stored in the liver and muscles (long-term energy reserve).
  - converted into fat and stored as adipose tissue.

✳ Cellulose assists in the removal of waste from the body.

Culinary Uses of Carbohydrates

The four types of carbohydrates fulfil different functions when they are used in cooking.

Sugar	Starch	Cellulose	Pectin
• Used as a flavouring in drinks, puddings and cakes. • Used in the aeration of creamed cakes. • Activates yeast, i.e. fermentation is quicker when sugar is used. • Is the main ingredient in icings and sweets. • Prevents the growth of micro-organisms. • When sugar is heated it caramel-ises. This is particularly useful in dessert making, e.g. caramel slices.	• Is used to thicken soups, sauces and gravies. • Is hygroscopic (absorbs moisture from air), which helps cakes keep for longer. • Dextrins cause browning in foods (toast).	• Gives a feeling of fullness without the kilocalories. • Adds texture; it can be used as a filler, e.g. meat loaf.	• Is found in ripe fruit. • Is used as a setting agent in jams and jellies.

Associated Dietary Disorders

Disorders occur due to people eating too much sugar and starch and not enough cellulose. There are three main consequences of dietary disorders:

✳ **Obesity:** From an over–consumption of high energy foods.

✳ **Dental caries:** From consuming too much sugar.

✳ **Bowel disorders:** From a lack of NSPs. (It is recommended that 25–35g of fibre is included in a person's diet daily.)

There are two main ways to counter dietary disorders: reducing sugar intake and increasing fibre intake.

Reducing sugar intake	Increasing fibre intake
• Choose low-sugar jams and jellies. • Use artificial sweeteners in place of sugar. • Choose non-sugary breakfast cereals. • Eat fresh fruit, or if it is canned ensure it is canned in its own juice.	• Add bran to breakfast cereals and home-made breads. • Eat fruit and vegetables with the skin on where possible. • Eat seeds and nuts. • Choose wholegrain bread, pasta, breakfast cereals and brown rice.

Energy Value of Carbohydrates:
1 gram of carbohydrates provides
4 kcal (17kJ)

Digestion of Carbohydrates

Digestion involves the breaking down of polysaccharides to disaccharides to monosaccharides (by the action of water (hydrolysis) and enzymes).

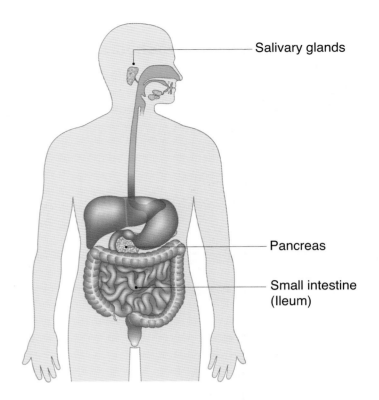

Fig 3.10: The digestive system.

Organ/Gland	Secretion	Enzymes	Substrate	Product
• Salivary glands	• Saliva	• Salivary amylase	• Starch	• Maltose
• Pancreas	• Pancreatic juice (sent into duodenum)	• Amylase	• Starch	• Maltose
• Ileum (part of small intestine)	• Intestinal juice	• Maltase • Sucrase • Lactase	• Maltose • Sucrose • Lactose	• Glucose • Glucose + Fructose • Glucose + Galactose

Mouth:
* Food is chewed.
* The enzyme **salivary amylase** breaks down some starch to maltose.

Small intestine:
* **Duodenum:** The enzyme **pancreatic amylase**, produced in the pancreas, changes more starch to maltose.

* **Ileum:** Three enzymes are found in the ileum:
  * Maltase changes maltose to glucose + glucose.
  * Lactase changes lactose to glucose + galactose.
  * Sucrase changes sucrose to glucose + fructose.

The digestion of carbohydrates is now complete.

Absorption and Utilisation of Carbohydrates

✻ Monosaccharides (containing one sugar unit, the smallest part of a carbohydrate) are absorbed through the villi of the small intestine into the bloodstream.

✻ The portal vein transports them to the liver where fructose and galactose are converted to glucose.

✻ In the liver:
 • Some glucose is oxidised to produce heat and energy.
 • Some glucose is converted to glycogen (long-term energy reserve in the liver).
 • Excess glucose is converted to fat (stored as adipose tissue).

Sample Questions and Answers
2005 Higher Level

Questions

1. Describe the chemical structure of each of the following:
   (a) monosaccharides
   (b) disaccharides
   (c) polysaccharides.
   Give one example of each. (24)

2. Name and explain three properties of carbohydrates that are useful in food preparation. (18)

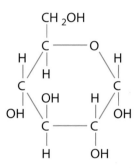

Fig 3.3: Chemical structure of a monosaccharide (glucose, $C_6H_{12}O_6$)

• Example: glucose.

Answers

1. Describe the chemical structure of each of the following:
   (a) monosaccharides
   (b) disaccharides
   (c) polysaccharides.

   7 marks x 3 sections = 21 marks.
   Plus 3 marks for each example.

   Monosaccharides:
   • One sugar unit.
   • Formula $C_6H_{12}O_6$

   Disaccharides:
   • Formed when two monosaccharides join together with the elimination of water (condensation reaction).
   • Formula $C_{12}H_{22}O_{11}$

   Monosaccharide + Monosaccharide = Disaccharide
   Glucose + Glucose = Maltose
   Glucose + Galactose = Lactose
   Glucose + Fructose = Sucrose

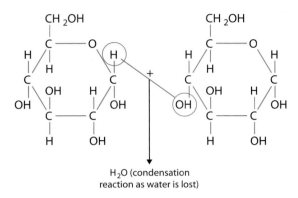

Fig 3.4: Chemical structure of a disaccharide $(C_{12}H_{22}O_{11})$.

Polysaccharides:
- Formed when three or more monosaccharides join together with the loss of a water molecule each time.
- They may be straight or branched chains.
- Formula $(C_6H_{10}O_5)^n$.
- Examples: starch, pectin, cellulose and gums.

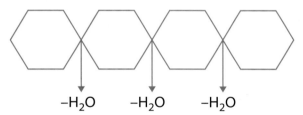

Fig 3.6: A polysaccharide $(C_6H_{10}O_5)^n$.

2. Name and explain three properties of carbohydrates that are useful in food preparation. (18)

   3 properties x 6 marks each = 18.

Caramelisation:
- When sugars are heated above their melting points, they produce a range of brown substances known as a caramel.
- There are ten gradual changes in sugar between melting and caramelisation (between 104°C and 177°C).
- Eventually, the heat will cause carbonisation (burning).
- Example: caramel squares.

Gelatinisation:
- When starch is heated in the presence of water, starch grains swell, burst and absorb the liquid, resulting in the thickening of the liquid.
- If starch is heated in water, the water penetrates the outer layers of the granules and the granules swell.
- As the size of the granules increases, the mixture becomes thicker and more gluey.
- As the temperature rises, this mixture becomes even more viscous, forming a sol. (A collodial solution containing particles that do not fully dissolve but are evenly dispersed in the liquid.)
- On cooling, this becomes a gel.
- Examples: using flour to thicken soups and sauces.

Crystallisation:
- This occurs if more sugar is added than can be absorbed by a liquid.
- Crystal particles are formed when the mixture cools.
- Crystallisation is used in the confectionery and sweet industry.

Lipids **4**

Composition of Lipids

> The term **'lipids'** covers fats and oils.
>
> **Lipids = Fats + Oils**
> **Fats = Solid at room temperature**
> **Oils = Liquid at room temperature**

There are two aspects to the composition of lipids: elemental and chemical.

Elemental:

* Carbon (C)
* Hydrogen (H)
* Oxygen (O).

Chemical:

The formation of a **triglyceride**:

* A triglyceride is the chemical name given to a fat.
* A triglyceride is formed when one glycerol molecule joins with three fatty acids to produce a triglyceride and water.
* Water is lost (condensation reaction).

$$
\begin{array}{ccccccc}
\text{H} & & \text{O} & & \text{H} & \text{O} & \\
| & & \| & & | & \| & \\
\text{H–C–OH} & & \text{H–O–C–R} & & \text{H–C–O–C–R} & & \\
| & & \quad\text{O} & & \quad\text{O} & & \\
& & \quad\| & & \quad\| & & \\
\text{H–C–OH} & + & \text{H–O–C–R} & = & \text{H–C–O–C–R} & + & 3H_2O \\
| & & \quad\text{O} & & \quad\text{O} & & \\
& & \quad\| & & \quad\| & & \\
\text{H–C–OH} & & \text{H–O–C–R} & & \text{H-C-O-C-R} & & \\
| & & & & | & & \\
\text{H} & & & & \text{H} & & \\
\end{array}
$$

Glycerol + 3 Fatty Acids = Triglyceride + Water

Fig 4.1: Formation of a triglyceride.

Classification of Fatty Acids

Fatty acids are classified into three groups:

* Saturated fatty acid.
* Monounsaturated fatty acid (**mono = one**).
* Polyunsaturated fatty acid (**poly = many**).

Saturated fatty acid	Monounsaturated fatty acid	Polyunsaturated fatty acid
• Each carbon atom is saturated with hydrogen. • There are **no** double bonds present between the carbon atoms. • They are generally solid at room temperature. • They originate from animal sources. • Examples: butyric acid in butter and stearic acid in meat.	• Each carbon atom is **not** saturated with hydrogen. • There is **one** double bond present. • These fatty acids are soft or liquid at room temperature. • They originate from plant sources. • Example: oleic acid found in olive oil.	• Each carbon atom is **not** saturated with hydrogen. • There is **more than one** double bond present. • These fatty acids are soft or liquid at room temperature. • They originate from plant/marine sources. • Examples: linoleic acid in corn oil and linolenic acid in vegetable oil.
Fig 4.2: Structure of saturated fatty acid	**Fig 4.3:** Structure of monounsaturated fatty acid	**Fig 4.4:** Structure of polyunsaturated fatty acid

$$\underset{\underset{\displaystyle H\ \ H\ \ H\ \ H}{|\ \ \ \ |\ \ \ \ |\ \ \ \ |}}{\overset{\overset{\displaystyle O\ \ H\ \ H\ \ H\ \ H}{\|\ \ \ |\ \ \ \ |\ \ \ \ |\ \ \ \ |}}{HO-C-C-C-C-C-H}}$$

$$\underset{\underset{\displaystyle H\qquad\quad H}{|\qquad\quad |}}{\overset{\overset{\displaystyle O\ \ H\ \ H\ \ H\ \ H}{\|\ \ \ |\ \ \ \ |\ \ \ \ |\ \ \ \ |}}{HO-C-C-C=C-C-H}}$$

$$\underset{\underset{\displaystyle H\qquad\qquad\quad H}{|\qquad\qquad\quad |}}{\overset{\overset{\displaystyle O\ \ H\ \ H\ \ H\ \ H\ \ H}{\|\ \ \ |\ \ \ \ |\ \ \ \ |\ \ \ \ |\ \ \ \ |}}{HO-C=C-C-C=C-C-H}}$$

What are fatty acids?

* Fatty acids are long hydrocarbon chains.
* Each fatty acid contains a methyl group (CH_3) at one end and a carboxyl group (COOH) at the other.
* Formula: $CH_3(CH_3)^n COOH$.

Cis and Trans Fatty Acids

Cis and trans fatty acids are based on the position of the **hydrogen atoms** at the **double bond**.

Cis fatty acids:
* Cis fatty acids occur when the hydrogen atoms are at the same side of the double bond.
* All unsaturated fatty acids are generally cis.
* Cis fatty acids are naturally occuring in foods.

$$\overset{\overset{\displaystyle H\ \ H}{|\ \ \ |}}{-C=C-}$$

Fig 4.5: Cis fatty acid.

Trans fatty acids:
Trans fatty acids occur when the hydrogen atoms are at opposite sides of the double bonds.

Fig 4.6: Trans fatty acid.

A Closer Look at Trans Fatty Acids

✳ It is during cooking (heating oils) and processing (manufacture of margarine/hydrogenation) that cis fatty acids are converted to trans fatty acids.

✳ Trans fatty acids are thought to increase the risk of coronary heart disease (CHD), in particular, trans fatty acids that are produced synthetically.

✳ Trans fatty acids are said to raise LDL levels in the body.

✳ Other sources of trans fatty acids include pastries and crisps.

Cholesterol

HDL = High Density Lipo-protein

Good cholesterol

LDL = Low Density Lipo-protein

Bad cholesterol

Fig 4.7: Sources of trans fatty acids.

Omega-3 Fatty Acids

✳ These are polyunsaturated fatty acids.

✳ Omega-3 relates to the positioning of the double bond.

✳ The double bond is between the third and fourth carbon atoms, counting from the methyl end (CH_3).

✳ Sources include oily fish (salmon, tuna, sardines).

✳ Omega-3 fatty acids are known as (EPA) eicosapentaenoic and (DHA) docoshexaenoic.

✳ Omega-3 fatty acids are thought to reduce the build-up of cholesterol in the arteries and increase brain activity.

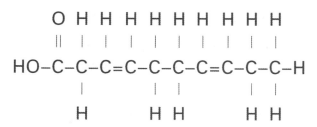

Fig 4.8: Omega–3 fatty acid.

Fig 4.9: Sources of omega–3 fatty acids.

Essential Fatty Acids

An essential fatty acid

is one that is not made in the body and therefore should be taken in through the food that we eat. They include: linoleic acid, found in corn oil; linolenic acid, found in vegetable oil; arachidonic acid, is found in animal fat. Linoleic acid is the most important of these as linolenic and arachidonic acid can be synthesised from linoleic acid.

Functions of Essential Fatty Acids:

✳ Build cell membranes.

✳ Counteract the hardening effect of cholesterol in the arteries.

✳ Help prevent CHD (coronary heart disease).

Classification of Lipids

Lipids are classified according to their sources and their degree of saturation.

Sources:

There are three sources of lipids: animal, plant and marine.

Animal	Plant	Marine
• Meat	• Vegetable oils	• Salmon
• Butter	• Olive oil	• Mackerel
• Cream	• Cereals	• Trout
• Egg yolk	• Soya beans	• Sardines

Degree of saturation:

✱ Fats and oils contain a variation of saturated and unsaturated fatty acid.
✱ The more double bonds, the greater the degree of unsaturation.
✱ It is the combination of fatty acids in a lipid that determines taste, consistency and texture.

	Saturated Fatty Acids	Monounsaturated Fatty Acids	Polyunsaturated Fatty Acids
Olive oil	10%	20%	66%
Sunflower oil	13%	74%	8%
Soft tub margarine	17%	47%	31%
Tuna	27%	26%	37%
Chicken fat	30%	45%	21%
Butter	40%	45%	11%

Table 4.1: How fatty acids are distributed in food.

Properties of Lipids

There are five properties of lipids: solubility, plasticity, hydrogenation, affected by heat, rancidity and emulsions.

Solubility:

✱ Lipids are insoluble in water.
✱ Lipids are soluble in solvents, e.g. ether and benzene.

Plasticity:

✱ A combination of saturated and unsaturated fatty acids. Allows for shape and structure of the lipid.
✱ This is useful in pastry making, e.g. margarine is used in the creaming method.

Hydrogenation:

✳ Hydrogenation occurs when hydrogen is forced through the double bond of unsaturated fatty acids in the presence of a nickel catalyst.

✳ This property is evident in the production of margarine.

> A **catalyst** is a substance that speeds up or slows down a reaction without itself changing.

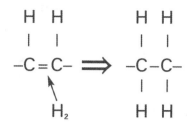

Fig 4.10: Hydrogenation.

Affected by heat:

There are varying temperatures that affect lipids (fats and oils).

Melting point	Smoke point	Flash point
• Solid fats melt when heated. • FATS: 30–40°C	• Lipids begin to decompose to glycerol and three fatty acids. • A blue haze emerges. • An acrid-smelling compound known as acrolein is present. • FATS: 200°C OILS: 250°C	• The decomposition of the lipids continues. • Lipids spontaneously burst into flames. • FATS: 310°C OILS: 325°C

Rancidity:

✳ This is the term used to describe lipids when they 'go off'.

✳ There are two types of rancidity: these are oxidative and hydrolytic.

✳ To prevent rancidity, store food correctly and use an anti-oxidant.

> **Anti-oxidants** occur naturally in vitamins A, C and E and occur artificially in BHA and BHT.

Oxidative	Hydrolytic
• This form of rancidity occurs when **oxygen** is forced through the double bond of an unsaturated fatty acid. It is the most common form of rancidity.	• This form of rancidity occurs when **enzymes and bacteria** react with the lipid. This occurs most commonly in freezers when enzymes are not destroyed.

Fig 4.11: Rancidity

Emulsions:

* There are two types of emulsions: oil in water and water in oil.
* When two immiscible liquids are forced together, an emulsion is formed.
* A temporary emulsion occurs when oil and vinegar are temporarily forced together, e.g. French dressing. This is caused by shaking and will separate on standing.
* A permanent emulsion occurs when oil and water are forced together in the presence of an emulsifier, e.g. mayonnaise (oil + water + emulsifier (lecithin in egg yolk) = emulsion)
* An emulsifier has two parts: a water-loving head (hydrophilic) and a water-hating tail (hydrophobic).

> **HYDRO** = Water
> **PHILIC** = Love
> **PHOBIC** = Hate

Working principle of an emulsifier:

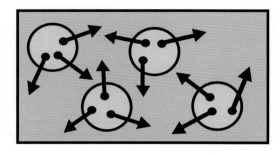

The hydrophilic head attaches to water, while the hydrophobic tail attaches to the oil.

Vinegar   Oil   Hydrophobic tail   Hydrophilic head

Fig 4.12: Working principle of an emulsifier.

* The hydrophilic head attaches itself to the water molecule.
* The hydrophobic tail attaches itself to the oil component of the emulsion.

| Oil | Water |

* Stabilisers are used to maintain an emulsion, e.g. in ice cream.
* An example of a stabiliser used in ice cream is alginates (E400).

Working principle of a stabiliser:

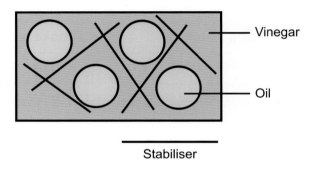

Vinegar

Oil

Stabiliser

Fig 4.13: Working principle of a stabiliser.

Functions of Lipids

* Lipids supply the body with heat and energy.
* Excess lipids are stored as adipose tissue under the skin. This insulates the body and maintains body temperature at 37°C.
* Lipids protect delicate organs, e.g. kidneys.
* Lipids are a source of the fat-soluble vitamins A, D, E and K.
* Lipids are a source of essential fatty acids.

> **Remember:**
> Essential fatty acids = linoleic acid, linolenic acid and arachidonic acid.

* Lipids delay the onset of hunger, as they take longer to digest than proteins and carbohydrates.

> **Energy Value of Lipids:**
> 1g of lipids provides 9kcal/37kJ.

Digestion of Lipids

Liver:

✳ The liver produces **bile**, which contains bile salts.

✳ Bile salts break down lipids into emulsified fats (emulsified fats are shorter chains of fats).

Pancreas:

✳ Pancreatic acid juice contains the enzyme **pancreatic lipase**.

✳ Lipase continues the breakdown of lipids into their basic component parts of one glycerol molecule and three fatty acids.

Ileum:

✳ Intestinal juice contains the enzyme **intestinal lipase**.

✳ This lipase completes the breakdown of lipids into one glycerol molecule and three fatty acids.

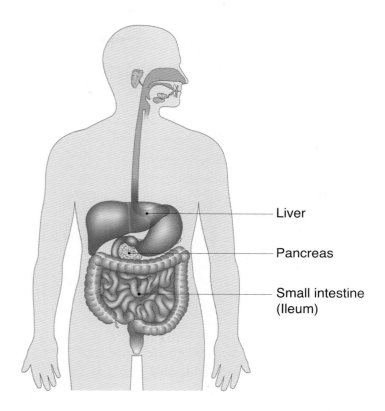

Fig 4.14: The digestive system.

Organ/Gland	Secretion	Enzyme	Substrate	By-product
• Liver	Bile	Bile salts	Lipids	Emulsified fats
• Pancreas	Pancreatic juice	Pancreatic lipase	Lipids	Glycerol + 3 fatty acids
• Ileum	Intestinal juice	Intestinal lipase	Lipids	Glycerol + 3 fatty acids

Absorption of Lipids

✳ When digested, the lipids (glycerol + three fatty acids) can be absorbed.

✳ Absorption takes places in the lacteals in the villi of the small intestine.

✳ Digested lipids are carried via the lymph system to the bloodstream at the subclavian vein in the neck.

Utilisation of Lipids

✳ The lipids are oxidised in the liver and muscles to:
  ● produce heat and energy.
  ● form cell membranes.

✳ Excess lipids are stored as adipose tissue underneath the skin. This:
  ● insulates the body.
  ● acts as an energy reserve.
  ● protects delicate organs.

Sample Exam Questions

Questions

1. Differentiate between:
   - a saturated fatty acid.
   - a monounsaturated fatty acid.
   - a polyunsaturated fatty acid. (18)

2. Give an account of three properties of lipids that are important in food production. (15)

Answers

1. Differentiate between:
   - a saturated fatty acid.
   - a monounsaturated fatty acid.
   - a polyunsaturated fatty acid. (18)

   (3 points @ 2 marks each) x 3 = 6 x 3 = 18.

Saturated fatty acid

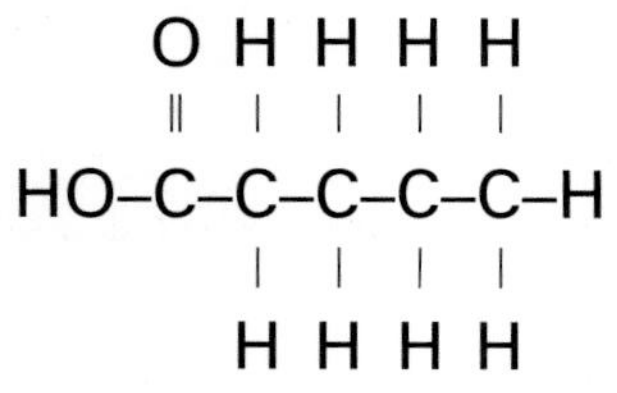

```
    O  H  H  H  H
    ‖  |  |  |  |
HO–C–C–C–C–C–H
       |  |  |  |
       H  H  H  H
```

Fig 4.2: Structure of saturated fatty acid.

- Each carbon atom is saturated with hydrogen.
- There are no double bonds present between the carbon atoms.
- They are generally solid at room temperature.
- They originate from animal sources.
- Examples include butyric acid in butter and stearic acid in meat.

Monounsaturated fatty acid

```
    O  H  H  H  H
    ‖  |  |  |  |
HO–C–C–C=C–C–H
       |        |
       H        H
```

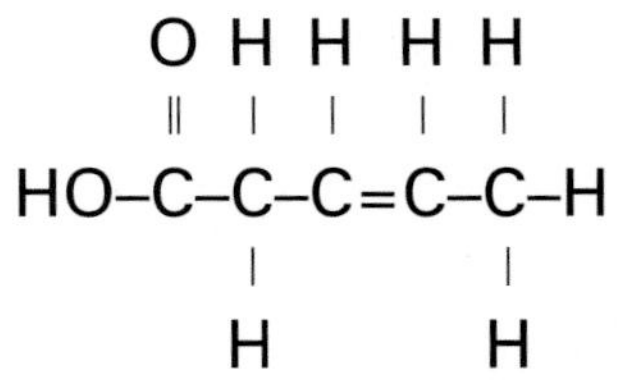

Fig 4.3: Structure of monounsaturated fatty acid.

- Each carbon atom is **not** saturated with hydrogen.
- There is one double bond present.
- These fatty acids are soft or liquid at room temperature.
- They originate from plant sources.
- Examples include oleic acid found in olive oil.

Polyunsaturated fatty acid

```
    O  H  H  H  H  H
    ‖  |  |  |  |  |
HO–C=C–C–C=C–C–H
       |        |
       H        H
```

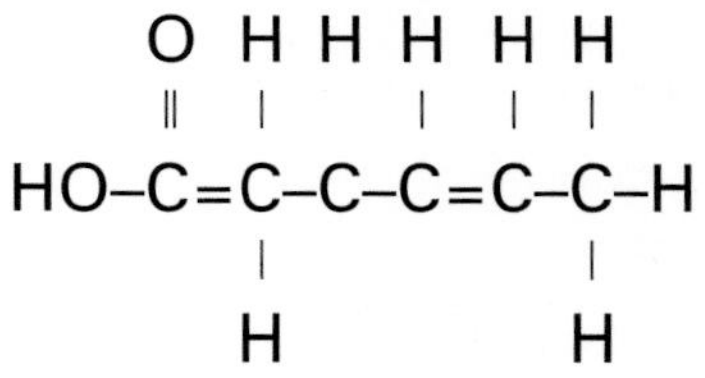

Fig 4.4: Structure of polyunsaturated fatty acid.

- Each carbon atom is **not** saturated with hydrogen.
- There is more than one double bond present.
- These fatty acids are soft or liquid at room temperature.
- They originate from plant and marine sources.

• Examples include linoleic acid in corn oil and linolenic acid in vegetable oil.

2. Give an account of three properties of lipids that are important in food production. (15)

    3 properties @ 5 marks each.

Emulsification:
*   There are two types of emulsion: oil in water and water in oil.
*   When two immiscible liquids are forced together, an emulsion is formed.
*   A temporary emulsion occurs when oil and vinegar are temporarily forced together, e.g. French dressing. This is caused by shaking and separates on standing.
*   A permanent emulsion occurs when oil and water are forced together in the presence of an emulsifier, e.g. mayonnaise (oil + water + emulsifier (lecithin in egg yolk) = emulsion.

Hydrogenation:
*   Hydrogenation occurs when hydrogen is forced through the double bond of unsaturated fatty acid in the presence of a nickel catalyst.
*   This property is evident in the production of margarine.

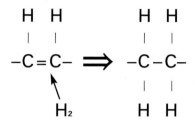

Fig 4.10: Hydrogenation.

Plasticity:
*   A combination of saturated and unsaturated fatty acids.
*   Allows for the shape and structure of the lipid.
*   This is useful in pastry making (margarine is used in the creaming method).

5 Vitamins

Classification of Vitamins

Vitamins are classified into two groups:

✳ Fat-soluble vitamins, i.e. A, D, E, K.
✳ Water-soluble vitamins, i.e. B group, C.

> **Vitamins** are micro-nutrients.
> They are essential to our diet as they
> are not made in the body.

Fat-Soluble Vitamins	Water-Soluble Vitamins
A, D, E, K	B group, C

Fat-Soluble Vitamins

Vitamin A

Vitamin A is found in two forms:

✳ Pure vitamin A (retinol).
✳ Pro-vitamin A (betacarotene).

Retinol

✳ Retinol is also known as pure vitamin A.
✳ Retinol is found in animal sources.

Properties	Functions	Deficiencies	Sources	RDA (µg/per day)
• Fat-soluble vitamin. • Insoluble in water. • Heat stable. • Yellow in colour. • Destroyed by oxygen when exposed to light and air.	• Necessary for healthy eyes. It is important in the production of rhodopsin. This enables the eye to adapt to dim light. • Maintains a healthy lining tissue in areas such as the eyes, nose and throat. • Assists/promotes growth. • Necessary for healthy hair and skin. • Necessary for metabolism.	• Night blindness – this is an inability of the eyes to adapt to dim light. • Xerophthalmia, also known as 'dry eye', in which the surface of the eyes dry out. This can lead to blindness. • May cause the mucus membrane to dry out. This causes a susceptibility to infection. • Stunted growth in children. • Follicular keratosis, a skin condition that causes dry skin.	• Liver • Cod liver oil • Fortified milk • Eggs • Cheese • Margarine	• Children 400–500 • Adolescents 600–700 • Adults 600–700 • Pregnant women 700 • Lactating women 950

Fig 5.1: Healthy eyes.

Carotenoids

These are pigments that are responsible for the colours of fruit and vegetables. They are converted to vitamin A in the gut.

Betacarotene is:

✳ also known as pro-vitamin A.

✳ found in green, orange and yellow fruit and vegetables.

✳ not as easily absorbed as retinol.

✳ must first be converted to retinol in the intestines.

✳ is converted in the ratio of 6:1 (whereby 6 betacarotene is needed to obtain 1 retinol).

Properties	Functions	Deficiencies	Sources	RDA (µg/per day)
• Fat-soluble vitamin. • Insoluble in water. • Heat stable. • Yellow/orange oil. • Powerful anti-oxidant.	• Necessary for healthy eyes. It is important in the production of rhodopsin. This enables the eye to adapt to dim light. • Maintains a healthy lining tissue in areas such as the eyes, nose and throat. • Assists/promotes growth. • Necessary for healthy hair and skin. • Necessary for metabolism. • The anti-oxidant activity of betacarotene has a protective property – helping to prevent coronary heart disease.	• Deficiencies are rare.	• Carrots • Red peppers • Apricots • Tomatoes • Spinach	• Children 400–500 • Adolescents 600–700 • Adults 600–700 • Pregnant women 700 • Lactating women 950

Vitamin D

There are two forms of vitamin D:

✳ Cholecalciferol (vitamin D_3).

✳ Ergocalciferol (vitamin D_2).

Cholecalciferol

• Found in animal sources.

• Made by the action of the sun.

Ergocalciferol

• Found in plant sources – fungi and yeasts.

• Made by the action of the sun.

Formation of Vitamin D:

Sunlight (ultra-violet light) converts 7-Dehydro-cholesterol found in the skin to vitamin D.

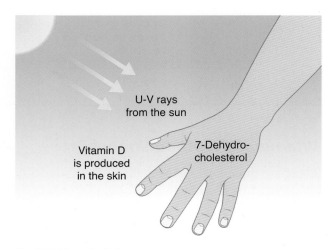

U-V rays from the sun

Vitamin D is produced in the skin

7-Dehydro-cholesterol

Fig 5.2: Vitamin D formation.

Vitamin D

Properties	Functions	Deficiencies	Sources	RDA (µg/per day)
• Fat-soluble vitamin. • Insoluble in water. • Heat stable. • Not affected by oxidation, acids and alkalis.	• Necessary for absorption of calcium and phosphorus. • Regulates the amount of calcium and phosphorus in teeth and bones. • Controls the level of calcium in the blood. • Prevents rickets and osteomalacia. • Reduces the kidneys' excretion of calcium and thus prevents the formation of kidney stones.	• Rickets in children (weak, malformed bones). • Osteomalacia (weakness of bones in adults). • Osteoporosis (brittle bones), high risk of fractures in the elderly. • Tooth decay.	• Liver • Fish liver oils • Oily fish • Sunlight • Eggs • Margarine • Milk	• Children 10 • Adolescents 15 • Adults 10 • Pregnant women 10 • Lactating women 10

Vitamin E (Tocopherols)

Properties	Functions	Deficiencies	Sources	RDA (µg/per day)
• Fat-soluble vitamin. • Insoluble in water. • Heat stable. • Acts as an anti-oxidant.	• As an anti-oxidant, vitamin E is believed to reduce the risk of heart disease and cancers. • It is thought to reduce the incidences of coronary heart disease (by oxidation of LDL). • Aids the absorption of vitamin A. • Is thought to protect blood cells.	• Deficiencies are rare as vitamin E is found in most foods.	• Cereals • Wheat germ • Nuts • Vegetable oil • Eggs • Poultry	• None

Vitamin K (Napthoquinones)

There are three forms of vitamin K: K_1, K_2 and K_3.

* **Vitamin K_1:** Phyllonapthoquinone, made by plants.
* **Vitamin K_2:** Menanapthoquinone, made by animals.
* **Vitamin K_3:** Menaphthone or menadione, is synthesised.

Properties	Functions	Deficiencies	Sources	RDA (µg/per day)
• Fat-soluble vitamin. • Insoluble in water. • Heat stable. • Destroyed when exposed to light.	• Necessary for the clotting of blood as it converts prothrombin to thrombin. • Regulates the level of calcium in the bones.	• A mild deficiency means that blood takes longer to clot. • A severe deficiency leads to a failure of blood to clot which, if it persists, can lead to death.	• Fish liver oils • Liver • Spinach • Cabbage • Peas • Cauliflower	• None

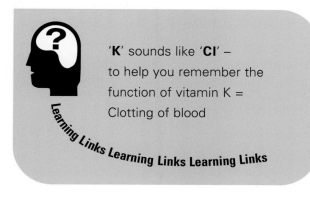

'K' sounds like 'Cl' –
to help you remember the function of vitamin K = Clotting of blood

Learning Links Learning Links Learning Links

Fig 5.3: A person with yellow skin because of a high vitamin A intake.

Hypervitaminosis

✳ Fat-soluble vitamins may be stored in the body for long periods of time.

✳ If this occurs with vitamins A and D, they can have a toxic effect on the body as they accumulate in the liver.

✳ The symptoms of hypervitaminosis include bone pain, loss of appetite, dry skin, hair loss and death.

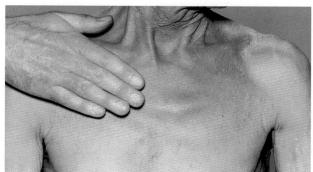

Water-Soluble Vitamins

Vitamin C (Ascorbic Acid)

Properties	Functions	Deficiencies	Sources	RDA (mg/per day)
• Water-soluble vitamin. • It is acidic. • It is destroyed by heat, alkali, light, metals, oxidase and oxygen. • Acts as an anti-oxidant.	• Helps in the formation of collagen, which promotes the healing of wounds. • It is necessary for the absorption of non-haem iron. • Prevents scurvy. • Acts as an anti-oxidant, preventing coronary heart disease.	• Delayed healing of wounds. • Scurvy. • Anaemia due to lack of absorption of iron. • Bruising and bleeding due to weakening of blood vessels and body tissue. **Fig 5.4:** Scurvy.	**Fruit:** • Kiwi • Blackcurrants • Strawberries • Oranges • Lemons **Vegetables:** • Tomatoes • Peppers • Cabbage • Spinach • Broccoli	• Children 45 • Adolescents 50–60 • Adults 60 • Pregnant women 80 • Lactating women 80

B Group Vitamins

There are six B vitamins. The vitamin B group complex includes:

* B$_1$: thiamine.
* B$_2$: riboflavin.
* B$_6$: pyridoxine.
* B$_{12}$: cobalamin.
* Niacin.
* Folate/folic acid.

Thiamine (B$_1$)

Properties	Functions	Deficiencies	Sources
• Water-soluble vitamin. • Destroyed by alkalis and high temperatures. • 70 per cent loss during milling.	• Assists the release of energy from carbohydrates and fats. • Necessary for healthy nerves and muscle functioning. • Aids growth.	• Beriberi. • Irratibility, memory loss, fatigue. • Retarded growth. 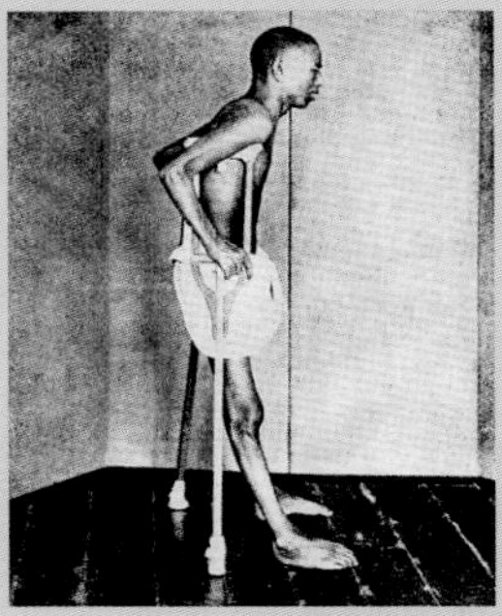 **Fig 5.5:** Beriberi.	• Wholegrain cereals • Fortified breakfast cereals • Milk • Eggs • Meat • Offal

Riboflavin (B$_2$)

Properties	Functions	Deficiencies	Sources
• Water-soluble vitamin. • Destroyed by alkalis. • Sensitive to light. • Unstable at high temperatures.	• Assists the release of energy from protein, carbohydrates and fats. • Promotes healthy membranes in the mouth and nose. • Promotes growth in children.	• Swollen red tongue • Eye infections • Lack of energy • Retarded growth	• Meat • Offal • Milk • Eggs • Dark green, leafy vegetables • Yeast extract

Niacin

Properties	Functions	Deficiencies	Sources
• Water-soluble vitamin. • 80–90 per cent loss in milling. • Stable to: • Heat. • Acids. • Alkalis.	• Assists the release of energy from carbohydrates. • Prevents pellagra. • Promotes healthy skin. • Necessary for a healthy nervous system.	• Tiredness. • Pellagra: causes the 5Ds (diarrhoea, dermatitis, depression, dementia and death). **Fig 5.6:** Pellagra.	• Meat and meat products • Fortified cereals • Bread

Pyridoxine (B$_6$)

Properties	Functions	Deficiencies	Sources
• Water-soluble vitamin. • Destroyed by oxygen. • Generally heat stable, but destroyed by high temperatures.	• Assists the releases of energy from carbohydrates, proteins and fat. • Necessary for production of red and white blood cells. • Thought to help relieve premenstrual tension and nausea in pregnancy. • Essential for healthy nervous system.	• Anaemia. • Convulsions in young babies. • Premenstrual tension – headaches, mood swings, anxiety. • Decreased immunity.	• Meat • Fish • Wheat germ • Dark green, leafy vegetables • Bananas

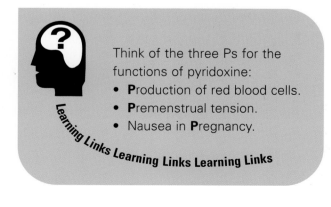

Think of the three Ps for the functions of pyridoxine:
• **P**roduction of red blood cells.
• **P**remenstrual tension.
• Nausea in **P**regnancy.

Learning Links Learning Links Learning Links

Folic Acid

Folate is the natural form of folic acid. It is found in foliage (dark green, leafy vegetables).
Folic acid is the synthesised form, therefore only found in supplements.

Properties	Functions	Deficiencies	Sources

• Water-soluble vitamin.
• It is unaffected by acids.
• Sensitive to oxygen and light and is easily destroyed by cooking.
	• Necessary for the manufacture of RNA and DNA (genetic material).
	• Essential for the formation of new cells in foetuses.
	• Helps protect foetuses from developing neural tube defects, e.g. spina bifida.
	• Helps the prevention of heart attacks, some cancers and strokes.
	• Helps maintain a healthy immune system.
	• Needed for protein metabolism. 

	Fig 5.7: A pregnant woman.
		• Neural tube defects, e.g. spina bifida.
		• Tiredness and fatigue.
		• Macrocytic anaemia, which means that red blood cells:
		  • Are enlarged.
		  • Are fewer in number.
		  • Contain less oxygen-carrying haemoglobin than normal cells.
			• Wheat germ
			• Fortified cereals
			• Wholemeal bread
			• Green leafy vegetables
			• Liver
			• Kidney

	µg per day
• Children	100–200
• Males	300
• Females	300
• Pregnant women	500
• Lactating women	400

Cobalamin (B₁₂)

Cobalamin is only found in animal foods.

Properties	Functions	Deficiencies	Sources
• Water-soluble vitamin. • Unaffected by light, acids and alkalis. • Heat stable to 100°C.	• Necessary for the metabolism of fatty acids and folic acid. • Necessary for the manufacture of red blood cells. • Necessary for the formation of myelin sheaths, which insulate the nerve fibres. • Promotes growth.	• Pernicious anaemia. • Weakness, fatigue and weight loss. • Deterioration of nerve fibres.	• Liver • Meat • Fish • Poultry • Eggs • Milk • Vegans must take supplements of B12, as it is only found in animal foods.

	µg per day
• Children	0.7–1
• Teenagers	1.4
• Adults	1.4
• Pregnant women	1.6
• Lactating women	1.9

Part Exam Question
Higher Level (2007)

Question

1. Give an account of folic acid/folate and refer to:
    (i) Sources in the diet.
    (ii) Properties.
    (iii) Biological functions.
    (iv) Recommended dietary allowances. (28)

Answer

Sources: 2 points @ 4 marks = 8 marks
Properties: 2 properties @ 4 marks = 8 marks

Biological functions: 2 functions @ 4 marks = 8 marks
RDA = 4 marks

• Folate is the natural form of folic acid.
• It is found in foliage (dark green, leafy vegetables).
• Folic acid is the synthesised form, therefore only found in supplements.

Sources	Properties	Biological functions
• Wheat germ • Fortified cereals • Wholemeal bread • Green leafy vegetables • Liver • Kidney	• Water-soluble vitamin. • Unaffected by acids. • Sensitive to oxygen and light and is easily destroyed by cooking.	• Necessary for the manufacture of RNA and DNA. • Essential for the formation of new cells in foetuses. • Helps protect foetuses from developing neural tube defects. • Aids the prevention of heart attacks, some cancers and strokes. • Needed for protein metabolism.

RDA

	µg per day
• Children	100–200
• Males	300
• Females	300
• Pregnant women	500
• Lactating women	400

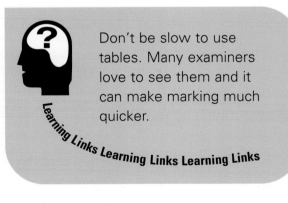

Don't be slow to use tables. Many examiners love to see them and it can make marking much quicker.

Learning Links Learning Links Learning Links

Test Yourself
eTest.ie

Minerals

6

Minerals are simple chemicals made up of single atoms or salts comprising a few atoms. There are two major types: macro minerals and trace minerals.

✳ **Macro minerals:** These are required in relatively large amounts – more than 100mg per day. Three of the macro minerals (sodium, potassium and chloride) – known as electrolytes – are important components of all body fluids.

✳ **Trace minerals:** These are required in smaller quantities. They are also known as trace elements.

Classification of Minerals

Macro minerals	Trace minerals
• Calcium	• Copper
• Chloride	• Fluoride
• Magnesium	• Iodine
• Phosphorus	• Iron
• Potassium	• Zinc
• Sodium	
• Sulphur	

Iron (Fe)

Iron is a very important mineral. Deficiency in iron is the most common mineral deficiency in humans. Iron is present in haemoglobin in the blood, myoglobin in the muscles, enzyme systems in the body cells, and is also stored in the liver, spleen and bone marrow.

Functions	Effects of deficiency	Sources
• Iron is necessary for the formation of haemoglobin, which carries oxygen around the body.	• Iron deficiency causes haemoglobin levels to fall, which means that there is not enough oxygen going to the body tissues.	The main sources of iron are: • Meat. • Meat products. • Chicken. • Cereals.

Iron (Fe) contd

Functions	Effects of deficiency	Sources

• It forms part of myoglobin, which carries oxygen to the muscles.
• It is an important part of enzyme systems that use oxygen to release energy from food.
	• It can lead to:
	  • Tiredness.
	  • Paleness.
	  • Breathlessness.
	  • Anaemia.
	• Anaemia is a common condition in Ireland, especially in women.
		• Eggs
		• Pulses
		• Green vegetables
		• Fish

Forms of Iron

There are two forms of iron: haem iron and non-haem iron.

Haem iron	Non-haem iron
• This is a ferrous iron. • Its chemical symbol is Fe^{2+}. • It is soluble and easily absorbed. • Sources of haem iron include meat, meat products, chicken.	• This is a ferric iron. • Its chemical symbol is Fe^{3+}. • It cannot be absorbed in the body and must be changed into ferrous iron to be absorbed. • Sources of non-haem iron include cereals, eggs, pulses, green vegetables, fish.

Fig 6.1: Sources of haem iron.

Fig 6.2: Sources of non-haem iron.

Absorption of Iron

Only about 10 to 15 per cent of iron intake is absorbed into the body. The most important factor influencing its absorption is the body's need for it.

Factors aiding iron absorption	Factors hindering iron absorption
• Eating **haem iron** (because it is more easily absorbed than non-haem iron). • Eating **non-haem and haem iron** together increases non-haem iron absorption. • **Vitamin C** is a reducing agent, as it changes ferric iron (Fe^{3+}) to the more easily absorbable ferrous iron (Fe^{2+}). • **Hydrochloric acid** in the stomach aids absorption by changing non-haem iron to haemiron.	• **Phytic acid**, in cereals and legumes, binds to iron, decreasing its absorption. • A dietary **fibre** intake above 35g per day has a tendency to bind iron, decreasing its absorption. • **Oxalic acid**, which is found in some fruit and vegetables (rhubarb and spinach), combines with iron, inhibiting its absorption. • **Tannins** in tea, coffee and cocoa decrease iron absorption.

RDA of iron:
- Children: 10mg
- Adolescents: 13–14mg
- Adults: males 10mg, females 14mg
- Pregnant or lactating women: 15mg

Calcium (Ca)

Ninety-nine per cent of calcium in the human body is present in the bones. It is also found in the blood, muscle and nerves.

Functions	Effects of deficiency	Sources
• Calcium plays a major role in the formation and development of bones and teeth. • Calcium is important in blood clotting. • Calcium is necessary for muscle contractions, normal functioning of nerves and membrane permeability. • Calcium is required to regulate metabolism in the cells.	• Rickets in children. • Osteomalacia in adults. • Osteoporosis in the elderly. • Tooth decay. • Poor blood clotting. • Failure of the muscles to relax (muscular spasms).	The main sources of calcium are: • Dairy products, e.g. milk, cheese, eggs. • Dark green vegetables, e.g. spinach, cabbage. • Canned fish, e.g. salmon, sardines. • Fortified flour. • Hard water.

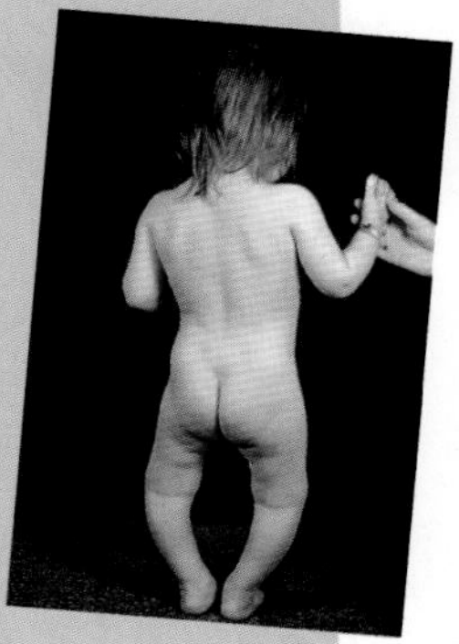

Fig 6.3: Rickets.

Absorption of Calcium

Approximately 20 per cent of calcium intake is absorbed. It is absorbed in the small intestine where it is bound to a specific carrier protein.

Factors aiding calcium absorption	Factors hindering calcium absorption
• **Vitamin D**, which stimulates calcium-binding protein and increases absorption. • **Parathormone** is a hormone that controls the level of calcium in the blood. (It is produced by the parathyroid gland.) • **Amino acids** combine with calcium, making soluble calcium salts, which are absorbed easily. • **Phosphorus** combines with calcium to form calcium phosphate. • An **acid environment** helps calcium absorption (eating vitamin C with calcium-rich foods).	• **Phytic acid**, present in cereals and grains, binds to calcium, preventing its absorption. • **Oxalic acid**, present in rhubarb and spinach, binds to the calcium, preventing its absorption. • **Fibre** binds to calcium, preventing its absorption. • **Excess saturated fat** forms insoluble soaps with calcium, preventing its absorption. • Overconsumption of **soft drinks**. • An **incorrect calcium/phosphorus** ratio. • Levels of oestrogen in postmenopausal women play a major role in the absorption of calcium. • Tannins in tea.

RDA for calcium:

- Children: 800mg
- Adolescents: 1200mg
- Adults: 800mg
- Pregnant or lactating women: 1200mg

Other Minerals

Mineral	Functions	Deficiency	Sources	RDA
Potassium (K)	• Maintains fluid balance in body tissue. • Ensures healthy nerve activity. • Ensures normal muscle contractions. • Necessary for the metabolism of protein.	• Deficiency is very rare. • Mus**C**ular weakness. • **C**ardiac arrest. • Mental **C**onfusion. Remember the 3Cs (sound like **K** for potassium).	• Green leafy vegetables • Meat • Milk • Fruit (especially bananas and oranges)	• Adult = 3.5g

Mineral	Functions	Deficiency	Sources	RDA
Sodium	• Maintains the fluid balance in body tissue. • Ensures healthy nerve activity. • Ensures normal muscle contractions.	• Deficiency is uncommon. • Deficiency leads to: – Low blood pressure. – Weakness. – Loss of appetite.	• Table salt • Processed foods • Smoked and cured meat • Cheese	• Adults = 1.6g
Iodine	• Helps the formation of thyroid hormones called thyroxine. • Growth and repair. • Regulates metabolism.	• Lack of thyroxide results in goitre (swelling of neck). • Stunted growth in children. • Lethargy. • Weight loss. • Cretinism, retardation in children.  **Fig 6.4:** Adult with goitre.	• Seafood • Iodised salt • Seaweed	• Children = 60–90µg • Adults = 140µg
Zinc	• Controls enzyme activity. • Promotes general health. • Assists in the healing of wounds. • Assists in the metabolism of protein and carbohydrates.	• Dry skin. • Slow growth. • Delayed healing.	• Dairy products • Meat • Poultry • Oysters	• Children = 4–7mg • Teenagers and adults = 7–10mg

Inter-Relationship between Vitamins and Minerals

Vitamin	Relationship with minerals
Vitamin D	• Works in the absorption of calcium and phosphorus.
Vitamin K	• Works with calcium in clotting blood.
Vitamin C	• Works in the absorption of iron and calcium.
Vitamin B_6, B_{12}, Folic Acid	• Works with iron in the formation of red blood cells.

Sample Exam Question

Questions

1. State the functions of calcium. (8)

2. State the RDA of calcium for a teenager. (5)

3. What factors assist the absorption of calcium in the diet? (10)

4. What factors prevent the absorption of calcium in the diet? (10)

Answers

1. State the functions of calcium. (8)

   4 functions x 2 marks each = 8.

   • Calcium plays a major role in the formation and development of bones and teeth.
   • Calcium is important in blood clotting.
   • Calcium is necessary for muscle contractions, normal functioning of nerves and membrane permeability.
   • Calcium is required to regulate metabolism in cells.

2. State the RDA of calcium for a teenager. (5)

   1 RDA x 5 marks = 5.

   The RDA is 1200mg per day (for adolescents).

3. What factors assist the absorption of calcium in the diet? (10)

   5 factors x 2 points each = 10.

   • Vitamin D, which stimulates calcium-binding protein and increases absorption.
   • Parathormone is a hormone that controls the level of calcium in the blood. (It is produced by the parathyroid gland.)
   • Amino acids combine with calcium, making soluble calcium salts, which are absorbed easily.

- Phosphorus combines with calcium to form calcium phosphate.
- An acid environment helps calcium absorption (eating vitamin C with calcium-rich foods).

4. What factors prevent the absorption of calcium in the diet? (10)

5 factors x 2 points each = 10.

- Phytic acid, present in cereals and grains, binds to calcium, preventing the absorption of calcium.

- Oxalic acid, present in rhubarb and spinach, binds to calcium, preventing the absorption of calcium.
- Fibre binds calcium, preventing the absorption of calcium.
- Excess saturated fat forms insoluble soaps with calcium, preventing its absorption.
- Overconsumption of soft drinks.
- Incorrect calcium/phosphorus ratio.
- Levels of oestrogen in postmenopausal women play a major role in the absorption of calcium.
- Tannins in tea.

7 Water

Elements of Water

Water is made up of two elements, hydrogen and oxygen, in the ratio 2:1 H_2O.

Sources	Functions	Properties
• Taps, wells, bottled water. • Fruit and vegetables. • Drinks, e.g. tea and coffee. • Variety of foods, except dried foods.	• Transports nutrients, oxygen, hormones and enzymes around the body. • Required for hydrolysis of nutrients during digestion. • Needed for all body fluids – urine, saliva, blood, sweat. • Part of all body cells. • Regulates body temperature – perspiration. • Supplies the minerals calcium and fluorine. • Quenches thirst.	• Colourless, odourless, tasteless liquid. • Boils at 100°C, freezes at 0°C. • Converts to a vapour at temperatures above 100°C. • Absorbs and retains heat easily. • Dissolves in a large number of substances (is an excellent solvent). • Neutral pH.

RDA:
Everyone: 2.5 litres per day.

DIET AND HEALTH

Section

8 Energy

9 Dietary Guidelines

10 Dietary and Food Requirements

1 2 3

8 Energy

Energy is the ability to do work. The amount of energy the body needs depends on a variety of factors, including: age, size and body weight, gender, levels of activity, occupation, climate, pregnancy, and illness.

Measuring Energy

Energy is measured in kilocalories (kcal) or kilo-joules (kJ). *(x4 to convert to joules.)*

Nutrient	Kcal/kJ
• 1g Protein	4kcal/17kJ
• 1g Carbohydrate	4kcal/17kJ
• 1g Fat	9kcal/37kJ
• 1g Alcohol	7kcal/29kJ

Age:

Young people require more energy as they are growing rapidly and tend to be very active. As people get older energy requirements decrease, together with their BMR (basal metabolic rate).

Size and body weight:

The larger a body, the more energy it needs.

Gender:

Men have a higher proportion of muscle to fat compared to women, therefore men require more energy.

Fig 8.1: Sedentary work.

Level of activity:

The more active people are, the more energy they need. Running requires more energy than playing a computer game.

Occupation:

Sedentary work, e.g. office work, requires less energy than manual work, e.g. construction work.

Climate:

More energy is needed in colder climates to main-tain a consistent body temperature.

Fig 8.2: Manual work.

Pregnancy:

During pregnancy and lactation, women require more energy.

* **Pregnancy**: Energy needed for the developing foetus.
* **Lactation**: Energy needed for the production of breast milk.

Illness:

During times of illness, different amounts of energy are required, e.g. less energy is needed during convalescence.

Role of Energy in the Body

Energy fulfils four main roles in the body:
* Growth.
* Physical activity.
* Generating heat.
* Basal metabolic rate.

Growth:

Energy is also required for growing by toddlers, young children, adolescents and pregnant women.

Physical activity:

* Energy is required for all physical tasks, including standing, walking and running.
* The more strenuous the physical activity, the more energy required.

Generating heat:

* To maintain the body temperature at 37°C, energy is required.
* This is known as thermogenesis.

Basal metabolic rate (BMR):

* The minimum amount of energy needed to keep internal organs working and to maintain body temperature.

* Each person's BMR is determined by their:
  * Body weight.
  * Age.
  * Gender.
* BMR is measured when a person is completely at rest, twelve hours after eating.

Energy Balance

* Energy balance is reached when: energy intake = energy output.
* If energy intake is greater than energy output, this means being overweight or obese.
* If energy intake is less than energy output, this means being underweight.
* Empty kilocalories provide energy but do not supply the body with any nutritional value, e.g. soft drinks.

Daily Energy Requirements (kilocalories):

	Male (kcal per day)	Female (kcal per day)
• Children	1,500	1,400
• Adolescents	2,800	2,300
• Adult (active)	2,800	2,450
• Adult (sedentary)	2,400	2,150
• Elderly people	2,200	1,800
• Pregnant women		2,400
• Lactating women		2,800

Dietary Guidelines

9

Current Healthy Eating Guidelines

* Eat a wide variety of foods, based on the recommendations of the food pyramid.
* Eat the correct amount of food for your body size.
* Eat five pieces of fruit and vegetables a day.
* Eat more fibre.
* Eat less fat.
* Eat less sugar.
* Eat less salt.
* Drink more water, at least eight glasses (2.5 litres) a day.
* Drink alcohol in moderation.

All of these recommendations have been formulated and are promoted by:
* The Department of Health and Children.

* The Health Promotion Unit (HPU).
* The Health Service Executive (HSE).
* The National Nutritional Surveillance Centre.
* The Irish Nutrition and Dietetic Institute.

These guidelines were formulated:
* To improve the nutritional status of the Irish diet.
* To promote an active and energetic lifestyle.
* To respond to growing concerns about childhood and adult obesity.
* To recommend a reduction in over-processed (high sugar, high salt, high fat) foods.
* To recommend an increase in fibre to prevent disorders of the bowel.
* To ensure that all food groups and servings are met.

Fig 9.1: The food pyramid.

Others (sparingly) → *good fats and oils.*

Meat, fish and alternatives (2 servings) *(nuts & beans.)* ↓ *small amounts.*

Milk and dairy group (3 servings) *3–5* *yoghurt, cheese, eggs.*

Fruit and vegetable group (5 servings) *(5–7)*

Cereal, bread and potato group (6+ servings) *3–5*

(6 shelves) new food pyramid

RDA:

This is found on food labels and shows the level of nutrient requirements that are needed by the public.

Lowest threshold intake (LTI):

This is the least amount of nutrient requirements that are needed by the public.

Dietary reference values (DRV):

These comprise a series of estimates of the amount of energy and nutrients needed by different groups of people.

> Terms found in nutritional literature from around the world.
> **RNI**: Reference nutrient intake
> **LRNI**: Lower reference nutrient intake
> **EAR**: Estimated average requirements

Food Composition Tables

These show the nutrient content of different foods per 100g of food or of liquid and they also show the energy value of foods. You are able to compare and contrast different foods under these headings. These tables are used for specific special diets by nutritionists and for nutritional food labels.

Food Composition Table

	Inedible waste (%)	Energy (kcal)	Energy (kJ)	Protein (g)	Fat (g)	Carbohydrates (as monosaccharides) (g)	Water (g)
Fruit							
Apples	20	46	297	0.3	0	12.0	84
Apricots, dried	0	182	776	4.8	0	43.3	15
Bananas	40	76	326	1.1	0	19.2	71
Blackcurrants	2	28	121	0.9	0	6.6	77
Gooseberries	1	27	116	0.9	0	6.3	87
Grapefruit	60	22	95	0.6	0	5.3	91
Lemons	60	7	31	0.3	0	1.6	91
Melons	40	23	97	0.8	0	5.2	94
Oranges	30	35	150	0.8	0	8.5	86
Orange juice, canned unconcentrated	0	47	201	0.8	0	11.7	87
Peaches, fresh	13	36	156	0.6	0	9.1	86
Peaches, canned (include syrup)	0	88	373	0.4	0	22.9	74
Pears	25	41	175	0.3	0	10.6	83
Pineapples	0	76	325	0.3	0	20.0	77
Plums	8	32	137	0.6	0	7.9	85
Prunes, dried	17	161	686	2.4	0	40.3	23

Food Composition Table (contd.)

	Inedible waste (%)	Energy (kcal)	Energy (kj)	Protein (g)	Fat (g)	Carbohydrates (as monosaccharides) (g)	Water (g)
Raspberries	0	25	105	0.9	0	5.6	83
Rhubarb	33	6	26	0.6	0	1.0	94
Strawberries	3	26	109	0.6	0	6.2	89
Sultanas	0	249	1,064	1.7	0	64.7	18
Nuts							
Almonds	63	580	2,397	20.5	53.5	4.3	5
Coconut, desiccated	0	608	2,509	6.6	62.0	6.4	3
Peanuts, roasted	0	586	2,428	28.1	49.0	8.6	5
Cereals							
Barley, pearl, dry	0	360	1,531	7.7	1.7	83.6	11
Biscuits, chocolate	0	497	2,087	7.0	24.9	65.3	3
Biscuits, cream crackers	0	471	1,985	18.1	16.2	78.0	4
Biscuits, plain	0	431	1,819	7.4	13.2	73.3	3
Biscuits, rich, sweet	0	496	2,084	5.6	22.3	72.7	3
Bread, white	0	251	1,068	8.0	1.7	54.3	39
Bread, wholemeal	0	241	1,025	9.6	3.1	46.7	38
Cornflakes	0	354	1,507	7.4	0.4	85.4	2
Crisp bread, Ryvita	0	318	1,325	10.0	2.1	69.0	6

Fig 9.2: Food composition table.

10 Dietary and Food Requirements

Factors Affecting Dietary Requirements

> The **gender**, **body size** and **activity level** of an individual will determine their energy requirements

Age

Babies

For the first six months of a baby's life, they are fed milk. This can be either breast milk or formulated milk, and both help with development and growth. Breast milk contains all the nutrients a baby needs and is recognised by health professionals as being the best milk for babies.

Breast-Feeding and Bottle-Feeding

The advantages of breast-feeding:
* Breast milk contains antibodies that build up the baby's resistance to diseases.
* Breast milk is always at the correct temperature.
* There is no need to prepare bottles or buy formula, which saves on time and eliminates cost.
* Breasts are sterile and do not need any preparation prior to feeding. Breast milk is readily accessible.
* It promotes bonding between mother and child.
* Babies are likely to gain the correct amount of weight.

* A breast-feeding mother can find it easier to lose excess baby weight.

Some possible reasons why a mother cannot breast-feed may include being HIV positive, use of illegal drugs and prescribed drugs.

Weaning

Solid foods are introduced when the baby is between four and six months old. When introducing solids, single-ingredient foods should be used (this gives time to notice any reactions – allergies or intolerances – the baby has to a particular food). Infant cereals are generally the first type of food given to babies, along with pureed fruit and vegetables.

The following should be taken into account when weaning babies:
* No sugar or salt should be added to babies' diet.
* A balance of foods from the four major food groups is recommended.
* Never give babies tea or coffee.
* Honey should also be avoided until the baby is one year old.
* Avoid additives by using fresh homemade food.

Children

Children need a highly nutritious diet as they continue to grow and develop.

What nutrients do they need and why?
* Protein: This promotes growth and is found in meat, eggs and cheese.
* Calcium and vitamin D: These help develop teeth and bones and are found in dairy products, particularly milk and cheese.
* Iron and vitamin C: These promote general health and foods such as fruit and vegetables are rich in these nutrients.

Below is a list of other requirements specific to this group.
* Children who are active need a high intake of energy foods.
* Sugary sweets and snacks should be avoided in order to reduce the risk of obesity and tooth decay.
* Portion sizes should be relative, i.e. for a child small portion sizes are key. It is also important that food is arranged attractively as children, like adults, 'eat with their eyes'.

* Lunches should be well balanced, e.g. sandwiches should have varied fillings. Fruit and yoghurt should be included with a healthy drink.

Adolescents

Adolescence is a time of continual development and change in a young person's life. It is therefore important that adolescents include enough protein, calcium, iron and certain vitamins in their diet:

What nutrients do they need and why?
* Protein: Needed for growth and is found in meat and fish.
* Calcium and Vitamin D: For healthy teeth and bones. Found in milk and cheese.
* Iron: Important for teenage girls as they begin menstruation, which leads to a loss of iron from the body; this in turn can lead to anaemia. They must, therefore, ensure they include iron-rich foods in their diet. Such foods include red meat and offal.
* Vitamin C: Increases the absorption of iron. It is also an important factor in the diet of teenagers, girls in particular. Vitamin C is found in fresh fruit and vegetables.

Below is a list of other requirements specific to this group:
* The energy required depends on the teenager's level of activity. Very active teenagers require high-energy foods.
* High-fibre foods are a good alternative to sugary foods.

There are various problems that are associated with the eating patterns of adolescents.

* Eating disorders, such as **anorexia nervosa** and **bulimia nervosa**.
* Missing meals.
* Eating a large amount of fast food and snacks.
* 'Faddy' eating.
* High-energy intake through snacks, etc. but low intake of nutrients.
* Start of alcohol consumption.
* Poor diet can contribute to problems such as acne and obesity.

Adults

What nutrients do they need and why?

* Protein: This is important to repair the body's cells. Protein is found in meat, fish and eggs.
* Fat: Polyunsaturated fats reduce the risks of coronary heart disease. Polyunsaturated fats are obtained from oily fish.
* Carbohydrates: These are used to provide energy. Adults should reduce refined carbohydrates and replace them with high-fibre foods, e.g. wholegrain bread.
* Vitamins: Vitamin B for the release of energy from food (obtained from a variety of foods). Vitamin C for the absorption of iron. Vitamin D for the absorption of calcium (oily fish, milk).
* Minerals: Iron for healthy blood and to prevent anaemia; calcium for strong bones and healthy teeth (milk, cheese).
* Water: Water is important to remain hydrated.

Below is a list of other requirements specific to this group:

* Smoking causes many diseases and it kills. Adults should not smoke.
* Adults should be aware of the damage alcohol can inflict on their bodies and reduce their alcohol consumption, or cut it out completely.
* Adults should cut down on their salt intake to prevent high blood pressure.

Elderly People

What nutrients do they need and why?

* Protein: This is necessary for the repair of body cells. Protein-rich foods include eggs, fish.
* Fat: This is necessary to provide energy. To maintain low cholesterol and to reduce the risk of coronary heart disease, unsaturated fats should be used, e.g. oily fish, polyunsaturated butter.
* Carbohydrates: Necessary for energy.
* Fibre: For a healthy digestive system and to prevent constipation. Fibre-rich foods include wholegrain cereals, skins of fruits and vegetables.
* Vitamins: Vitamin C (fruits and vegetables) for iron absorption and the healing of wounds. Vitamin A (liver, eggs, carrots) for healthy eyes and skin. Vitamin D (milk, yoghurt) for the absorption of calcium.
* Minerals: Calcium (milk, cheese) for strong bones and to prevent osteoporosis. Iron (offal, dark green vegetables) to prevent anaemia.
* Water: This is necessary to remain hydrated.

Below is a list of other requirements specific to this group:

* Sugar intake should be reduced to prevent the onset of diabetes mellitus.

* Salt intake should be reduced to prevent high blood pressure.
* Spicy foods should be avoided to prevent indigestion.
* Foods that are easily digestible, such as white fish, eggs and milk, should constitute a sizeable portion of food intake to compensate for the loss of any teeth (or use of false teeth), which can make chewing food difficult.

Convalescents

What nutrients do they need and why?

* Protein: This is necessary for the repair of body cells. Protein foods include eggs, fish.
* Fat: The amount of fat being eaten should be reduced, as there is less energy being used. Reduce saturated fat and replace with polyunsaturated fat.
* Carbohydrates: These are necessary for energy.
* Fibre: This is needed to prevent constipation.
* Vitamins: General vitamin intake for healing is advised.
* Minerals (calcium and iron): These are important to promote recovery, e.g. to heal wounds and to prevent anaemia. Milk, cheese, eggs, offal and dark green vegetables should be included.
* Water: This is important to maintain hydration, as dehydration during an illness is very common.

Below is a list of other requirements specific to this group:
* Small portions that are easy to eat are preferable.
* Meals prepared in a hygienic environment (because of an increased susceptibility to illness).
* Foods that are easily digestible, such as white fish, eggs and milk, should constitute a sizeable portion of food intake.

Pregnant and Breast-Feeding Women

What nutrients do they need and why?

* Protein: This is necessary for the growth of new body cells.
* Fat: Essential fatty acids (oily fish, eggs, liver) are necessary for a foetus's nervous system.
* Carbohydrates: These are necessary for energy.
* Fibre: This is needed for a healthy digestive system and to prevent constipation. Fibre-rich foods include wholemeal bread, pasta, skins of fruit and vegetables.
* Vitamins: Vitamin B folic acid (fortified cereals, leafy green vegetables) is necessary to prevent neural tube defects, such as spina bifida, in foetuses. Vitamin C is important for the pregnant woman's absorption of iron. Vitamin D is important for the pregnant woman's absorption of calcium.
* Minerals: Calcium (dairy products) for strong bones and healthy teeth. Iron for healthy blood and to prevent anaemia in both mother and baby.
* Water: This is necessary for hydration.

Below is a list of other requirements specific to this group:
* Extra energy is needed during pregnancy. This should be obtained from healthy sources.
* Salt intake should be reduced to prevent high blood pressure and water retention (oedema).
* Pregnant women should not smoke or drink alcohol.
* Pregnant women should not eat raw eggs, cooked chilled foods, cream cheese, shellfish, etc. to prevent the risk of food poisoning, such as salmonella and listeria. This could also lead to miscarriage.

Dietary Requirements for Modified Diets

Vegetarians

A vegetarian is a person who does not eat meat or meat products and replaces these foods with foods that come predominantly from plants.

There are a number of different types of vegetarian:
* **Pesco vegetarians:** Do not eat meat, but eat fish.
* **Lacto vegetarians:** Do not eat meat, but consume milk and milk products.

* **Lacto-ovo vegetarians:** Do not eat meat, but eat eggs and dairy products.
* **Pollo vegetarians:** Do not eat red meat, but eat chicken.
* **Vegans:** Do not consume any products derived from animals.

Why People Become Vegetarians

People become vegetarian for a variety of reasons.

* **Ethical reasons:** People believe that it is wrong to kill animals for the benefit of humans.
* **Aesthetic:** Some individuals do not like the look, smell or taste of meat.
* **Economic reasons:** Meat is generally expensive, therefore families on a low-income budget may not be able to afford it.
* **Health reasons:** Meat contains saturated fat and it is recommended to people suffering from coronary heart disease that they omit meat from their diet, or choose a healthier alternative, textured vegetable protein (TVP).
* **Religious reasons:** Some religions exclude meat from their diet. The Hindu religion respects and worships the cow, therefore Hindus choose not to eat meat. Orthodox Jews believe pig meat is unclean.
* **Family influence:** When the majority of individuals in a family choose to be vegetarian, other family members often conform to this practice.

Advantages of a Vegetarian Diet

* A vegetarian diet contains less saturated fat and therefore reduces the risk of a person suffering from high cholesterol.
* A vegetarian diet is generally high in fibre, which also minimises the risk of bowel disorders.
* Vegetarians are less likely to be obese as they have a high intake of fruit and vegetables in their daily diet.
* Few vegetarians develop diabetes.
* Less salt in the diet of vegetarians leads to low levels of hypertension.

Key Points in Planning a Vegetarian Diet

* It is important to include food from the four major vegetarian food groups
* Ensure there are sufficient quantities of vegetable protein in the diet. Textured vegetable protein, tofu and Quorn are good alternatives to animal protein.
* Always consider the type of vegetarian, e.g. if preparing food for a lacto vegetarian, incorporate foods such as milk, cheese and yoghurt.
* Wholemeal cereals are ideal as they provide vegetarians with adequate roughage and B group vitamins.
* In the case of vegans, alternative dairy foods are a necessity; these include products made from soya beans (soya milk, etc.).
* Salt should be replaced with herbs and flavourings.
* Vegetable stock cubes should be used in place of animal stock cubes.

Vegetarian food is divided into five categories:

* Pulse vegetables.
* Grains and nuts.
* Milk and dairy products.
* Fruit.
* Vegetables.

Vegetarians must monitor their diet closely to ensure they do not suffer from diseases caused by deficiencies in their diet. Below is a list of nutrients that must be provided in the diet of a vegan.

Nutrient	Plant source
• HBV protein	Soya protein is a good HBV protein. Seeds and nuts are also good sources of vegetable protein.

Nutrient	Plant source
• Riboflavin (B_2)	Like most B group vitamins, riboflavin is obtained from wholegrain cereals. Other sources include leafy green vegetables, nuts and seeds.
• Cobalamin (B_{12})	Fortified cereals and/or fortified soya milk provide cobalamin. In some cases, supplements could be an option.
• Vitamin D	Also known as the sunshine vitamin, a good source of vitamin D is the sun. Food sources of vitamin D include fortified margarine and fortified breakfast cereals.
• Calcium	Fortified soya milk, fortified juices and leafy green vegetables are sources of calcium.
• Iron	Dark, leafy green vegetables, wholegrains, prunes and dried fruit are excellent sources of plant (non-haem) iron.
• Zinc	Wholegrains, nuts and beans are good sources of zinc.

Coeliac Disease

✳ Coeliac disease occurs when gluten, a protein found in wheat and wheat-based products, damages the lining of the small intestine.

✳ As a result of consuming gluten, the villi of the small intestine become damaged and are unable to absorb an adequate supply of nutrients from food.

Symptoms

There is a range of symptoms to verify that an individual is a coeliac. Some of these are listed below.

Children:
✳ Weight loss.
✳ Crankiness.
✳ Pale, offensive-smelling stools.
✳ Slow growth.

Adults:
✳ Weight loss.
✳ Mouth ulcers.
✳ Tiredness.
✳ Abdominal discomfort.

Dietary guidelines

✳ The most effective way to overcome being coeliac is to adopt a gluten-free diet.

✳ Natural gluten-free foods include fresh meat, fish, cheese, eggs and milk. With an increased awareness of this problem, many gluten-free products – such as gluten-free biscuits, pasta and crackers – are widely available.

✳ Sources of gluten, which someone suffering from coeliac disease must avoid, include all wheat and wheat-based products, such as bread, cakes, breaded foods and pasta.

✳ Hidden sources of gluten include sausages, and some sauces and gravies.

Fig 10.1: Gluten-free symbol.

Diabetes Mellitus

✳ Diabetes is the most common of the endocrine disorders.

✳ Insulin, a hormone produced by the pancreas, controls the amount of glucose in a person's blood.

✳ If there isn't enough insulin, large amounts of glucose remain in the bloodstream.

* People with diabetes either do not produce enough insulin or the insulin produced is ineffective and does not work as it should.

There are two forms of diabetes:
* **Type 1:** Insulin-dependent diabetes, formerly known as juvenile-onset diabetes.
* **Type 2:** Non-insulin-dependent diabetes, formerly known as maturity-onset diabetes.

Insulin-Dependent Diabetes (IDD)

This form of diabetes usually begins in childhood or adolescence. Patients with IDD have a total lack of insulin and must inject insulin into their bloodstream daily or take oral medication.

There are a number of *dietary guidelines* a person with IDD should follow:
* Synchronise meals with times of insulin treatment. This enables the injected insulin to control the body's glucose level, which rises when food is consumed.
* Reduce saturated fat intake, as a high fat intake could lead to coronary heart disease.
* Salt intake should be low, as salt increases the risk of high blood pressure.
* Maintain a high-fibre diet.

Non-Insulin Dependent Diabetes (NIDD)

This condition occurs in middle or later life and is associated with weight gain. Today, it is the most dominant form of diabetes and accounts for 90% of all cases of diabetes worldwide. Patients with NIDD either do not have enough insulin or the insulin they do produce is ineffective.

This form of diabetes is controlled by a rigid diet and, in some cases, medication is prescribed.

There are a number of *dietary guidelines* a person with NIDD should follow:
* Body weight should be reduced by eating fewer calories.
* The intake of saturated fat should be reduced.
* The intake of fruit and vegetables, which are healthy alternatives to sugary snacks, should be increased.

* Salt intake should be kept low.
* Low glycaemic index (low GI) foods should be consumed as they release energy slowly, e.g. starch.

Hypoglycaemia and Hyperglycaemia

Hypoglycaemia occurs when a person's *blood sugar level drops* considerably and their *insulin levels* remain *high*. In such cases, a glucose intake is essential in order to overcome a hypoglycaemic attack. Symptoms of hypoglycaemia include feeling ill, irritability, hunger and perspiration.

Hyperglycaemia occurs when there is *not enough insulin* in the body and a person's *blood sugar level rises*. Insulin is needed to prevent diabetic coma. Symptoms include vomiting, heavy breathing, diabetic coma.

Coronary Heart Disease

Coronary heart disease (CHD) is a major concern in most westernised countries. It is caused by an increase in the consumption of saturated fatty acids, which deposit on the walls of arteries, thereby restricting the flow of blood around the body.

CHD can lead to:
* Heart attack.
* Angina.
* Sudden death.

The major cause of these problems is atherosclerosis, the hardening of arteries within the body.

Heart attack:
This occurs when the blood flow to the heart muscle becomes severely restricted by a blood clot. This clot inhibits the flow of oxygen to the heart.

Angina:
This occurs when blood flow around the heart muscle is restricted. Reduced amounts of oxygen are carried to the heart muscle. This puts extra pressure on the heart, particularly when extra demands are involved, e.g. climbing stairs can cause breathlessness.

Sudden death:

This can occur if problems relating to the heart are not dealt with immediately.

The following are factors associated with CHD:
* High blood cholesterol.
* Cigarette smoking.
* High blood pressure.
* Stress.
* Age (men over the age of 45 and women over the age of 55).
* Obesity.
* Diabetes.
* Gallstones.

There are a number of dietary guidelines a person with CHD should follow:
* The intake of saturated fats should be reduced.
* The intake of oily fish should be increased.
* The intake of fruit and vegetables should be increased.
* Salt should be omitted from the diet.
* Refined carbohydrates, especially sugar, should be avoided.
* Intake of fibre should be increased.
* Low-fat options should always be chosen by a person suffering with CHD.

An increase in exercise is a very important life change essential for a person suffering from CHD. Other important changes that a person with CHD should make include losing weight and not consuming alcohol and cigarettes.

Cholesterol

* Cholesterol is necessary for the production of hormones, which are needed for growth and reproduction.
* Cholesterol is a vital component in the production of the cell wall (in the production of new cells).
* It is an essential ingredient of bile salts produced in the liver, which help in the digestion of emulsified fats.

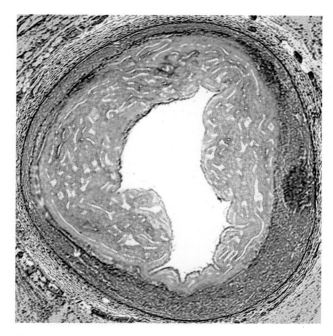

Fig 10.2: Cholesterol in an artery.

The body binds cholesterol with protein to form lipo-protein. There are two types of lipo-protein:

* HDL(high-density lipo-protein) = 'good cholesterol'

* LDL (low-density lipo-protein) = 'bad cholesterol'

LDL is deposited on the walls of the arteries, whereas the 'good' HDL mops up loose cholesterol from the arteries, before carrying it back to the liver where it is broken down and excreted. HDL levels are increased through exercise.

Guidelines to Reduce Levels of 'Bad' Cholesterol in the Body

There are things that people can do to reduce the levels of 'bad' cholesterol in their bodies:
* Reduce the intake of saturated fats.
* Increase the intake of omega-3 and omega-6 fatty acids, which are mainly obtained from oily fish.
* Reduce the intake of food high in cholesterol.
* Check cholesterol level regularly.

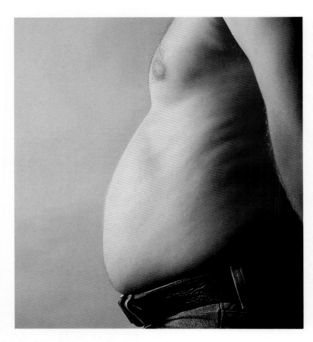

Fig 10.3: An obese man.

Obesity

Fat should account for between 15 and 20 per cent of body weight in healthy young adult men and between 20 and 25 per cent in healthy young adult females. Definition: People who are 20 per cent or more over their ideal weight for their height are said to be obese, and it is estimated that a third of adults in developed nations are obese. Obesity is caused by an imbalance between energy intake and energy expenditure. Severe obesity is defined as a body mass index of 30kg/m or higher.

Causes of Obesity:

There are seven main causes of obesity:

* When a person's energy intake is greater than energy expenditure.
* A person's genetic inheritance.
* Some people store more fat than others.
* A diet high in convenience foods.
* A lack of exercise.
* Certain drugs cause gradual increase in body weight.
* A hormonal imbalance, such as in the thyroid gland.

Risks Associated with Obesity:

There are nine main consequences of obesity to a person's health and well being:

* Coronary heart diseases, caused by the cholesterol build-up in the arteries.
* Breathing difficulties.
* Psychological problems, especially feelings of depression and low self-esteem due to a bad self-image.
* Gallstones caused by high cholesterol.
* Back pain due to excess weight.
* Diabetes, in particular maturity-onset diabetes.
* Arthritis and joint pain can be caused by excess weight.
* Varicose veins.
* High blood pressure.

Dietary Guidelines for Tackling Obesity:

People can use their diet to overcome obesity and reduce the risks it causes to their health:

* Weight loss is key; however, it is important that this is monitored, as excessive weight loss over a short period of time is not as effective as slow, gradual weight loss.
* Increase the intake of fruit and vegetables.
* Increase the intake of high-fibre foods.
* Reduce the intake of saturated fat.
* Avoid convenience foods, which are generally high in additives.
* Eat a balanced diet.
* Drink plenty of water.
* It is important to consult a doctor.

Dental Caries

Dental caries is the decay of the enamel of teeth. The two main forms of dental disease are:

* Periodontal disease.
* Dental cavities.

Plaque is the main cause of these diseases. It is a sticky film composed mostly of bacteria and minerals from saliva. Plaque can harden on teeth and if it is not removed, it causes a plaque build-up, which can lead to irritation of the gums.

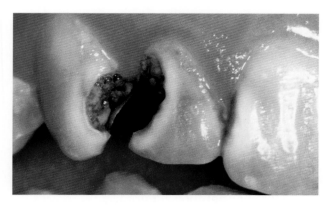

Fig 10.4: Tooth decay.

How to Prevent Cavities:

There are some basic measures that people can take to prevent cavities.

* Increase the resistance of the tooth by regular brushing at least twice a day.
* Remove bacteria by using a mouthwash.
* Floss regularly to remove lodged food from between teeth.
* Visit a dentist at least twice a year.
* Use artificial sweeteners instead of sugar.
* Drink fluoridated water instead of fizzy drinks.

Osteoporosis

Osteoporosis is a common disease among the elderly, and women in particular. It is where bone density is less than expected for a person's age so that bones become lighter and thinner and break very easily. Osteoporosis is commonly known as 'brittle bone' disease.

Factors in Developing Osteoporosis:

The factors associated with developing osteoporosis include:

* **Hereditary factors:** In some families there is a history of osteoporosis.
* **Age:** Post-menopausal women are at higher risk, as they no longer produce the female hormone oestrogen that maintains calcium levels.
* **Calcium intake:** If a person's diet is lacking or low in calcium and vitamin D, they are more prone to the disease.

* **Lack of exercise:** To keep bones healthy, people require regular exercise (thirty minutes three times a week is deemed sufficient).
* **Gender:** Women are more at risk of developing osteoporosis.

Preventing Osteoporosis

The main methods used to prevent the development of osteoporosis are:

* Eating a well-balanced diet, rich in calcium and vitamin D. Such a diet is particularly important during stages of growth such as childhood, adolescent and during a woman's child-bearing years.

* Taking regular exercise.
* Avoiding smoking and avoiding the consumption of alcohol.
* Women taking HRT (hormone replacement therapy) after menopause, as this can reduce calcium loss and thereby decrease the risk of fractures later.

Fig 10.5: A woman with osteoporosis.

* Reducing the intake of caffeine and salt as these are associated with decreasing bone mass density.

Bowel Disorders

Bowel disorders are caused by a lack of fibre in a person's diet. They are becoming more prevalent in developed countries where a lot of processed foods are eaten. They include:

* Constipation.
* Haemorrhoids (piles).
* Diverticulitis.
* Colon cancer.
* Irritable bowel syndrome.

Constipation

This occurs when the faeces become hard and difficult to pass. Fibre absorbs a large amount of water, thus making faeces soft and bulky, therefore preventing constipation.

Haemorrhoids (Piles)

These are swollen veins on the rectum and anus. They form as a result of severe straining during defecation. They can lead to excessive itching and, in some cases, blood loss.

Diverticulitis

* As a consequence of the extra pressure required to remove waste when constipated, the intestinal wall can become damaged, forming small pouch-like structures called diverticula.
* These can become full of food waste. The bacteria present will produce acids and gases. Inflamation will occur, causing extreme pain.

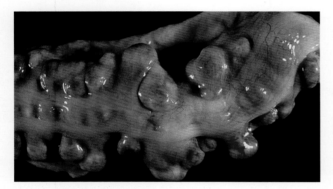

Fig 10.6: Diverticulitis in the intestine.

Colon Cancer

Cancer of the bowel is caused by a lack of fibre in a person's diet. Too much saturated fat and a lack of fruit and vegetables can cause this form of cancer.

Irritable Bowel Syndrome

This causes bloating and extreme cramps in the stomach. Diarrhoea or constipation can be two of the major effects.

Tips to increase fibre intake in the diet:
* Choose wholegrain options, i.e. bread, flour, pasta and rice; these aid peristalsis.
* Drink plenty of water, as fibre absorbs water and this aids the movement of food through the digestive system.
* Increase intake of fruit and vegetables, in particular their skins, as these are a rich source of fibre.
* Exercise regularly.

The advantages of a diet high in fibre:
* A high-fibre diet is low in fat.
* Fibre gives a feeling of fullness.
* Fibre prevents bowel disorders.

Anaemia

This is a disorder that occurs when there is an insufficient quantity of iron in the body. Teenage girls tend to suffer from anaemia.

Symptoms of Anaemia:

The symptoms of anaemia include:
* Tiredness.
* Giddiness.
* Pale complexion.
* Weakness.
* Feeling 'run down'.

Causes of Anaemia:

Anaemia is caused by:
* Lack of iron in the diet.
* A low intake of vitamin C.
* Heavy blood loss.

Eating Disorders

There are two types of eating disorder:
* Anorexia nervosa.
* Bulimia nervosa.

Psychotherapy and special dietary treatment are necessary to treat both conditions.

Anorexia Nervosa

This is a psychological condition whereby an individual has a fear of becoming obese. It most commonly affects teenage girls. A person with anorexia tries to lose weight by:

Fig 10.7: A girl with anorexia.

* Starvation.
* Self-induced vomiting.
* An abuse of laxatives.

If medical attention is not given, death may occur through starvation.

Symptoms of anorexia nervosa:

Symptoms associated with anorexia nervosa include:

* Periods stopping.
* Excess hair growth; this occurs as the body seeks to maintain its temperature.
* A thinning of hair.

Bulimia Nervosa

A person with bulimia nervosa generally turns to food to alleviate stress. They will try to lose weight by:

* Binge eating followed by self-induced vomiting.
* Abusing laxatives.

Symptoms of bulimia nervosa:

* Tooth decay (mottling of the teeth).
* Throat irritation due to vomiting.
* Dehydration.
* Inflammation of the oesophagus.
* A swelling of the salivary glands.

Exam Question
Higher Level (2007)

Questions

'Coronary Heart Disease (CHD) remains the leading cause of death in Ireland, accounting for over 7,000 deaths annually.'
(*CHAIR – Coronary Heart Attack Ireland Register*)

1. Identify and elaborate on:
    (i) the lifestyle changes.
    (ii) the dietary guidelines
    that should be followed in order to reduce the incidence of coronary heart disease. (16)

2. Plan a day's menu for a person with coronary heart disease (CHD). Include **one** *functional food* in the menu and state a reason for its inclusion. (22)

3. Write an informative account of cholesterol. (12)

Answers

1. Identify and elaborate on:
    (i) the lifestyle changes.
    (ii) the dietary guidelines
    that should be followed in order to reduce the incidence of coronary heart disease. (16)

    4 points x 4 marks each = 16.

1. (i) **Lifestyle changes to reduce CHD**
   - An increase in exercise is a very important life change essential to a person suffering from coronary heart disease.
   - Weight loss is essential, together with avoidance of alcohol and smoking.

   (ii) **Dietary guidelines to reduce CHD**
   - Reduce intake of saturated fat.
   - Increase intake of oily fish.
   - Increase intake of fruit and vegetables.
   - Omit salt from the diet.
   - Avoid refined carbohydrates, especially sugar.
   - Increase intake of fibre.
   - Always choose low-fat options.

2. Plan a day's menu for a person with coronary heart disease (CHD). Include **one** *functional food* in the menu and state a reason for its inclusion. (22)

   3 meals x 5 marks each = 15.

   Functional food = 3 marks if included; reason for its inclusion = 4 marks. Total = 7.

Breakfast
Glass of freshly squeezed orange juice
Bowl of hot porridge made with low-fat milk and water
Wholemeal brown bread and Flora pro.activ spread
Tea

Lunch
Chicken Caesar salad with low-calorie dressing
Benecol yoghurt drink
Glass of chilled water

Dinner
Fish and tomato bake served with steamed mixed vegetables and potatoes
Fresh fruit salad
Glass of chilled water

Snacks during the day
Apple or pear with skin, water, low-fat yoghurt

Reasons for breakfast choice:

- The orange juice is a good source of vitamin C, which is necessary for general health and stimulates the appetite.
- The porridge is a low GI food, i.e. slow energy-releasing food, which will give the person a feeling of fullness for longer and they therefore won't want to be snacking.
- The wholemeal brown bread is a good source of fibre, which aids in the removal of waste from the body, gives a feeling of fullness and prevents constipation.
- Low-fat spread is used here, as a person with coronary heart disease should always use low-fat products instead of full-fat products where possible.

Lunch:

- The chicken in the Caesar salad has less saturated fat than red meat.
- The lettuce leaves have little to no fat content.
- The low-calorie dressing can be served on the side so that it is used sparingly.
- Water hydrates the body and prevents a feeling of being bloated.

Dinner:

- Tuna is the fish used in this dish. It is an oily fish which is high in polyunsaturated fatty acids. Polyunsaturated fatty acids are thought to help lower cholesterol and reduce the incidence of CHD.
- Tomatoes used in this main course are low in kilocalories.
- The vegetables are steamed in order to retain as many vitamins and minerals as possible. No salt will be added during cooking or serving. (Salt is thought to increase the incidence of hypertension.)
- Fresh fruit salad for dessert ensures that the person gets as many vitamins and minerals as possible. The fruit salad is served in its own juices so as not to increase the sugar content.

Snacks:

- The snacks throughout the day are low-calorie foods. The fruit (apple or pear) provides more roughage when eaten with the skin on.

Functional food included and reason for its inclusion:

Functional Food	Added ingredient	Health Benefit
• Flora pro.activ	Plant sterols	Reduces cholesterol build-up and the risk of coronary heart disease.

3. Write an informative account of cholesterol. (12)

3 points x 4 marks each = 12.

Functions of cholesterol:

- Cholesterol is necessary for the production of hormones.
- These hormones are needed for growth and reproduction.
- Cholesterol is a vital component in the production of the cell wall (in production of new cells).
- It is an essential ingredient of bile salts

produced in the liver (which help in the digestion of emulsified fats).

The body binds cholesterol with protein to form lipo-protein. There are two types:
- HDL (high-density lipo-protein).
- LDL (low-density lipo-protein).

HDL (good cholesterol):
- HDL mops up loose cholesterol from the arteries, then carries it back to the liver where it is broken down and excreted.
- HDL levels are increased through exercise.

LDL (bad cholesterol):
- LDL deposits on the wall of the arteries.

FOOD COMMODITIES

11 Meat

12 Poultry

13 Fish

14 Eggs

15 Milk

16 Butter

17 Cream

18 Yoghurt

19 Cheese

20 Alternative Protein Foods

21 Fruit

22 Vegetables

23 Nuts and Legumes

24 Cereals

25 Fats and Oils

26 Meal Management and Planning

27 Food Preparation and Cooking Processes

28 Food Preparation and Cooking Equipment

29 Recipe Modification

30 Aesthetic Awareness of Food

31 Sensory Analysis

32 The Irish Diet

33 The Irish Food Industry

Section

1 2 3

11 Meat

Classification of Meat

Meat can be classified in four categories: carcass, poultry, game and offal.

Carcass	Poultry	Game	Offal
Beef	Chicken	Rabbit	Liver
Pork/Bacon	Duck	Pheasant	Kidney
Lamb/Mutton	Turkey	Deer	Heart

Composition

Meat is composed of protein, fat, vitamins, minerals and water. It doesn't contain any carbohydrates, vitamin C or calcium.

Protein	Fat	Carbohydrate	Vitamins	Minerals	Water
20–30%	10–30%	0%	B group	Iron Potassium Sulphur Phosphorus Zinc	50–60%

Nutritive Value/Nutritional Significance

Nutrients	Explanation
Protein	• The type of protein present is animal protein (high biological value). • Meat fibres contain the proteins myosin, actin and globulin. • Connective tissue contains the proteins collagen and elastin.

Nutrients	Explanation
Fat	• The type of fat present is animal fat (saturated fat). • The amount of fat depends on the type/cut of meat. • Visible fat can be found, e.g. the rind of rashers. • Invisible fat is marbled throughout the connective tissue, e.g. mince.
Carbohydrates	• There is no carbohydrate present in meat; however, a small amount of glycogen can be found in the liver.
Vitamins	• B group (niacin, thiamine B_1, riboflavin B_2, pyridoxine B_6 and cobalamin B_{12} are present in meat). • Vitamins A and D are found in offal.
Minerals	• Haem iron is found in meat. • Potassium, zinc, phosphorus and sulphur are present in meat in small amounts.
Water	• The water content in meat varies: the higher the fat content, the less water present.

Think!
Who is it good for? Why is it good for them? What are its advantages?

Dietetic Value/Contribution to the Diet

- Meat contains HBV protein that is necessary for growth in children, teenagers, pregnant women.
- Meat is an excellent source of **haem iron**, which prevents anaemia in teenage girls.
- Meat contains **saturated fat** that can lead to coronary heart disease and high cholesterol, therefore people with coronary heart disease should lower their intake of red meat.
- Meat lacks three Cs: carbohydrates, calcium, vitamin C, therefore it is good served with foods rich in these things. For example, carbohydrate is found in potatoes, pasta and rice. Calcium is found in milk and cheese. Vitamin C is found in fresh fruit and vegetables.
- Meat is widely available to consumers, therefore it can be used in a wide variety of dishes.
- Some meats can be purchased cheaply, e.g. offal is relatively inexpensive and is very nutritious.

Structure of Meat

✳ Meat is made up of: connective tissue, meat fibres and fat globules.
- Connective tissue contains the proteins elastin and collagen.
- Meat fibres contain water, proteins (actin, myosin and globulin), minerals and extractives.
- Extractives are substances which are dissolved in water and improve the flavour. They are found in the meat fibres, e.g. lactic acid.
- Fat globules can be found in two forms: invisible fat (which is 'marbled' throughout the meat fibres) and visible fat (which is found under the animal skin and is known as adipose tissue).

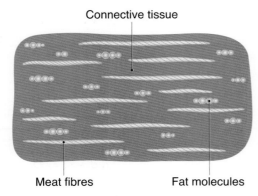

Connective tissue

Meat fibres — Fat molecules

Fig 11.1: The structure of meat.

Selecting and Buying Meat

* Always buy meat from a clean, reliable source.
* Ensure the staff maintain good hygienic practices.
* Make sure meat has a fresh smell.
* Look for moist flesh with a good colour.
* Choose cheaper, more economical cuts which are just as nutritious as more expensive cuts of meat.
* Avoid buying meat with a lot of visible fat, bone or gristle.
* Always buy meat suitable for the cooking method intended.
* Check for traceability.

Storing Meat

* Refrigerate meat below 5°C.
* Place meat in the fridge as soon after purchasing as possible.
* Remove packaging and place the meat on a plate. Vacuum-packed meats should remain in their packaging.
* Always cover to prevent meat drying out.
* Always use meat within two or three days of purchase.

Cooking Methods

* Grilling.
* Baking.
* Frying.
* Pan-frying.
* Stir-frying.
* Casseroling.
* Barbecuing.
* Stewing.

Causes of Toughness in Meat

Tough meat = long meat fibres

Tender meat = short meat fibres

Age of the animal:

The older the animal, the tougher the meat.

Activity of the animal:

Different parts of the animal have longer meat fibres because they are used when the animal is active, e.g. the legs and neck are more active than the back. Cuts of meat from these areas will be tougher than meat from the back.

Treatment of the animal prior to slaughter:

Prior to slaughter, animals should be allowed to rest, as this enables the glycogen levels to build up in the muscles of the animal.

Treatment of the animal after slaughter:

* After slaughter, the glycogen converts to lactic acid. This has a tenderising effect on the meat.
* If meat isn't hung properly, this will result in toughening of the meat.

Fig 11.2: Carcasses of beef hanging.

Incorrect cooking method:

✳ Tough cuts of meat require long, slow, moist methods of cooking, e.g. stewing.

✳ Tender cuts of meat can be cooked by fast methods, e.g. frying and grilling.

✳ An incorrect method of cooking for a particular cut of meat will result in the meat becoming tough.

Tenderising Meat

There are various ways in which meat can be made tender.

Injecting the animal with proteolytic enzymes prior to slaughter:

✳ These protein-splitting enzymes break down meat structure, thus having a tenderising effect.

Mechanical methods:

These include:

✳ Mincing meat with a mincer.

✳ Piercing the meat with a sharp knife.

✳ Pounding the meat with a steak hammer.

Fig 11.3: Meat hammer.

Meat Processing

There are five main methods of processing meat.

Commercially prepared tenderisers:

✳ These can be sprinkled on the meat and include:
  ● Ficin from figs.
  ● Papain from the paw-paw fruit.
  ● Bromelin from pineapple.

Cooking methods:

✳ Slow, moist cooking methods, e.g. boiling, stewing or casseroling, tenderise meat.

Marinades:

Marinades contain a combination of acids, herbs and spices which tenderise the meat and add flavour.

Cooking Meat

Cooking meat changes some of its attributes.

✳ The protein in meat coagulates; this causes a shrinkage of the meat fibres. Meat shrinks in size by up to 20 per cent during cooking.

✳ Collagen (protein in connective tissue) is converted to gelatine, making the meat more digestible.

✳ B group vitamins and some minerals are lost during cooking.

✳ Bacteria are destroyed.

✳ Fat melts, adding flavour to the meat.

✳ Extractives are squeezed out of the fibres, causing flavours to develop.

✳ When meat is overcooked, it becomes tough and indigestible.

✳ Colour change: meat changes from red to brown.

Process	Method	Effects
Freezing	● Meat is commercially frozen at -30° C.	● Quick freezing enables little loss of nutrients. ● Some extractives and B group vitamins are lost in freezing.

Process	Method	Effects
Vacuum Packing	• Meat is sealed in strong polythene from which the air is removed, e.g. bacon rashers.	• Freezer burn may occur if packaging is torn. • There is little effect on the nutritive value of meat.
Canning	• Meat is heated to high temperatures. • There are two methods of canning: in-container canning and aseptic canning (see Food preservation p. 219).	• There is a loss of B group vitamins. • There is a change in the colour, flavour and texture of the meat. • The fat content of meat is increased.
Curing	• Brine solutions are injected into the carcass of the meat and the meat is then soaked for five days to enable flavour to develop. • This form of processing can involve smoking.	• There is an increase in the salt content of the meat. • There is a change in the colour and flavour of the meat.
Dehydration	• This is the removal of water from meat, used in packet soups and sauces.	• The B group vitamins are lost. • There is a change in the colour, flavour and texture of the meat.

Meat Products

✱ Sausages.
✱ Salami (dried sausage).
✱ Beefburgers.
✱ Pâté.
✱ Gelatine.
✱ Cooked meats.

Fig 11.4: Selection of meat products.

Offal

Offal is the edible internal organs of an animal, such as liver, kidneys, heart, etc. It is a good source of iron, protein and B group vitamins. Liver is also a good source of vitamins A and D. Offal increases the nutritive value of a dish.

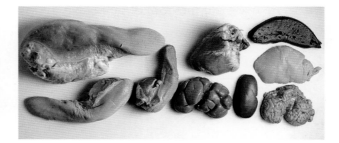

Fig 11.5: Selection of offal.

BSE (Bovine Spongiform Encephalopathy)

BSE is also known as 'mad cow disease'. It affects the brain and the spinal cord of an animal and results in lesions ('holes') in its brain, making it look 'spongy'. BSE occurred when animals were fed bone meal. This meal was composed of the bones and spinal cords of other animals and this is how the disease was transmitted. The human form of the disease is nvCJD (new variant Creutzfeldt-Jakob disease). It affects the nervous system of an individual and often results in death.

Beef Quality Assurance Scheme

* This scheme was set up by An Bord Bia.
* Its aim is to improve the quality of the meat available to consumers.

* Using HACCP as a frame of reference, safety management systems must be in place.
* Regular inspections are carried out by An Bord Bia.
* Quality marks are awarded where high standards and regulations are met.

Fig 11.6: Beef Quality Assurance logo.

Sample Exam Questions

Questions

1. What are the effects of cooking on meat? (12)

2. Explain how to store meat. (8)

Sample Answers

1. What are the effects of cooking on meat? (12)

   4 points x 3 marks each = 12.

   The effects of cooking on meat are:
   * The protein in meat coagulates, causing the shrinkage of the meat fibres. Meat shrinks in size by up to 20 per cent during cooking.
   * Collagen (protein in connective tissue) is converted to gelatine, making the meat more digestible.
   * B group vitamins and some minerals are lost during cooking.
   * Colour change: meat changes from red to brown.

2. Explain how to store meat. (8)

   2 points x 4 marks each = 8.

   * Place meat in the fridge (below 5°C) as soon after purchasing as possible.
   * Remove packaging and place the meat on a plate. Vacuum-packed meats should remain in their packaging.

12 Poultry

Nutritive Value/Nutritional Significance

Nutrient	Explanation
Protein	• The type of protein present is animal protein (high biological value).
Fat	• The type of fat present is animal fat (saturated fat). • The percentage of fat depends on the type of bird, i.e. duck, goose, chicken.
Carbohydrates	• There are no carbohydrates present.
Vitamins	• Water-soluble B group vitamins: thiamine (B_1), riboflavin (B_2), and niacin are present.
Minerals	• There is less iron in poultry than in red meat. • Trace amounts of calcium, phosphorus and zinc can be found.
Water	• The amount of water varies depending on the amount of fat; for example, chicken contains more water than duck.

Dietetic Value/Contribution to the Diet

- Poultry has HBV protein which is important for growing children.
- Poultry is easy to digest, therefore particularly suitable for the elderly.
- The HBV protein is important for people recovering from illness (convalescents) as it helps repair body cells.
- Turkey and skinless chicken breasts have a low fat content and are therefore suitable for people on low-cholesterol/low-kilocalorie diets.
- Poultry can be used in a wide range of dishes, e.g. chicken curry, Cantonese duck.
- It is relatively inexpensive.
- Carbohydrates can be added to make a balanced dish, e.g. sweet-and-sour chicken and rice, duck in a plum sauce with noodles.

Buying Poultry	Storing Poultry	Cooking Poultry
<ul><li>Buy from a clean, hygienic shop.</li><li>Check the use-by date on packaging.</li><li>Ensure there is no unpleasant smell or bruising.</li><li>Ensure the flesh is firm and plump.</li><li>Ensure frozen poultry is frozen solid.</li></ul>	<ul><li>Fresh poultry should be stored as for meat (in a refrigerator below 5°C).</li><li>Frozen poultry should be put into the freezer as soon as possible.</li></ul>	<ul><li>Fresh poultry: remove giblets and wash meat thoroughly.</li><li>Frozen: defrost thoroughly.</li><li>Wash hands and areas that came into contact with poultry to prevent cross-contamination.</li><li>Any leftovers should be cooled quickly, stored in the fridge and used up in one or two days.</li></ul>

Processing Poultry

Poultry can be processed in many ways before it is cooked and eaten.

✱ **Fresh:** whole, breasts, boned and rolled.
✱ **Frozen:** products, e.g. chicken burgers, chicken nuggets, ready-made meals, e.g. sweet-and-sour chicken, chicken curry.

13 Fish

Classification of Fish

Fish can be classified in three ways, according to:

* **Shape:** flat or round.

* **Habitat:** demersal (swim near the seabed) or pelagic (swim near the surface of the water).

* **Nutritive value and appearance**.

Types of Fish

There are three types of fish: white, oily and shellfish.

White	Oily	Shellfish
• Whiting • Cod • Haddock • Hake	• Mackerel • Herring • Salmon • Tuna	**MOLLUSCS (found in a shell)** • Mussels • Scallops • Oysters • Squid

Fig 13.1: White fish.

Fig 13.2: Oily fish.

Fig 13.3: Molluscs.

CRUSTACEANS (have claws)
* Prawns   • Crab
* Shrimp   • Lobster

Fig 13.4: Crustaceans.

Average Composition of Fish

	Protein	Fat	Carbohydrates	Vitamins	Minerals	Water
• White fish	17%	0.5%	0%	B group	1.5%	80%
• Oily fish	18%	10–15%	0%	A, D, B group	2%	65%
• Shellfish	16%	2.5%	0%	B group	2%	79%

Nutritive Value/Nutritional Significance

Nutrient	Explanation
Protein	• Fish is a good source of high biological value protein. • The proteins present include actin, myosin and collagen.
Fat	• Oily fish contains polyunsaturated fatty acids (omega-3 fatty acids), which lower blood fats, helping to make blood less sticky so it flows more easily around the body and is less likely to clot. • White fish contain only trace amounts of fat, as the fat in white fish is found in the liver, which is removed during preparation.
Carbohydrates	• Fish contains no carbohydrates because the glycogen is converted to lactic acid during the struggle when the fish is caught.
Vitamins	• Fish contains B group vitamins. • Oily fish contains the fat-soluble vitamins A and D.
Minerals	• Fish is an excellent source of iodine. • Fish is a good source of phosphorus and potassium. • Canned fish contains calcium, which is good for bones and teeth.
Water	• Fish is composed of 65–80 per cent water. • White fish contains the most water.

Dietetic Value of Fish/Contribution to the Diet

- Fish contains HBV protein, which is necessary for growth of children, teenagers and pregnant women.
- Tinned fish contains calcium, which is important for bone development.
- Fish is an excellent source of omega–3 fatty acids, which may help reduce the risk of coronary heart disease, essential for people with high cholesterol.
- Fish is low in fat and therefore an excellent meat substitute. This is particularly important for those who are obese or overweight.
- Fish lacks carbohydrates, therefore is good served with carbohydrate-rich foods, e.g. potatoes.
- Fish is widely available to consumers.
- Fish can be used in a wide variety of dishes.
- Fish in season can be purchased cheaply.
- Fish does not take long to prepare and has a very short cooking time.

Structure of Fish

* Fish is made up of bundles of short fibres called myomeres.
* Myomeres are held together by connective tissue (collagen). Collagen is converted to gelatine during cooking, causing fish to flake easily.
* The fat present in oily fish can be found amongst the fibres.
* There is less connective tissue than in meat.

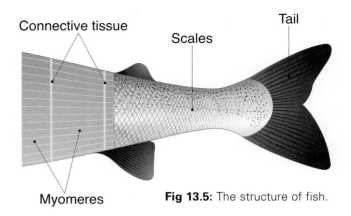

Fig 13.5: The structure of fish.

Fish Cuts

Fish can be bought in three ways: whole, filleted or in cutlets/steak.

Whole:

* Large fish, such as salmon, turbot, can be descaled and cleaned by removing the intestines.
* Smaller fish, such as trout or sole, can be served whole or as a portion.

Fillets:

* A fillet is a long, thin piece of flesh cut the length of the fish on either side of the bone.
* Four fillets can be obtained from flat fish.
* Two fillets can be obtained from round fish.

Cutlets and steak:

* Steaks and cutlets are large slices of fish that are cut vertically through the fish, including the bone, with the skin intact.
* Large round fish are best suited for this cut.

Buying Fish

Fish should be bought at its freshest. Signs of freshness are:
* No unpleasant smells.
* Flesh is firm, shiny and moist.
* Colour is distinct.
* Gills are bright red or pink in colour.
* Eyes are bright and bulging.

Other points to note:
* Buying fish in season will ensure freshness and value.

Whole fish

Fish fillet

Fish cutlet

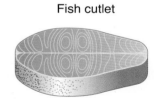

Fish steak

Fig 13.6: Different cuts of fish.

* Buying from a reliable source will ensure the fish has been stored in the correct way to retain freshness.
* When buying fresh molluscs, always make sure that the shells are closed or close when they are touched.
* When buying frozen fish, make sure that the fish is frozen solid.

Storing Fish

Ideally, fish should be bought as required and used immediately. If it is to be stored, do the following:
* Remove packaging and rinse fish in cold water.
* Store on the top shelf of the refrigerator.
* Fish should be stored separately from other foods. When opened, tinned fish should be used immediately.

* Fish that will be stored for more than one day should be frozen.
* Frozen fish should be stored in the freezer compartment of the fridge.

Cooking Methods

* **Poaching:** This involves placing the fish in simmering liquid and maintaining the simmer, allowing the fish to cook.
* **Steaming:** Fish is placed on a lightly greased plate, covered and cooked over boiling water.
* **Grilling:** This is a fast method of cooking. A moderate heat ensures correct cooking. Turn fish only once to prevent it breaking.
* **Frying:** This is the most popular method of preparing fish as it adds great flavour: but it increases the calorie content.

* **Baking:** This is a healthy alternative to frying. Fish can be stuffed, seasoned and wrapped in foil or baked in a casserole dish.
* **Microwaving:** This is suited to fish, as the high moisture content and relatively thin cut of fish ensures rapid and even cooking.
* **Barbecueing:** Fillets and whole fish can be wrapped in foil and seasoned well still acquiring the charcoal-smoked flavour from the barbecue.

Effects of Cooking on Fish

* Protein coagulates, the fish shrinks and flesh becomes opaque.
* Connective tissue changes to gelatine (fish breaks easily).
* Bacteria are destroyed.

* There is some loss of B group vitamins.
* If fish is cooked in water, i.e. poached, soluble vitamins and minerals leach into the cooking liquid.

Preparing Fish for Cooking

1. Dip fingers in salt for a better grip.
2. Descale fish.

3. Remove head, tail and fins.
4. Remove intestines and wash inner cavity.
5. Wash the outside of the fish.

Remove scales.

Remove head, tail and fins.

Cut underside and remove insides.

Wash fish thoroughly.

Fig 13.7: Preparing fish.

Spoilage of Fish

Fish is a very perishable food that spoils easily because of:

* **Oxidative rancidity**: Fish reacts with oxygen in the air.
* **Enzymic activity**: Enzymes cause deterioration of fish flesh. These enzymes remain active even at low temperatures.
* **Bacterial action**: When a fish is caught, it struggles violently, which uses up all the glycogen stores in the muscle and liver. When a fish dies, therefore, there is no supply of glycogen, as it has generally been converted to lactic acid. Lactic acid has a preservative effect on foods. Without it, bacteria act on fish flesh, breaking it down and producing a strong-smelling nitrogen compound, trimethylamine.

Preserving and Processing Fish

There are three methods of preserving fish: freezing, canning and smoking.

Process	Method	Effects
Freezing	• Commercially frozen fish is blast frozen at −30°C, resulting in loss of vitamin B and some minerals. • Microbes are inactivated at temperatures less than 0°C and therefore freezing effectively stops microbial growth.	• This method of preserving is probably the best, as it maintains the colour, flavour, texture and nutritive value of any food.
Canning	• Most fish are suitable for canning. • The high temperature used during the canning process kills the micro-organisms that can cause decay.	• The one big nutritional advantage of canning is that it softens the bones, thus making fish a good source of calcium.
Smoking *(cold, hot and artificial)*	• The underlying principles of smoking are that creosote and formaldehyde (the chemicals in smoke) prevent the action of micro-organisms. There are three types of smoking: cold smoking, hot smoking and artificial smoking. • **Cold smoking**: This involves smoke from wood chips or dust which is blown over the fish. The temperature does not exceed 27°C, therefore the fish needs to be cooked before it is eaten. • **Hot smoking**: The temperature is gradually increased during smoking to approximately 80°C and held there for a short cooking period. • **Artificial smoking**: Some fish can be soaked in food colours and flavours, e.g. lemon yellow for white fish and annatto for kippers.	• Colour changes and there is a change in the flavour from an increase in the salt content.

Fish Products

Fish is used to make many ready-to-eat products, e.g. breaded fish, scampi, fish fingers and fish cakes.

Fish fingers:

* These are made from blocks of frozen, filleted white fish.
* The fish is cut into fingers, dipped into a batter or breadcrumbs and refrozen.

* Fish fingers generally contain 50–70 per cent fish, depending on the cooking process.

Fish cakes:

* These contain minced fish, potatoes, herbs and seasoning.
* They are usually shaped into rounds, coated in batter or breadcrumbs and frozen.
* They must contain a minimum of 35 per cent fish.

Part Exam Questions
Higher Level (2004)

Questions

1. Give a detailed account of the nutritive value of fish. (12)

2. State why oily fish is recommended for a person with coronary heart disease. (6)

Sample Answers

1. Give a detailed account of the nutritive value of fish. (12)

   4 points x 3 marks each = 12.

2. State why oily fish is recommended for a person with coronary heart disease. (6)

   2 points x 3 marks each = 6.

   Oily fish is recommended for a person with coronary heart disease for the following reasons.
   * Oily fish contains polyunsaturated fatty acids (omega-3 and 6 fatty acids.
   * Fatty acids lower blood fats, helping to make blood less sticky so it flows more easily around the body and is less likely to clot. This is essential for people suffering from coronary heart disease.

Nutritive Value/Nutritional Significance

Nutrient	Explanation
Protein	• Fish is a good source of high biological value protein. • The proteins present include actin, myosin and collagen.
Carbohydrates	• Fish contains no carbohydrates because the glycogen is converted to lactic acid during the struggle when the fish is caught.
Vitamins	• Fish contains B group vitamins. • Oily fish contains the fat-soluble vitamins A and D.
Minerals	• Fish is an excellent source of iodine. • Fish is a good source of phosphorus and potassium. • Canned fish contains calcium, which is good for bones and teeth.

14 Eggs

Nutritional Composition of an Egg

Nutrient	Whole egg	White	Yolk
Protein	13%	12%	16%
Fat	12%	0.25%	32%
Carbohydrates	0%	0%	0%
Vitamins	A, B, D	B group	A, B, D
Minerals	1%	0.75%	2%
Water	74%	87%	49%

Nutritive Value/Nutritional Significance

Nutrient	Explanation
Protein	• The type of protein present is animal protein (high biological value). • In the white, the proteins present are ovalbumin and globulin. • In the yolk, the proteins present are vitellin and livetin.
Fat	• The type of fat present is animal fat (saturated fat). • Eggs contain the emulsifier lecithin. • Cholesterol is present in eggs.
Carbohydrates	• There are no carbohydrates found in eggs.
Vitamins	• **Water soluble**: B_1 thiamine, B_2 riboflavin, B_{12} cobalamin and niacin. • **Fat soluble**: A, D, E.
Minerals	• The minerals present are: calcium, iron, phosphorus, sulphur.
Water	• There is 74 per cent water in eggs.

Dietetic Value/Contribution to the Diet

- Eggs have HBV protein for growth of body cells, which is important for children and adolescents.
- Eggs are easy to digest and are a suitable food for the elderly.
- Eggs have HBV protein for repair of body cells. This is particularly important for convalescents.
- Eggs contain cholesterol and saturated fat, therefore people on low-cholesterol/low-kilocalorie diets need to limit their consumption of eggs.

- Eggs are a good meat alternative and are suitable for lacto vegetarians.
- Can be used in a wide range of dishes, e.g. quiches and omelettes.
- Inexpensive to buy.
- Carbohydrate foods can be served with eggs to make a balanced dish, e.g. omelette and chips, quiche Lorraine with baby new potatoes.

Structure of Eggs

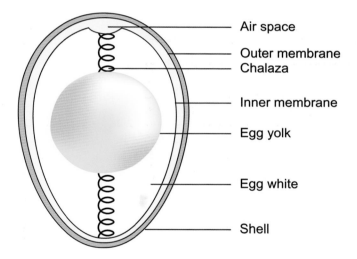

Air space
Outer membrane
Chalaza
Inner membrane
Egg yolk
Egg white
Shell

Fig 14.1: An egg.

Shell:

The shell:
* Is 10 per cent of the egg.
* Is a hard, protective layer made up of calcium carbonate.
* Sporous.

* Can be white or brown in colour.
* Has a thin membrane inside, which keeps the egg in place.

White:

The white:
* Is 60 per cent of the egg.
* Is a viscous, colourless liquid.
* Is mainly made up of water.
* Is high in the proteins ovalbumin and globulin.
* Is a good source of vitamins and minerals.

Yolk:

The yolk:
* Is 30 per cent of the egg.
* Is held in the centre of the egg by string-like structures called chalazae.
* Is high in the proteins vitellin and livetin.
* Is high in saturated fat.
* Is high in cholesterol.
* Is high in lecithin (natural emulsifier).
* Is a good source of vitamins A and D.

Buying Eggs

* Check best-before date.
* Check that they are heavy for their size.
* Check there are no cracked or broken eggs.
* Decide whether you want to buy free range or organic eggs.
* Check for Quality Assurance logo.

Storing Eggs

* Eggs should be stored in a refrigerator.
* Eggs should be stored pointed end downwards; this prevents the chalazae from breaking.
* Eggs should be stored away from strong-smelling foods, as the shell is porous.
* Leftover egg yolks can be covered with water.
* Leftover egg whites can be stored in a container in the fridge.

Fig 14.2: An egg box.

Cooking Eggs

* Protein coagulates (sets).
* Bacteria are destroyed.
* Egg white becomes opaque.
* There is a loss of B group vitamins, especially thiamine.
* Eggs can curdle if overcooked.
* A green ring can form around the yolk if it is overcooked – this is a reaction between iron and sulphur.
* Overcooking also makes eggs tough and hard to digest.

Labelling and Grading of Eggs

The following information is found on an egg box:
* Name and address of packer.
* Country of origin.
* Number of eggs.
* Registration of the packer.
* Use-by date.
* Quality Assurance mark.
* Storage instructions.
* Grade size:
  * large, 63g–72.9g
  * medium, 53g–62.9g
  * small, under 53g
  * A: top quality
  * B: ideal for baking
  * C: for sale to industry only.

Properties of Eggs

Property	Application
Coagulation • When heated, the egg solidifies and the white becomes opaque. • The egg white coagulates at 60°C and the yolk at 68°C.	• **Cooking:** Fried, boiled and poached eggs. • **Binding:** When cooked, the egg coagulates and sets and holds the other ingredients together, e.g. burgers. • **Coating:** When cooked, the egg coagulates and holds the breadcrumbs onto the food, e.g. chicken Kiev.

Properties of Eggs

Property	Application
• When heated, protein chains unravel, straighten and bond around small pockets of water.	• **Thickening:** The cooking causes the egg to coagulate and the liquid mixture is set, e.g. custard. • **Glazing:** The egg coagulates and gives a golden glossy sheen to the food, e.g. pastry on apple tart.

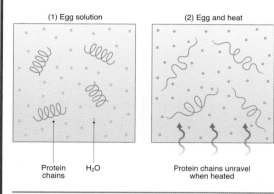 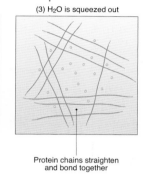

Fig 14.3: Coagulation.

Trapping air • Egg protein can trap air and produce a foam. • When egg is beaten or whisked, air bubbles are formed. • Beating creates enough heat to coagulate the albumin slightly. • Whisking causes the protein chains to unravel, straighten and bond around the air bubbles. • This forms a thin layer around the bubbles and the mixture becomes stiff. • Heat or gelatine are used to set the foam or it will collapse over time.	• **Aerating cakes**: Air is introduced into the mixture by beating or whisking, e.g. sponge cakes, soufflés and meringues.

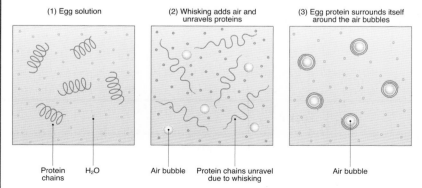

Fig 14.4: Trapping air.

Property	Application
Emulsifying • Lecithin is a natural emulsifier that is present in egg yolk. • When two liquids which do not normally mix are forced to do so, the lecithin surrounds the droplets and prevents them separating out again (See p.32.)	• **Mayonnaise and vinaigrette**: The oil and vinegar are mixed and held together by the lecithin in the egg yolk. • **Cakes**: Fat and sugar are emulsified. • **Hollandaise sauce**: Butter and vinegar are emulsified. – Lecithin holds the mixture together for a certain length of time, but after a while the mixture will separate out. Industrial emulsifiers are stronger and will hold an emulsion in place indefinitely.

EMULSIFYING

(1) Oil and vinegar separate   (2) Add an emulsifier   (3) Vinegar and oil do not separate

Oil   Vinegar

Hydrophobic tail (water-hating)   Hydrophilic head (water-loving)

Egg yolk (lecithin added)   Emulsifier (note: head attaches to vinegar, tail attaches to oil)

Fig 14.5: Emulsifying.

Culinary Uses of Eggs

Binding	Burgers, fish cakes.
Enriching	Rice pudding.
Thickening	Custard, quiches.
Have on their own	Boiled, scrambled, poached.
Coating	Fish.
Aerate	Sponge cakes, meringues.
Glaze	Scones, pastry.
Emulsifier	Mayonnaise.

Remember
BETH CAGE

Learning Links Learning Links Learning Links

Testing an Egg for Freshness

There are two ways to test whether an egg is fresh.

Test 1	Test 2
• Place an egg in bowl of salted water. • Fresh egg = sinks Stale egg = floats	• Crack an egg onto a small plate. • Fresh egg = well-rounded yolk, jelly-like white.

Test 1	Test 2
• This is due to the fact that the air space has got bigger.	• Stale egg = flat yolk and watery white

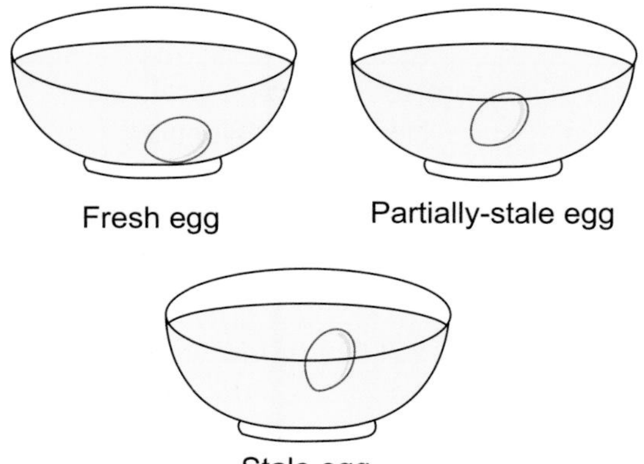

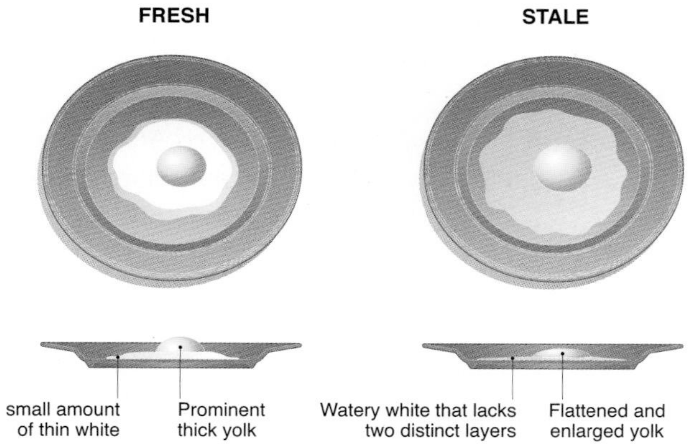

Fresh egg

Partially-stale egg

Stale egg

Fig 14.6: Bowl test.

FRESH

STALE

small amount of thin white — Prominent thick yolk

Watery white that lacks two distinct layers — Flattened and enlarged yolk

Fig 14.7: Visual test.

Eggs Quality Assurance Scheme

✳ This was set up to prevent any risk of food poisoning to consumers by salmonella or other bacteria.

✳ Implemented by the Department of Agriculture and Food.

✳ Hens are tested and certified as salmonella-free.

✳ Heat-treated chicken feed is used.

✳ All eggs must be fully traceable.

✳ All farms are inspected and monitored.

✳ The Quality Assurance mark is awarded by An Bord Bia.

✳ This logo is found on every egg, along with the best-before date.

QUALITY ASSURANCE SCHEME
BORD BIA – IRISH FOOD BOARD
APPROVED QUALITY PROCESS

Fig 14.8: Quality Assurance logo.

Sample Exam Questions

Questions

1. Evaluate the nutritive value of eggs. (12)

2. Name and describe the properties of eggs relevant to food preparation. Give an example of each property. (18)

3. Summarise the effects of heat on eggs. (6)

4. Give an account of the Quality Assurance scheme in relation to eggs. (8)

1. Evaluate the nutritive value of eggs. (12)

    4 points x 3 marks each = 12.

Nutrient	Explanation
Protein	• The type of protein present is animal protein (high biological value). • In the white, the proteins present are ovalbumin and globulin. • In the yolk, the proteins present are vitellin and livetin.
Fat	• The type of fat present is animal fat (saturated fat). • Eggs contain the emulsifier lecithin. • Cholesterol is present in eggs.
Carbohydrates	• There are no carbohydrates found in eggs.
Vitamins	• **Water soluble**: B_1 thiamine, B_2 riboflavin, B_{12} cobalamin and niacin. • **Fat soluble**: A, D, E.

2. Name and describe the properties of eggs relevant to food preparation. Give an example of each property. (18)

    3 properties x 5 marks each, plus 3 examples at 1 mark each = 18.

Property	Application
Coagulation • When heated, the egg solidifies and the white becomes opaque. • The egg white coagulates at 60°C and the yolk at 68°C.	• **Cooking:** Fried, boiled and poached eggs. • **Binding:** When cooked, the egg coagulates and sets and holds the other ingredients together, e.g. burgers.

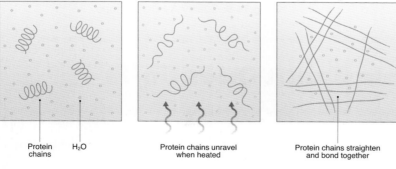

(1) Egg solution

Protein chains H_2O

(2) Egg and heat

Protein chains unravel when heated

(3) H_2O is squeezed out

Protein chains straighten and bond together

Fig 14.3: Coagulation.

Property	Application
• When heated, protein chains unravel, straighten and bond around small pockets of water.	• **Coating:** When cooked, the egg coagulates and holds the breadcrumbs onto the food, e.g. chicken Kiev. • **Thickening:** The cooking causes the egg to coagulate and the liquid mixture is set, e.g. custard. • **Glazing:** The egg coagulates and gives a golden glossy sheen to the food, e.g. pastry on apple tart.
Trapping air • Egg protein can trap air and produce a foam. • When egg is beaten or whisked, air bubbles are formed. • Beating creates enough heat to coagulate the albumin slightly. • Whisking causes the protein chains to unravel, straighten and bond around the air bubbles. • This forms a thin layer around the bubbles and the mixture becomes stiff. • Heat or gelatine are used to set the foam or it will collapse over time.	• **Aerating cakes**: Air is introduced into the mixture by beating or whisking, e.g. sponge cakes, soufflés and meringues.

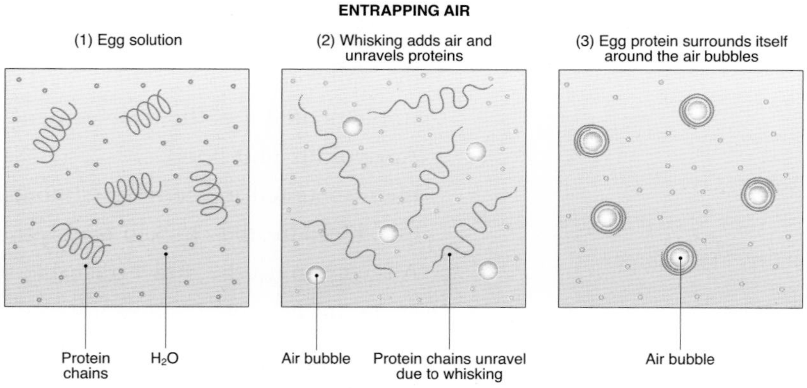

ENTRAPPING AIR

(1) Egg solution

(2) Whisking adds air and unravels proteins

(3) Egg protein surrounds itself around the air bubbles

Protein chains   H₂O

Air bubble   Protein chains unravel due to whisking

Air bubble

Fig 14.4: Trapping air.

Property	Application
Emulsifying • Lecithin is a natural emulsifier that is present in egg yolk. • When two liquids which do not normally mix are forced to do so, the lecithin surrounds the droplets and prevents them separating out again.	• **Mayonnaise and thousand island dressing**: The oil and vinegar are mixed and held together by the lecithin in the egg yolk. • **Cakes**: Fat and sugar are emulsified. • **Hollandaise sauce**: Butter and vinegar are emulsified. – Lecithin holds the mixture together for a certain length of time, but after a while the mixture will separate out. Industrial emulsifiers are stronger and will hold an emulsion in place indefinitely.

EMULSIFYING

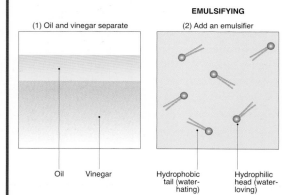
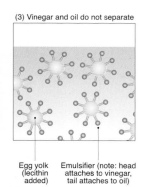

(1) Oil and vinegar separate — Oil, Vinegar
(2) Add an emulsifier — Hydrophobic tail (water-hating), Hydrophilic head (water-loving)
(3) Vinegar and oil do not separate — Egg yolk (lecithin added), Emulsifier (note: head attaches to vinegar, tail attaches to oil)

Fig 14.5: Emulsifying.

3. Summarise the effects of heat on eggs. (6)

   3 points x 2 marks each = 6.

   Three effects of heat on eggs are:
   • Protein coagulates (sets).
   • Bacteria are destroyed.
   • Egg white becomes opaque.

4. Give an account of the Quality Assurance scheme in relation to eggs. (8)

   2 points x 4 marks each = 8.

   • This was set up to prevent any risk of food poisoning to consumers by salmonella or other bacteria. Implemented by the Department of Agriculture and Food.
   • Hens are tested and certified salmonella-free. Heat-treated chicken feed is used. All eggs must be fully traceable. All farms are inspected and monitored.

Test Yourself
eTest.ie

Milk 15

Milk is a whole food. An infant's body can sustain life for the first six months with milk alone. This is due to sufficient quantities of iron and vitamin C in an infant's body. These are the nutrients that are lacking in milk. Milk is used to make milk products such as yoghurt, butter and cheese.

Composition

Type of Milk	Protein	Fat	Carbohydrates	Vitamins	Minerals	Water
• Whole	3.5%	4%	4.5%	A, B, D	Calcium Phosphorus	87%
• Skimmed	3.5%	0.2%	5%	B	Calcium Phosphorus	90%
• Human	2.25%	3.5%	6.5%	A, B, C, D	Calcium Phosphorus	87.4%

Nutritive Value/Nutritional Significance

Nutrient	Explanation
Protein	• Milk is a good source of HBV protein. • Proteins found in milk include caseinogen, lactoglobulin, lactalbumin. • During the digestion of milk, caseinogen is converted into casein. This is known as a derived protein. A derived protein is one which is caused by a chemical or enzymic reaction on a protein.
Fat	• Milk contains mainly saturated fat. • Milk is an oil-in-water emulsion, with tiny fat droplets dispersed throughout the milk. Lecithin helps stabilise the emulsion. • Milk is easily digested. • Homogenisation is a process that ensures that the fat droplets will not coalesce and rise but will remain permanently dispersed throughout the milk.
Carbohydrates	• The milk sugar present in milk is lactose, which is a disaccharide. • Lactic acid bacteria cause fermentation of milk (break down the lactose into lactic acid), which causes the milk to sour. • Pasteurisation destroys pathogens and also some of the lactic acid and delays souring.

Nutrient	Explanation
Vitamins	• Milk is a good source of B group vitamins, in particular thiamine and riboflavin. It lacks vitamin C. • Fat-soluble vitamins are present in milk fat but are removed when milk is skimmed. In particular, vitamins A and D are removed when milk is skimmed. • In summer, milk contains more vitamin D, as cows are exposed to sunlight.
Minerals	• Milk is a rich source of calcium, which is necessary for healthy bones and teeth. • Milk is a good source of phosphorus, which is also needed for healthy bones and teeth. • Milk contains trace amounts of sodium and potassium.
Water	• Milk contains 87% water. The high percentage of water makes it relatively easy to digest.

Dietetic Value/Contribution to the Diet

- Contains HBV protein, necessary for growth of body cells. It is a suitable food for babies, infants, toddlers, adolescents and pregnant woman.
- HBV protein is necessary for repair of body cells, particularly in the elderly and convalescents.
- Low-fat varieties are available, which are suitable for people on weight-reducing diets.
- Super Milk contains omega-3 fatty acids, which reduce the incidence of coronary heart disease, and is therefore suitable for people with high cholesterol.
- Milk has a wide variety of uses.
- Milk is a cheap, complete food and is easily available.
- As milk is lacking in starch, fibre and iron, it is best combined with foods rich in these, e.g. cereals.

Culinary Uses of Milk

* Milk can be a refreshing **drink** served on its own or with a meal.
* Milk is a main ingredient for many **sauces**, e.g. white sauce.
* Milk can be added to a variety of recipes to **increase the nutritional value** of a meal.
* **Baked foods**, such as scones and cakes, contain milk.
* Milk is used to **glaze** dishes, such as the top of scones, to give a smooth, shiny surface.
* Milk is used to **cool beverages**, such as tea and coffee.
* Milk is a main ingredient in **batters**.
* Milk is a key component in **desserts** such as rice pudding and custard.

Buying Milk

* Buy from a clean shop.
* Always check the use-by date.
* Ensure there is a good turnover of milk in the shop where the milk is purchased.

Storing Milk

* Store milk in a fridge as soon after purchase as possible.
* Do not mix milk with different use-by dates.
* Do not store milk near strong-smelling food.

Cooking Milk (Effects of Heat)

* Protein coagulates. This can be seen by the presence of a skin on the surface of the milk after heating.
* There is a change in the colour and the flavour of the milk. This change is caused by the caramelisation of the carbohydrate lactose.
* There is a loss of B group vitamins, in particular thiamine.
* High temperature destroys pathogenic micro-organisms.
* Milk curdles when combined with acid.

Fig 15.1: Different types of milk.

Types of Milk

Whole milk	Contains 4 per cent fat.
Semi-skimmed (low-fat milk)	Contains 2 per cent fat.
Skimmed milk	Contains 0.2 per cent fat. Note: when fat is removed, so too are the fat-soluble vitamins.
Super milk	Contains 2 per cent fat and is fortified with vitamins and minerals.
Buttermilk	Soured milk used in bread-making.
UHT milk	Milk that can be kept unrefrigerated for up to six months but, once opened, must be treated as fresh milk.
Dried milk	When water has been removed from the milk.
Evaporated milk	Canned milk with a long shelf life.
Condensed milk	Sweetened milk used for making desserts.
Soya milk	Made from soya beans, this is a milk substitute.

Spoilage of Milk

* Milk is high in protein, which is an ideal medium for bacteria to grow in.
* Unpasteurised milk may contain pathogenic bacteria, such as tuberculosis or brucellosis.
* It also contains non–pathogenic bacteria, such as lactic acid bacteria, which break down lactose bacteria into lactic acid.
* Lactic acid bacteria cause pH levels to drop and casein is denatured and separates from the liquid. This causes milk to curdle.

Processing Milk

Milk is processed to:
* Improve its flavour.
* Increase the time it can be kept.
* Make it safer to drink.
* Increase its nutritive value.

Methods of Processing

Homogenisation:

Homogenisation means 'to make uniform'. Milk is heated to 60°C. It is then forced at high pressure through tiny holes. This causes the fat globules to break up into very small droplets. As a result, the milk is creamier throughout and is more easily digested.

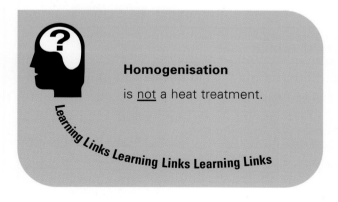

Homogenisation

is <u>not</u> a heat treatment.

Learning Links Learning Links Learning Links

Heat treatments:

* **Pasteurisation:** Milk is heated to 72°C for 15–25 seconds and cooled rapidly to 10°C.
  Effects:
  * This is the time and temperature necessary to destroy all pathogens (but it does not change the flavour of the milk).
  * Pasteurised milk will keep for four to five days.

* **Sterilisation:** Milk is first homogenised, bottled and sealed. Sterilisation is carried out in one of two ways.
  * The **batch process**, in which bottles of milk are heated to 104°–113°C and held at this temperature for between 15 and 40 minutes. Bottles then cool naturally.
  * The **continuous process** involves milk bottles being passed through water tanks on a conveyor belt and then passed into a steam chamber under pressure at 107°–113°C for between 15 and 40 minutes. The bottles are then cooled in water tanks.
  Effects:
  * Pathogenic micro-organisms are destroyed.
  * Loss of B group vitamins.
  * Flavours change.
  * Keeps for several weeks unopened.

* **UHT (ultra-heat-treated):** First the milk is homogenised, then heated to 132°C for one second. The milk is packed into tetra cartons.
  Effects:
  * This heat treatment method kills off all micro-organisms.
  * This type of milk can last for up to six months, but once opened must be treated as fresh milk.
  * This form of heat treatment causes little change to the flavour and colour of the milk.
  * All bacteria are destroyed.

* **Evaporated milk:** This is unsweetened, concentrated milk. Evaporated milk has no added sugar. The milk is placed in sealed cans and sterilised for 20 minutes at 115°C.

Effects:
- Unopened cans may be stored indefinitely.
- The nutrients are more concentrated in evaporated milk because of the loss of water.

✳ **Condensed milk:** This is sweetened, concentrated milk. Milk is homogenised and heated to 80°C for 15 minutes, **15 per cent sugar is added** and the milk is then heated under a vacuum. It is evaporated to one-third of its initial volume.

Effects:
- The final product is twenty-two times more concentrated than milk.
- Bacteria are destroyed.
- Flavour is changed.
- Sugar content is increased.

✳ **Dehydrated milk:** As milk is 87 per cent water, removing the water reduces its bulk and weight. Dehydrated milk is powdered milk, which has been homogenised and then evaporated to 60 per cent of its original volume. There are two forms of drying: spray drying and roller drying.

- **Roller drying:** Roller-dried milk is produced when the evaporated milk is poured over heated rotating rollers. As the milk dries on these rollers, it is scraped off as a powder.

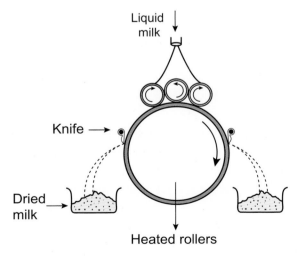

Fig 15.2: Roller drying.

- **Spray drying:** This involves spraying milk under pressure into a hot air chamber. As the droplets fall, the water is evaporated and the dried droplets fall to the bottom of the chamber where they are removed and cooled quickly. Milk is packed into airtight containers.

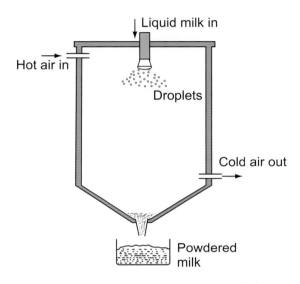

Fig 15.3: Spray drying.

Effects:
- Dehydrated milk does not taste as good as pasteurised milk.
- It lacks vitamins and some amino acids.
- Bacteria are destroyed.
- Reconstitutes easily with the addition of water.

Milk Quality

✳ Untreated milk, is not safe to consume (untreated = unpasteurised).

✳ Milk contains pathogenic micro-organisms when untreated.

✳ These micro-organisms are destroyed by heat treatments.

✳ Cattle on farms are regularly tested for diseases such as tuberculosis (TB), E. coli 0157: H7.

* All dairy farms must be registered with the Department of Agriculture and Food.
* Inspections are compulsory and frequent.
* Hygiene practices must be carried out and monitored at all stages of production.

Part Sample Exam Questions

Questions

1. Explain the following heat treatments: (15)
   * pasteurisation.
   * UHT.
   * sterilisation.

2. Outline the dietetic value of milk. (12)

Sample Answers

1. Explain the following heat treatments: (15)
   * pasteurisation.
   * UHT.
   * sterilisation.

   3 types x 5 marks = 15.

Pasteurisation:
Milk is heated to 72°C for 15–25 seconds and cooled rapidly to 10°C.
Effects:
* This is the time and temperature necessary to destroy all pathogens (but does not change the flavour of the milk).
* Pasteurised milk will keep for four to five days.

UHT (ultra–heat–treated):
First, milk is homogenised, then it is heated to 132°C for one second. The milk is packed into tetra cartons.

Effects:
* This heat treatment method kills off all micro-organisms.
* This type of milk can last for up to six months, but when opened must be treated as fresh milk.
* This form of heat treatment causes little change to the flavour and colour of the milk.
* All bacteria are destroyed.

Sterilisation:
Milk is first homogenised, bottled and sealed. Sterilisation occurs in two ways.
* The **batch process** in which bottles of milk are heated to 104°–113°C and held at this temperature for between 15 and 40 minutes. Bottles then cool naturally.
* The **continuous process** involves milk bottles being passed through water tanks on a conveyor belt and then passed into a steam chamber under pressure at 107°–113°C for between 15 and 40 minutes. The bottles are then cooled in water tanks.
Effect:
* Pathogenic micro-organisms are destroyed.
* Loss of B group vitamins.
* Flavours change.
* Keeps for several weeks unopened.

2. Outline the dietetic value of milk. (12)

4 points x 3 marks each = 12.

Dietetic Value of Milk

Dietetic Value/Contribution to the Diet

- Contains HBV protein, necessary for growth of body cells. It is a suitable food for babies, infants, toddlers, adolescents and pregnant woman.
- HBV protein is necessary for repair of body cells, particularly in the elderly and convalescents.
- Low-fat varieties are available, which are suitable for people on weight-reducing diets.
- Super Milk contains omega-3 fatty acids, which reduce the incidence of coronary heart disease, and is therefore suitable for people with high cholesterol.
- Milk has a wide variety of uses.
- Milk is a cheap, complete food and is easily available.
- As milk is lacking in starch, fibre and iron, it is best combined with foods rich in these, e.g. cereals.

16 Butter

Butter is manufactured from milk. It is an oil-in-water emulsion.

Fig 16.1: Different types of butter.

Nutritive Value/Nutritional Significance

Nutrient	Explanation
Protein	• There is a small amount of HBV protein in butter.
Fat	• The type of fat present is animal fat (saturated fate). • The fatty acid in butter is butyric acid.
Carbohydrates	• There are trace amounts of lactose (milk sugar) found in butter.
Vitamins	• Fat-soluble vitamins A, D and E are present in butter.
Minerals	• The minerals sodium and chloride are added during the production of butter. • Traces of calcium and phosphorus are found in butter.
Water	• There are small amounts of water (14–16 per cent) present in butter.

Composition of Butter

Protein	Fat	Carbohydrate	Vitamins	Minerals	Water
1%	82%	0.5%	0.5%	2%	14%

✱ **By law, butter must contain at least 80 per cent fat to be called butter.**

Production of Butter

1. Cream (fat from milk) is pasteurised.
2. Cream is cooled and the fat hardens.
3. Cream is churned and the fat clumps together.
4. The liquid part, called buttermilk, is drained off.
5. Salt (1.5 per cent) is added.
6. The butter is packaged for sale.

Types of Butter

* Salted: Salt is added.
* Unsalted: No salt is added to the butter.
* Low-fat: The fat content of the butter is reduced by 50 per cent.
* Spreadable: The butter is churned for longer periods of time to allow for the fat globules to separate. This allows for a more spreadable product.

17

Cream

Milk is a fat-in-water emulsion. Cream is made from the fat of milk.

Nutritive Value/Nutritional Significance

Nutrient	Explanation
Protein	• There is approximately 3 per cent protein in cream. • This is HBV protein (animal protein). • The type of protein present in cream is called casein.
Fat	• There are varying quantities of saturated fat present in cream, depending on the type of cream.
Carbohydrates	• There is approximately 2–4 per cent carbohydrate in cream. • This carbohydrate is present in the form of the milk sugar lactose.
Vitamins	• The vitamins present in cream include A and D. • Small amounts of B group vitamins are found in cream.
Minerals	• Cream contains calcium.
Water	• The water content varies according to the type of cream.

Types of Cream

* Half cream.
* Single cream.
* Double cream.
* Whipping cream.
* Aerosol cream.
* Sour cream.

Fig 17.1: Different types of cream.

Type of cream	Use
Half cream	• This cream contains **12 per cent** fat. • It is a pouring cream used in desserts.
Single cream	• This cream contains **18 per cent** fat. • It is a pouring cream used in desserts and sauces.
Double cream	• This cream contains **48 per cent** fat. • It is used for decoration of desserts.
Whipping cream	• This cream contains **35 per cent** fat. • It is used for decoration of desserts.
UHT cream	• This cream contains **35 per cent** fat. • It is used in trifles.
Sour cream	• This cream contains **18 per cent** fat. • It is used in savoury dishes, e.g. sweet and sour.
Cream alternatives	• Crème fraîche – 30 per cent fat. • Natural yoghurt – 3 per cent fat.

18 Yoghurt

Types of Yoghurt Available

* Low-fat/non-fat yoghurt.
* Custard yoghurt.
* Frozen yoghurt.
* Active/live yoghurt.
* Drinkable yoghurt.
* Set yoghurt.
* Greek yoghurt.

Production of Yoghurt

1. Milk is homogenised.
2. Milk is pasteurised at 90°C for 15–30 minutes to destroy bacteria.
3. Milk is cooled to 40°C to stop protein coagulating.
4. A starter culture of lactobacillus bulgarius and streptococcus thermophilus is added. This is known as inoculation.
5. It is incubated for six to eight hours at 37°C.
6. Fermentation occurs during this time. Lactose changes to lactic acid, milk proteins coagulate and the distinctive flavour of yoghurt develops.
7. Yoghurt is cooled to 4.5°C.
8. Other ingredients are added as necessary: fruit, nuts, sweeteners, colourings and flavourings. Stabilisers, such as pectin, prevent the separation of the yoghurt. Vitamins A and D are added to increase the food value of the yoghurt.
9. The yoghurt is packaged and labelled.

Fig 18.1:
Different types of yoghurt.

Nutritive Value/Nutritional Significance

Nutrient	Explanation
Protein	• The type of protein present is animal protein (high biological value).
Fat	• The type of fat present is animal fat (saturated fat). • The amount of fat depends on the type of milk used in its production: low-fat, skimmed or full-fat milk.

Nutrient	Explanation
Carbohydrates	• The type of carbohydrate present is the milk sugar lactose. • Sugar is also introduced by the addition of fruit and sweeteners.
Vitamins	• **Fat-soluble**: Vitamins A and D **Water-soluble**: Vitamin B_1 thiamine, Vitamin B_2 riboflavin, niacin
Minerals	• The mineral calcium is present. • Small amounts of potassium and phosphorus are also present.
Water	• The water content varies according to the fat content of the yoghurt produced.

Dietetic Value/Contribution to the Diet

- Yoghurt contains HBV protein necessary for growth, therefore it is a suitable food for children and teenagers.
- Yoghurt is easily digested and is suitable for the elderly and convalescents.
- Yoghurt contains HBV protein necessary to repair cells, essential for those recovering from illness.

- Low-fat yoghurts are available and are particularly suitable for those on low-kilocalorie diets.
- Yoghurt can be used in a wide variety of dishes.
- Yoghurt is available in a wide variety of flavours.
- Yoghurt is relatively inexpensive to buy.

Storing Yoghurt

Storing yoghurt:
* Store in a refrigerator (below 5°C).
* Use within the best-before date.

Using Yoghurt

Yoghurt can be used:
* On its own.
* In smoothies.
* On desserts, e.g. fruit salad.
* In desserts, e.g. cheesecake.
* For dips.
* In savoury dishes, e.g. served with curry.

19 Cheese

Classification of Cheese

There are four types of cheese: hard, semi-hard, soft and processed.

Hard cheese	Semi-hard cheese	Soft cheese	Processed cheese
• Cheddar • Parmesan • Swiss 	• Stilton • Gouda 	• Cottage • Brie • Mozzarella • Feta 	• Cheese spread • Cheese slices • Smoked cheese

Fig 19.1: Hard cheese.

Fig 19.2: Semi-hard cheese.

Fig 19.3: Mozzarella.

Fig 19.4: Processed cheese.

Average Composition of Cheese

Type	Protein	Fat	Carbohydrate	Vitamins	Minerals	Water
• Hard	26%	33%	0%	A, B_2	Calcium	37%
• Soft	14%	4%	4%	A, B_2	Calcium	77%

Nutritive Value/Nutritional Significance

Nutrient	Explanation
Protein	• The HBV protein caseinogen is present in cheese.
Fat	• The fat in cheese tends to be saturated. • Hard cheese has a higher proportion of fat than soft cheese.
Carbohydrates	• There are no carbohydrates present in hard cheese, as they are lost during processing. • In soft cheese, however, there is a small proportion of the disaccharide lactose present.
Vitamins	• Cheese is a good source of vitamins A, B_2 (riboflavin) and D. • There is no vitamin C present.
Minerals	• Hard cheese is a very good source of calcium.
Water	• Hard cheese contains about 33% water. • Soft cheese can contain up to 75% water.

Dietetic Value of Cheese/Contribution to the Diet

- Cheese is rich in protein and calcium, two nutrients essential for growth in children, adolescents, pregnant woman and nursing mothers.
- Cheese is a high-energy food and is suitable for active people.
- Low-fat varieties are available for those on weight-reducing diets. Cottage cheese contains only 4 per cent fat, making it a better cheese alternative for those on low-kilocalorie/low-cholesterol diets.

- Cheese is versatile. It can be used in a wide range of dishes.
- Cheese is economical with little or no waste.
- Because cheese lacks carbohydrates, it should be eaten with foods rich in carbohydrate, e.g. brown bread.
- Cheese is a quick and convenient, high-energy, nutritious snack.

Cheese-Making

1. Milk is pasteurised.
2. Starter culture (lactic acid bacteria) is added to milk. This changes lactose (milk sugar) to lactic acid.
3. Milk is warmed to approximately 30°C.
4. Rennet is added. Rennet is an enzyme which causes the milk protein, caseinogen, to convert to casein. The mixture is left for between 30 and 45 minutes until the milk protein, casein, changes to curds (solid) and whey (liquid).
5. Whey is drained off and the curds are chopped. **Cottage cheese is produced at this point**.
6. The curds are heated again (to 40°C) to shrink them further and to squeeze out more whey. This is known as scalding.
7. The curds are cut into blocks and packed on top of each other to remove any remaining whey. This is known as cheddaring.
8. Two per cent salt is added and more whey is drained off.

Fig 19.5: Making cheese in a factory.

9. The cheese is pressed into moulds.

10. For protection, the cheese is sprayed with hot water and this forms a rind.

11. The cheese is removed from moulds and wrapped in polythene bags, where it is left to ripen. Ripening time varies with the type of cheese, e.g. Cheddar cheese is left to ripen for up to one year at 10°C. **Cheddar cheese is produced at this point**.

11. The cheese is date-stamped, graded and packed.

Buying Cheese

* Cheese should be bought in small amounts.
* Cheese should be used quickly.
* Pre-packed cheese should be fully sealed after opening.
* Buy cheese from a hygienic shop.
* Check the use-by date.

Storing Cheese

* Open cheese should be wrapped in separate polythene bags to retain moisture and flavour.
* Always store cheese in a refrigerator.
* Blue cheeses need air and therefore should be stored in a polythene box.
* Cheese is best eaten at room temperature.

Cooking Cheese

* Fat melts and separates out.
* Protein coagulates – it shrinks and becomes indigestible, hard and tough.
* When heated, cheese gives a golden colour to food.
* There is little loss of nutrients.
* It is very easy to overcook cheese, so it is advisable to add it towards the end of cooking to prevent carbonisation.

Culinary Uses of Cheese

Cheese can be used:
* As a cold snack in a sandwich.
* As a hot snack, e.g. cheese on toast.
* In sauce-making, e.g. cheese sauce for lasagne.
* In fillings, e.g. in omelettes.
* As a topping, e.g. on pizzas.
* As dips and spreads.
* As a course at the end of a meal, e.g. cheese board.
* As a protein alternative in a main course.
* To enhance the nutritive value of a dish.

Alternative Protein Foods 20

Alternative Protein from Plant Foods

✱ Also known as 'novel foods'.
✱ Sources – plant foods and micro–organisms.

Soya Beans

Nutritive Value/Nutritional Significance

Nutrient	Explanation
Protein	• The type of protein present is of high biological value. It is 74 per cent high biological value, even though it is a vegetable protein food.
Fat	• The type of fat present is vegetable fat (unsaturated fat). • It contains the polyunsaturated fatty acid linoleic acid.
Carbohydrates	• The carbohydrates present are starch and fibre.
Vitamins	• Soya beans contain the B group vitamins.
Minerals	• Soya beans contain the minerals calcium and iron (non-haem).
Water	• There is a low amount of water at 14 per cent.

Dietetic Value/Contribution to the Diet

- Soya beans are high in protein and low in saturated fat, therefore suitable for all age groups.
- They contain polyunsaturated fat, which helps to reduce cholesterol, and are suitable for those on low-cholesterol/low-kilocalorie diets.
- Soya beans are a nutritionally good meat alternative, so ideal for vegetarians.

- Many different soya products are available.
- Easy to use.
- Can be used in a wide variety of dishes.

Fig 20.1: Soya foods.

Examples of Soya Foods

* Textured vegetable protein (TVP).
* Tofu (made from soya milk, this is a soya bean curd which can also be smoked or marinated).
* Tempeh (a chewy, fermented soya bean 'cake').
* Miso (a soya bean paste used in stews and soups).
* Soy sauce.
* Soya milk (made from soya beans, it is a dairy milk alternative).

Buying TVP

* TVP can be bought in dehydrated form.

Storing TVP

* Store in a cool, dry place.

Cooking TVP

* Follow the instructions on the packaging.
* Place in water for between 15 and 30 minutes.
* Once it has been reconstituted it can be used like meat.
* Make the dish in the usual way.
* Use with meat to bulk up the meal.
* Use as a meat substitute in dishes with strong flavours, e.g. Bolognese sauce, curries, etc.

Manufacture of Textured Vegetable Protein (TVP)

1. Oil is extracted from the soya bean.
2. Soya beans are ground into flour.
3. Carbohydrates are removed. All that remains is the protein.
4. Oil, flavouring and additives are added.
5. The mixture is heated and extruded through a nozzle into a reduced pressure environment, in order to get the correct texture.
6. It is dehydrated to make cubes or mince.
7. The TVP is fortified with cobalamin (vitamin B_{12}) and packaged for sale.

Advantages of TVP	Disadvantages of TVP
• Cheap alternative to meat • Low in saturated fat • Can be used in a wide variety of dishes. • Good source of fibre. • No shrinkage during cooking.	• Inferior to meat in terms of taste and flavour. • Inferior to meat in terms of texture. • Due to its bland nature, extra flavouring is needed, and it is only suitable for dishes with strong flavours.

Other Plant Sources

Seitan (wheat protein): This is made from gluten and is available in health stores.

Alternative Protein from Micro-organisms

Mycoprotein

Nutritive Value/Nutritional Significance

Nutrient	Explanation
Protein	• The protein present is comparable to the protein in meat. It is of high biological value. • The protein present, methionine, is an essential amino acid.
Fat	• Mycoprotein is low in saturated fat.
Carbohydrates	• Mycoprotein contains fibre.
Vitamins	• Contains B group vitamins.
Minerals	• Contains zinc and iron (non-haem).
Water	• There is a low water content in mycoprotein.

Manufacture of Mycoprotein

1. Mycoprotein is derived from the mycelium of a species of the fungus Fusarium graminearum.
2. These fungus cells are grown in a fermenter. The fermenter is sterilised to provide the correct environment for the growth of myco-protein, i.e. the correct temperature, correct pH, correct oxygen level.
3. Oxygen, glucose and nitrogen are added. Minerals, such as potassium, magnesium and phosphate, are also supplied.
4. The temperature in the fermenter is a constant 65°C.
5. The mixture is then harvested – this occurs when cells are removed from the fermenter.
6. The material is then filtered in huge cen-trifuges.
7. The harvested product absorbs a wide variety of colours and flavourings.
8. Its fibrous texture resembles meat.

Fig 20.2: Quorn products.

9. It can be prepared according to the cut required (sliced, diced or shredded).
10. Quorn is suitable for vegetarians but not for vegans, since a small amount of egg white is added.

21 Fruit

Classification of Fruit

Type	Examples
Citrus fruit	• Oranges, grapefruit, lemons, limes.
Berries	• Raspberries, strawberries, gooseberries, blueberries, blackberries.
Dried fruit	• Dried apricots, sultanas, prunes, dates.
Hard fruit	• Apples, pears.
Stone fruit	• Peaches, nectarines, cherries, plums.
Miscellaneous (exotic, tropical and others)	• Kiwi, bananas, pineapples, passion fruit.

Composition of Fruit

Protein	Fat	Carbohydrate	Vitamins	Minerals	Water
0.5%	0%	5–10%	A, C	Calcium Iron	80–90%

Nutritive Value/Nutritional Significance

Nutrient	Explanation
Protein	• The type of protein present is vegetable protein (low biological value). There are trace amounts of protein present in fruit.
Fat	• There is no fat present in fruit, except in avocados and olives. The type of fat present in these is polyunsaturated fat.

Nutritive Value/Nutritional Significance

Nutrient	Explanation
Carbohydrates	• Unripe fruit contains starch. • Ripe fruit contains 5–10 per cent sugar in the form of glucose and fructose. • Dried fruit has a high percentage of sugar. Non-starch polysaccharide (NSP) or fibre is contained in the skins. • Pectin is present in some fruit, such as apples.
Vitamins	• Vitamins, particularly vitamin C, are present. • Carotene (pro-vitamin A) is present in orange/yellow fruits, such as apricots and peaches, and also in darker fruit, such as blackcurrants.
Minerals	• Some fruits contain calcium. • Dark fruits, such as blackcurrants, contain traces of iron (non-haem).
Water	• Fruit has a high water content of 80–90 per cent. (Dried fruit has considerably reduced water content.)

Dietetic Value of Fruit/Contribution to the Diet

- Fruit contains no fat, therefore it is useful for people on low kilo-calorie diets.
- It is sweet and can replace sugary foods, such as cakes.

- Fruit is a good source of fibre, especially if the skins are eaten. It is therefore suitable for high fibre diets.
- Fruit is rich in vitamin C and associated with reducing the risk of common colds and is therefore ideal for general health.

Culinary Uses of Fruit

✱ Fruit can be used:
  - On its own.
  - In smoothies and juices.
  - As a garnish, e.g. lemon wedges with fish.
  - In desserts, e.g. fresh fruit salad.
  - In jams and preserves.

Buying Fruit

✱ Buy fruit in season, as this is when it is at its best, both nutritionally and in terms of value for money.

✱ Choose young fruit. This ensures maximum vitamin content and maximum flavour.
✱ Buy fresh fruit, as this ensures best quality in flavour, colour and texture.
✱ Check for damage and bruising.

Storing Fruit

✱ Use fruit quickly.
✱ Remove from any packaging as soon as possible after purchase.
✱ Allow air to circulate to prevent any mould growth.

Cooking Fruit

✳ Heat softens the cellulose and makes the fruit easier to digest and softer to eat. Overcooking makes the fruit mushy.

✳ Vitamin C is heat-sensitive and, as a water-soluble vitamin, is lost in cooking.

✳ There is loss of some colour and flavour.

✳ Micro-organisms are destroyed.

Changes During Ripening

✳ Starch is a carbohydrate present in unripe fruit. It is converted to fructose (the fruit sugar) as the fruit ripens.

✳ Enzymes in fruit bring about changes in the colour and flavour.

✳ Pectose in unripe fruit (protopectin) becomes pectin in ripe fruit and pectic acid in over-ripe fruit.

✳ Ethylene gas is given off during ripening.

✳ Enzymes, yeasts and moulds eventually decompose fruit. The store of sugar is used up and the fruit shrivels.

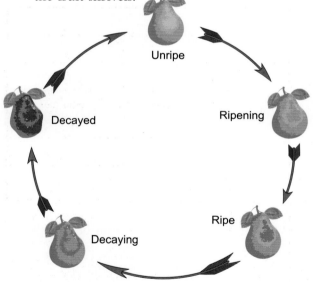

Fig 21.1: Ripening pears.

> **Note:**
> • To speed up ripening – under-ripe fruit is sprayed with ethylene gas.
> • To delay ripening – fruit is sprayed with CO_2 and O_2.

Organic Fruit and Vegetables

✳ Organic farming is the most traditional method of farming on Earth.

✳ The idea behind organic farming is that it is much better to feed the soil than the plant.

✳ As a result, organic crops are grown without the aid of any artificial fertilisers, chemicals or pesticides.

✳ Only natural animal manure and vegetable waste are used to produce nutrients for the soil.

✳ For that reason, organic foods are seen as good for the environment and good for soil.

✳ Many supermarket outlets carry an ever growing choice of organic products, many of which are sourced from Irish suppliers who must meet EU regulations and carry one of the logos of the accreditation bodies. These logos are:

Fig 21.2: Irish Organic Food Growers Association (IOFGA).

Fig 21.3: The Soil Association.

Fig 21.4: The Organic Trust.

Vegetables 22

Classification of Vegetables

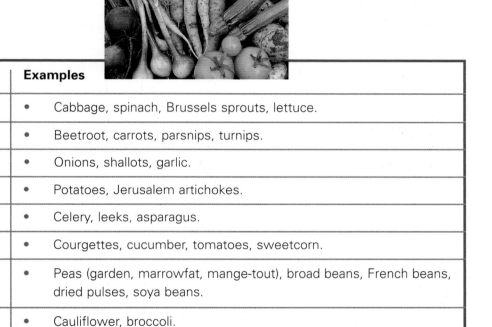

Type	Examples
Green leafy vegetables	• Cabbage, spinach, Brussels sprouts, lettuce.
Roots	• Beetroot, carrots, parsnips, turnips.
Bulbs	• Onions, shallots, garlic.
Tubers	• Potatoes, Jerusalem artichokes.
Stems	• Celery, leeks, asparagus.
Fruit	• Courgettes, cucumber, tomatoes, sweetcorn.
Pulses	• Peas (garden, marrowfat, mange-tout), broad beans, French beans, dried pulses, soya beans.
Flowers	• Cauliflower, broccoli.
Fungi	• Mushrooms (cup, button, flat).

Composition of Vegetables

	Protein	Fat	Carbohydrate	Vitamins	Minerals	Water
• Greens	3%	0%	3%	A, B_6, Folate, C	Calcium and iron	90–95%
• Roots	2%	0%	5–10%	A, C	Calcium and iron	70–90%
• Fruit	1%	0%	2–5%	A, C	Calcium and iron	90–95%
• Pulses	2–8%	0%	3–20%	A, B_1, B_2, B_6, C	Calcium and iron	75%

Nutritive Value/Nutritional Significance

Nutrient	Explanation
Protein	• A low amount of low biological value (LBV) protein is present. • Soya beans have high biological value (HBV) protein – 74 per cent.
Fat	• The lipid content is low, except in soya beans. • Nuts, olives and seeds, such as rapeseed and cottonseed, contain oil. • The type of oil present is polyunsaturated.
Carbohydrates	Vegetables contain three forms of carbohydrate: • Sugar, e.g. tomatoes, peppers, onions and carrots. • Starch, e.g. potatoes. • Fibre, e.g. the skin and husks are made up of cellulose.
Vitamins	• Betacarotene (pro-vitamin A), e.g. carrots, dark green, leafy vegetables and peppers. • Vitamin B_1 (thiamine) is present in pulses. • Vitamin C is present in all vegetables, especially in green, leafy vegetables, such as cabbage and spinach. There is only a small amount in potatoes, but because of the large amount of potatoes eaten in Ireland, they are a useful source.
Minerals	Vegetables contain the following minerals: • Iron, e.g. dark green, leafy vegetables. • Spinach contains a high amount of iron, but the oxalates (chemicals which inhibit iron absorption) present in spinach prevent the iron being absorbed. • Calcium and potassium are also present in vegetables. • Iodine is present in vegetables grown near the sea.
Water	• Vegetables contain a high percentage of water, some having over 90 per cent.

Dietetic Value/Contribution to the Diet

- Vegetables are an excellent source of vitamins and minerals and should be included in everyone's diet to reduce the risk of common colds.
- As vegetables contain no fat, they are suitable for those on weight-reducing diets.
- As vegans do not eat eggs or dairy products, they should include pulse vegetables in their diet, because these are the only vegetables that provide protein.
- Vegetables can be used in a wide variety of ways and in many different dishes.
- Vegetables are relatively inexpensive to buy with very little waste.
- Wide selection to choose from to suit different tastes.
- Vegetables are cheapest when in season and are also at their most nutritious.

Dietetic Value/Contribution to the Diet

- Vegetables do not contain any vitamin D or vitamin B_{12}. Strict vegetarians (vegans) must obtain vitamin D from sunshine or supplements and vitamin B_{12} from supplements.
- Dark green, leafy vegetables should be included in the diet to provide iron and to prevent anaemia. This is particularly important for adolescent girls, pregnant women and nursing mothers.
- Vegetables provide the body with roughage and fibre, especially if the skins are eaten.

Buying Vegetables

✳ Buy vegetables that are in season.
✳ Buy fresh, quality vegetables.
✳ Buy loose or netted vegetables to prevent mould growth.
✳ Buy in usable amounts. This prevents waste.
✳ Avoid bruised or damaged vegetables, as one damaged vegetable will rot the rest.

Storing Vegetables

✳ Store in a cool, dry, dark place.
✳ Remove from plastic packaging immediately.
✳ Put salad ingredients into salad drawer of fridge.
✳ Use vegetables soon after purchase, as they are at their most nutritious.

Cooking Vegetables

✳ Water-soluble vitamins and minerals dissolve into cooking water. Vitamins C and B_1 are lost due to high temperatures.
✳ Cell walls soften and become more digestible.
✳ Loss of colour, flavour and texture.
✳ Starch grains burst and the starch becomes digestible.

Methods of Cooking

✳ Boiling.
✳ Baking.
✳ Frying.
✳ Stir frying.
✳ Steaming.
✳ Microwaving.
✳ Barbecuing.
✳ Grilling.

EU Grading of Vegetables

Extra Class	Excellent quality.
Class 1	Good quality – no bruising.
Class 2	Some minor defects in size and colour – reasonable quality.
Class 3	Blemishes in shape and colour – marketable quality.

Spoilage of Vegetables

✳ The enzyme **phenolase** oxidises cell components in vegetables, resulting in bruising and brown patches.
✳ Vegetables with an 'open' structure wilt, turn yellow and eventually become slimy, e.g. lettuce.
✳ Some vegetables, mostly roots, go limp, woody and develop spongy patches, as the water content evaporates and the vegetables continue to shrivel in size.
✳ Vegetables are not as easily damaged as fruits during storage.

Processing Vegetables and Fruit

✳ Freezing.
✳ Canning.
✳ Drying.
✳ Commercial freezing.
✳ Irradiating.

Freezing	Drying	Canning	Irradiation
Suitable foods: • Carrots. • Peas. • Blackcurrants. • Rhubarb.	**Suitable foods:** • Peas. • Beans. • Grapes.	**Suitable foods:** • Peas. • Beans. • Sweetcorn. • Pears. • Peaches.	**Suitable foods:** • Onions. • Potatoes. • Dried fruit. • Rhubarb.
Effects: • Enzymes and micro-organisms are inactivated. • Change in texture. • Little change to nutritive value, colour or flavour.	**Effects:** • Enzymes and micro-organisms are inactivated. • Change in texture. • Loss of water-soluble vitamins. • Dried fruit is high in sugar.	**Effects:** • Enzymes and micro-organisms are inactivated. • Change in colour, texture and flavour. • Heat causes loss of vitamins and minerals. • Canned fruit in syrup is high in sugar.	**Effects:** • Destroys enzymes and micro-organisms. • No change to flavour and texture. • Some vitamin loss. • Prolongs shelf life. • Prevents sprouting.

Fig 22.1: Radura symbol.

Preparing and Cooking Fruit and Vegetables

✱ Always use a sharp knife to cut fruit and vegetables, as a blunt one will tear the cells and liberate an enzyme called **oxidase**, which destroys nutrients.

✱ Only use fresh, good-quality fruit which is not bruised and eat it raw, with the skin on, if possible.

✱ Only use fresh, good-quality vegetables and avoid cooking if possible. Use vegetables in salads.

✱ Prepare just before cooking.

✱ Use cooking water for soups and sauces.

✱ Never use bread soda to retain colour when cooking. It destroys vitamin C.

✱ Avoid overcooking vegetables. They should be served *al dente* to reduce vitamin loss and maintain texture.

✱ Avoid steeping in liquid for long periods of time, as vitamins and minerals leach into the water.

✱ Steaming maintains nutrients, as there is no direct contact with water.

✱ Use a tight-fitting lid when cooking, as an open saucepan encourages oxidation.

✱ Avoid reheating vegetables or keeping them warm for long periods of time.

✱ Always use boiling water.

Sample Paper Exam Questions

1. Outline the nutritional significance of vegetables in the diet. (12)

2. List four effects of heat on vegetables. (12)

3. Identify six ways of retaining nutrients in vegetables. (18)

1. Outline the nutritional significance of vegetables in the diet. (12)

   4 points x 3 marks each = 12.

Nutrient	Explanation
Protein	• A low amount of low biological value (LBV) protein is present. • Soya beans have high biological value (HBV) protein – 74 per cent.
Fat	• The lipid content is low, except in soya beans. • Nuts, olives and seeds, such as rapeseed and cottonseed, contain oil. • The type of oil present is polyunsaturated.
Carbohydrates	Vegetables contain three forms of carbohydrate: • Sugar, e.g. tomatoes, peppers, onions and carrots. • Starch, e.g. potatoes. • Fibre, e.g. the skin and husks are made up of cellulose.
Vitamins	• Betacarotene (pro-vitamin A): carrots, dark green, leafy vegetables and peppers. • Vitamin B_1 (thiamine) is present in pulses. • Vitamin C is present in all vegetables, especially in green, leafy vegetables such as cabbage and spinach. There is only a small amount in potatoes, but because of the large amount of potatoes eaten in Ireland, they are a useful source.

2. List four effects of heat on vegetables. (12)

   4 effects x 3 marks each = 12.

   • Water-soluble vitamins and minerals dissolve into cooking water. Vitamins C and B_1 are lost due to high temperatures.

   • Cell walls soften and become more digestible.
   • Loss of colour, flavour and texture.
   • Starch grains burst and the starch becomes digestible.

3. Identify six ways of retaining nutrients in vegetables. (18)

6 ways x 3 marks = 18.

- Always use a sharp knife to cut fruit and vegetables, as a blunt one will tear the cells and liberate an enzyme called **oxidase**, which destroys nutrients. Prepare just before cooking.
- Use cooking water for soups and sauces.
- Never use bread soda to retain colour when cooking. It destroys vitamin C.
- Avoid overcooking vegetables. They should be served *al dente* to reduce vitamin loss and maintain texture.
- Avoid steeping in liquid. Steaming maintains nutrients, as there is no direct contact with water.
- Use a tight-fitting lid when cooking, as an open saucepan encourages oxidation.

Nuts and Legumes

23

Nuts

Nutritive Value/Nutritional Significance

Nutrient	Explanation
Protein	• Nuts contain LBV protein.
Fat	• High in polyunsaturated fatty acids.
Carbohydrates	• Nuts are a good source of cellulose.
Vitamins	• Some B group vitamins present.
Minerals	• The minerals calcium and iron are present.
Water	• There is a small amount of water, generally 5 per cent.

Dietetic Value of Nuts/Contribution of the Diet

- Nuts supply the body with protein required for growth and repair of body cells and are therefore suitable for all diets.
- For a vegan, nuts are a good source of protein, which is needed for growth.
- Nuts are available in a variety of different types, e.g. almonds, hazelnuts and peanuts.
- They keep well, due to the small amount of water present.
- Nuts add texture to a dish.
- They can be used in sweet and savoury dishes, e.g. cashew nuts in stir fries.

Uses of Nuts

Nuts can be used in:
* Salads, e.g. Waldorf salad.
* Main courses, e.g. curry, stir fry.
* Biscuits, e.g. chocolate and peanut cookies.
* Decorating cakes, e.g. toasted walnuts on a coffee cake.
* Snacks, e.g. peanuts.

Legumes

Legumes is the collective name given to peas, beans and lentils.

Nutritive Value/Nutritional Significance

Nutrient	Explanation
Protein	• Low biological value (LBV) protein. • The exception to this is soya beans, which contain high biological value (HBV) protein.
Fat	• Legumes contain little or no fat. • Any fat present is polyunsaturated.
Carbohydrates	• Legumes contain starch and fibre.
Vitamins	• Vitamin C and B group vitamins are found in fresh legumes. • Legumes that have been processed in some form tend to lack vitamin C.
Minerals	• Legumes contain calcium and non-haem iron.
Water	• Water content varies depending on the type of legume.

Storing Legumes

✱ Legumes should be stored in a cool, dry, dark place.
✱ Use within five to six months.

Preparing Legumes

✱ Follow the manufacturer's instructions.
✱ To reduce cooking time, soak pulses overnight to reconstitute them.
✱ Some legumes, e.g. kidney beans, must be cooked at high temperatures to destroy toxins present.

Cereals 24

Cereals are the grains of cultivated grass plants. Some common cereals are wheat, rye, barley, oats, maize (corn) and rice.

Classification of Cereal Composition

Protein	Fat	Carbohydrate	Vitamins	Minerals	Water
12%	2%	72%	B group, E	Iron Calcium	12%

Nutritive Value/Nutritional Significance

Nutrient	Explanation
Protein	• The type of protein present is LBV protein. • The proteins present include gluten, lysine, threonine and tryptophan. • The protein content of cereal varies according to the variety.
Fat	• The type of fat present is polyunsaturated fat. • This fat contains essential fatty acids. • The fat content is found in the germ of the cereal grain.
Carbohydrates	• Cereals are an excellent source of carbohydrates. • Cereals contain a high proportion of starch (64 per cent). • The outer husk contains 8 per cent cellulose, which is removed during the production of white flour.
Vitamins	• B group vitamins – niacin, thiamine B_1, riboflavin B_2 – are present in cereals. • The germ is a good source of vitamin E.
Minerals	• Non-haem iron is found in cereals together with calcium and a small amount of phosphorus.
Water	• The water content is low; this makes cereals ideal for storage.

Dietetic Value/Contribution to the Diet

- Cereals are made up mainly of starch, which is a very good energy food for all groups.
- The outer husks of cereal grains are high in fibre, which aids digestion by stimulating peristalsis, essential for healthy diets.
- Whole grains are a good source of B group vitamins, non-haem iron and calcium, which are present in adequate amounts.
- Coeliacs are unable to digest gluten, the protein present in cereals, therefore their diet should omit such foods as barley, oats, wheat and rye.

- Gluten-free products provide an alternative to these foods, e.g. rice flour.
- Economical: cereals are a comparatively cheap food.
- Cereals are versatile; they can be used in many ways.
- Cereals are readily available.

Structure of Cereal Grains

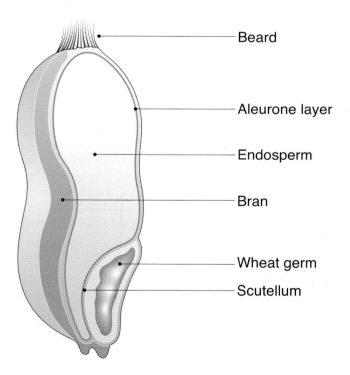

Beard

Aleurone layer

Endosperm

Bran

Wheat germ

Scutellum

Fig 24.1: Cross-section of a wheat grain.

Part of Cereal Grain	Percentage	Nutrients Present
• Bran	13%	• **Cellulose** is the main nutrient present in the bran layer. Cellulose cannot be digested by humans; however, it is useful in aiding digestion. • This part of the cereal grain contains the **B vitamin niacin** in particular. • The minerals present include **non-haem iron and calcium**.
• Endosperm	85%	• This forms the largest part of the cereal grain. • **Starch** is the main nutrient present in the endosperm. • The **protein gluten** is also present with some B group vitamins.
• Germ	2%	• This is a very nutritious part of the cereal grain. • The germ is a rich source of **protein.** • The vitamins present in the germ include **vitamins B and E.** • The fat is polyunsaturated and contains some **essential fatty acids**.

Types of Wheat

There are two types of wheat: winter wheat and summer wheat:

* **Winter wheat**: As its name suggests, this type of wheat is sown in the winter and harvested in the autumn. This type of wheat is generally grown in climates that have mild winters, e.g. Ireland. The flour made from this wheat tends to have a lower gluten content than spring wheat.

* **Spring wheat**: This is sown in the spring and harvested in the late summer. This type of wheat is generally sown in countries that have colder winters, e.g. Canada.

Flour

Flour Milling

1. The wheat is **cleaned** to remove any pieces of dirt. This cleaning process involves passing the grain through a series of sieves. The wheat is then washed.
2. Moisture is then added through the use of a machine known as a **conditioner**.
3. Different varieties of wheat are then **blended** together. The blended wheat is referred to as a grist.
4. The grain is passed through a series of rollers, which **breaks** the wheat grain apart. These rollers move at various speeds which separate the endosperm and germ (wholegrain flour is produced).
5. The wheat is **sieved** to separate the germ, the bran and the endosperm. Air is blown through the grain to separate the light bran from the heavy endosperm. The germ and bran are packaged and sold at this point.

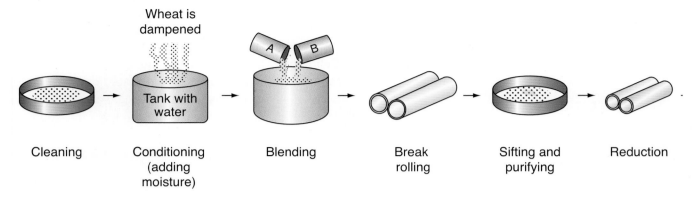

Wheat is dampened

Cleaning → Conditioning (adding moisture) → Blending → Break rolling → Sifting and purifying → Reduction

Fig 24.2: The process of making flour.

6. The wheat is **reduced** to produce fine flour and ensure the germ is completely extracted.
7. The next process is **air classification**, which is essential to ensure the correct protein quantity of the flour. Flour is separated according to size; the smaller particles have high protein content. The manufacturer will add such particles if a high-protein flour is needed.
8. **Additives**, such as nutrients and improvers, are added to the flour at this stage: they include calcium, vitamin C (an improver that aids gluten quality) and bleaching agents.
9. The flour is **packed** and ready for distribution and sale.

Flour Milling
Can **C**olm **B**ring **B**ack
Some **R**efreshments **A**fter
Andrew's **P**arty?

Learning Links Learning Links Learning Links

Types of Flour

There are many types of flour: wholemeal, wheatmeal (brown), white (cream), self-raising, strong, gluten-free and high-ratio.

Fig 24.3: Types of flour.

Flour type	Description	Extraction
• Wholemeal	This flour contains the whole grain. It is highly nutritious flour.	100%
• Wheatmeal/Brown	A lot of the bran has been removed. It is brown in colour.	85%

Flour type	Description	Extraction Rate
• White (cream)	The bran and germ layer have been removed.	70%
• Self-raising	Similar to cream flour except a raising agent (sodium bicarbonate) is added to the flour.	70%
• Strong	This flour has a higher percentage of gluten. It is ideal for yeast baking.	–
• Gluten-free flour	Gluten has been removed.	–
• High-ratio flour	This has low gluten content. It is milled very finely and is ideal for confectionery baking.	50%

Note: Extraction rate refers to the amount of the grain used for flour production.

Effects of Heat on Cereals

* Dry heat causes the starch grains to swell and burst and absorb fat. This is what happens in the production of popcorn.
* Moist heat causes the starch grains to swell, burst and absorb the cooking liquid. This causes gelatinisation and thus thickens the liquid.
* Cellulose is softened.
* Dextrinisation and caramelisation occur; this causes the surface of bread loaves and cakes to turn brown.
* B group vitamins are destroyed.
* The protein (gluten) coagulates and sets the risen bread.
* Starch becomes more digestible.

Cereal Products

These include:
* Breakfast cereals.
* Pasta.

Breakfast cereals:

There is a wide range of breakfast cereals on the market today which are made from a selection of cereals. These cereal grains can be flaked, puffed or shredded. A mixture of other ingredients can be added to these breakfast cereals, e.g. honey, nuts, fruit, sugar, or they can be fortified with vitamins and minerals.

Pasta:

Pasta is made from durum wheat, which has a high gluten content. Durum wheat is milled into semolina,

Fig 24.4: Different types of pasta.

which is then mixed with eggs, oil, salt, water and, in some instances, tomato puree or spinach. The dough is moulded into various shapes. It can be sold as either fresh or dried pasta.

Other Cereals

Other cereals include:
* Oats.
* Barley.
* Maize.
* Rice.

Oats

Oats are high in protein, fat and minerals. The flour made from oats cannot be used in bread-making. Oats are used to make oat flakes (porridge) and flapjacks.

Barley

Barley is grown in Ireland predominantly to be used in the production of malt. Other uses of barley include pearl barley and barley water.

Maize

Maize is the cereal used to produce cornflakes, sweetcorn, corn on the cob and popcorn.

Rice

Rice contains less protein, fat and minerals than other cereals. It is the staple food of Asian countries. There is a variety of different types of rice available, including:
* **Short grain rice:** This is used to make rice puddings and sweet dishes containing rice.
* **Medium grain rice:** This is generally used for risottos and salads, e.g. arborio rice.
* **Long grain rice:** This is used in savoury dishes, e.g. to accompany a curry, e.g. Patna rice.
* **Basmati rice:** This is grown in India and is considered the best type of rice for its flavour and texture.
* **Brown rice:** Only some of the bran has been removed in this rice, therefore it is a richer source of fibre than the other types, but it takes longer to cook than the other types of rice.

Rice Products

* Rice Krispies breakfast cereals.
* Rice flour, used as a thickening agent in soups.
* Cans of rice pudding.
* Boil in the bag rice.
* Rice paper is an edible, paper-like substance.

Fats and Oils

Classification of Fats and Oils

There are three types of fat: animal, plant and marine.

Animal fat	Plant fat	Marine fats
Examples of saturated fat from animals: • Suet. • Dripping. • Butter. • Eggs. • Cream.	Plant fat is mainly unsaturated. Examples include: • Vegetable oils, e.g. olive oil. • Soya oil. • Margarine. • Nut oil, e.g. almond oil. • Seed oil, e.g. rapeseed oil.	Examples of polyunsaturated fat from marine sources include: • Oily fish. • Halibut liver oil. • Cod liver oil.

Nutritive Value/Nutritional Significance

Nutrient	Explanation
Protein	• Butter and margarine contain traces of protein. • The type of protein is high biological value.
Fat	• The fat content varies from 82 per cent in butter to 99 per cent in cooking oil. • Low-fat equivalents contain 40 per cent fat.
Carbohydrates	• Fats contain only a trace of carbohydrates.
Vitamins	• Margarines are fortified with vitamins A and D. • Butter produced during the summer months is a richer source of vitamin D because the cows are exposed to sunlight.
Minerals	• There are trace amounts of calcium in margarine and butter.
Water	• The quantity of water present in fat depends on the fat type.

Dietetic Value/Contribution to the Diet

- All groups require fats as they provide the body with heat and energy.
- Fat provides fat-soluble vitamins and essential fatty acids in the diet.

- Polyunsaturated fats are recommended to replace saturated fats and thereby reduce cholesterol build-up in the arteries. This is particularly important for low-calorie/low-cholesterol diets.
- Fats add flavour to food.

Production of Oil

1. The seeds, nuts or grains are cleaned, crushed by break rollers and heated.
2. Extraction of the oil can be done either physically or with the use of a solvent.
3. Many vegetable oils contain impurities that must be removed, as they would lead to an inferior flavour, odour or colour of the product. This process of removal is known as the refining process. It involves many stages, including:

✽ **Degumming:** This removes impurities by adding hot water followed by centrifuging.

✽ **Neutralising:** This process removes impurities by mixing the oil with an alkali. The alkali changes the fatty acids into an insoluble compound, which can be easily removed. This leaves the oil clear and free from fatty acids.

✽ **Bleaching and filtration:** This process allows for the removal of colour from the oil. The oil is then filtered to give a clear, colourless liquid.

✽ **Deodorisation:** Removes any odours from oil.

✽ **Packaging:** The oil is packaged after being deodorised and then filtered.

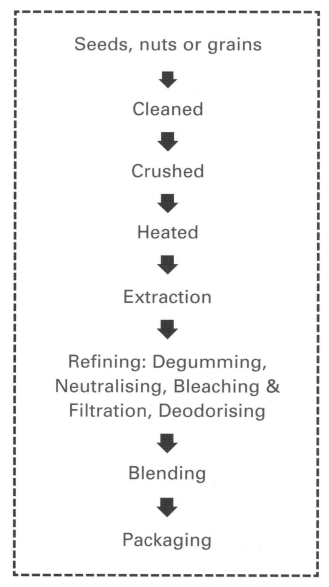

Fig 25.1: Oil production.

Margarine

Production of Margarine

Stages of production	Explanation of stages
• Oil extraction	Oil is extracted and refined.
• Hydrogenation	Hydrogen is forced into the oil in the presence of a nickel catalyst, converting the unsaturated nature of the oil to a solid, saturated fat.
• Blending	The different fats and oils are blended together. The variety of the blend will depend on the desired end product.
• Addition of ingredients	The ingredients added to the mixture can include: salt, whey, skimmed milk, water. It can also be fortified with vitamins A and D.
• Emulsification	To prevent the fat and liquid in the margarine from separating, the process of emulsification must be carried out. This involves placing the mixture in a VOTATOR and mixing it. Stabilisers are also used at this stage, and the margarine is chilled and kneaded until the desired texture has been achieved.
• Packaging	The margarine is weighed and packed and labelled.

Types of Margarine

Block margarine:

* This form of margarine is made chiefly of vegetable oil; however, some may contain animal and/or marine oil.
* It comes in rectangular blocks wrapped in foil or waxed paper.
* It is generally high in saturated fats.
* It is used for baking and frying.

Soft margarine:

* This margarine is made chiefly from vegetable oil and is designed to spread straight from the fridge (soft consistency)
* It is packed in plastic tubs.
* It is high in saturated fat, but it has less fat than block margarine.

* Soft margarine is used for baking, cooking and spreading on bread.

Dairy spreads

Low-fat spreads:

* Low-fat spreads are used particularly by slimmers to reduce their intake of fat, as they generally contain 40 per cent fat.
* These spreads are used for spreading, e.g. on bread, or in cooking.
* They should not be used for pastry-making or frying, as their high water content is not conducive to high temperatures.
* Example: Dairygold light.

Functional food spreads:

✳ Such spreads have been proven medically to reduce incidents of high cholesterol.

✳ These spreads contain **plant sterol esters**, an ingredient that reduces the absorption of cholesterol in the small intestine.

✳ They contain little, if any, trans fatty acids and virtually the same quantity of hydrogenated fatty acids.

✳ Examples of such spreads include: Flora pro.activ and Benecol.

Fig 25.2: Flora pro.active.

Storing Fats and Oils

✳ Oils should be stored in a cool, dark place.
✳ Fats should be covered to prevent the absorption of odours.
✳ Store fats in a refrigerator.
✳ Always check the use-by date.

Culinary Uses of Fats and Oils

✳ **Addition of flavour**: Fats and oils add flavour to food.

✳ **Anti-staling**: Fats have an anti-staling quality essential in cake and biscuits, which prevents such foods from drying out and maintains their keeping quality.

✳ **Creaming**: Fats are useful in baking as they allow for the addition of air, which allows food to rise.

✳ **Shortening agent**: This gives pastry the desired crumbly texture.

✳ **Emulsion**: An emulsion is formed when fat and water combine, as is the case with mayonnaise.

✳ **Frying**: Fats and oils are used to fry foods, either by shallow frying or deep frying.

Sample Exam Questions

Questions

1. Explain the stages involved in the production of oil. (20)

2. Outline how fats/oils should be stored. (6)

Sample Answers

1. Explain the stages involved in the production of oil. (20)

   5 stages x 4 marks each = 20.

There are four steps in the production of oil.
   • The seeds, nuts or grains are cleaned, crushed by break rollers and heated.

• Extraction of the oil can be done either physically or with the use of a solvent.

• Many vegetable oils contain impurities that must be removed, as they would lead to an inferior flavour, odour or colour of the product. This process of removal is known as the refining process. It involves many stages, including:

   Degumming: This causes the removal of impurities by adding hot water followed by centrifuging.

   Neutralising: This process removes impurities by mixing the oil with an alkali. The alkali changes the fatty acids into an insoluble compound, which can be easily removed. This leaves the oil clear and free from fatty acids.

Bleaching and filtration: This process allows for the removal of colour from the oil. The oil is then filtered to give a clear, colourless liquid.

Deodorisation: Removes any odours from oil.

- Packaging: The oil is packaged after being deodorised and then filtered.

2. Outline how fats/oils should be stored. (6)

2 points x 3 marks each = 6.

- Oils should be stored in a cool, dark place. Store fats in a refrigerator.
- Fats should be covered to prevent the absorption of odours.
- Always check the use-by date.

26 Meal Management and Planning

Planning a Meal

Time:

This refers to the amount of time a person has to prepare for a meal.

* Consider the time needed for cooking and serving.

Money:

The amount of money a person has will affect what food they buy.

* The bigger the budget, the more extravagant and expensive the food items that can be purchased, e.g. caviar.
* Note that less expensive cuts of meat (e.g. offal) are just as nutritious as the expensive ones.

People:

The number of people who have to be fed, together with their likes and dislikes, will affect the planning of the meal.

* The age of the people being cooked for should also be taken into consideration.

Skills:

The skills of the cook will have a definite impact on what is cooked. A person only able to boil an egg will produce a very different meal from one cooked by a professional chef.

Equipment:

* Labour- and time-saving pieces of equipment, e.g. food processors, can really speed up the preparation of a meal.

* Read a recipe thoroughly before you start making the dish to see if special equipment is needed.

Healthy eating guidelines:

Current healthy eating guidelines recommend that we eat less fat, less sugar, less salt and more fibre. It is important to remember this when planning a meal.

Special dietary needs:

Special diets, e.g. for people with coeliac disease or diabetes and for vegetarians, will affect the choice of foods for meals.

Occasion:

The type of occasion will affect the choice of foods to be selected, e.g. a barbecue, a buffet, a child's birthday party or a retirement party.

Availability of food:

* The time of year and a person's access to the food available will affect food choices. A person living in a small rural area with only a small grocery shop may not be able to get the same variety of foods available in a bigger supermarket.
* When food is in season, it is more readily available and cheaper.

Religious beliefs:

If you are preparing meals, it is important to be aware of any religious beliefs of your guests that might affect the choice of food.

Food Preparation and Cooking Processes

27

Food Preparation

Changes that Occur During Food Preparation

Physical Changes	Chemical Changes
• **Tenderising of meat:** This can be done by physically breaking down the meat fibres using a meat hammer. • **Increase in size:** This can be seen when dried pulses, e.g. marrowfat peas, absorb water when they are rehydrated. • **Loss of nutrients:** Vitamin C is the most unstable of all the vitamins and is easily lost. Two examples of this are when vitamin C is steeped in water or exposed to air. Vitamin C, for example, is lost if cabbage is steeped in water before cooking or if oranges are cut and left exposed to air.	• **Tenderising of meat**: This can be done by the use of proteolytic enzymes or by using a marinade (which contains acid e.g. vinegar, which breaks down the meat fibres). • **Increase in size**: This can be seen when we use yeast in cookery and the dough gets bigger while it is proving. • **Colour change**: This can be seen when we cut open apples or bananas to make fruit salad. The apples and bananas will go black due to a reaction between an enzyme that is released on cutting fruit and exposing it to air. This browning is known as enzymic browning. When making a fruit salad we generally add some lemon juice or a syrup, which prevents browning.

Cooking Food

Reasons for Cooking Food

✳ To destroy micro-organisms.
✳ To destroy enzymes.
✳ To make food digestible.
✳ To improve the colour, flavour and taste of the food.

✳ To make food more appetising.
✳ To combine different ingredients to give variety in texture.
✳ To extend the shelf life of food, i.e. to preserve food.

Changes that Occur During Cooking

Physical Changes

- **Colour change**: This can be seen when we cook meat – it goes from red to brown.
- **Micro-organisms and enzymes are destroyed**: Heat destroys these and makes food safe to eat.
- **Nutrient loss**: Water-soluble vitamins, e.g. vitamin B$_1$ (thiamine) and vitamin C, are lost easily as they are very heat sensitive. Minerals will leach into the cooking liquid.
- **Change in size**:
  - *Gets smaller*: Water is evaporated from meat when it is cooking, and so the meat shrinks.
  - *Gets bigger*: Air is a natural raising agent and can be incorporated into recipes by sieving, kneading, whisking, and rubbing in. This will help make breads and cakes rise.
- **Thickening**: This can be seen when flour is added to a sauce to thicken it.
- **Change in texture**: Generally food becomes more digestible as it is cooked.
- **Tenderising meat**: Meat becomes digestible as connective tissue changes to gelatine on cooking.

Chemical Changes

- **Maillard reaction (non-enzymic browning)**: This is the browning of food caused by an interaction between amino acids, carbohydrates and dry heat, e.g. roast potatoes.
- **Caramelisation**: This can be seen when sugar is heated and gradually changes to a caramel colour.
- **Dextrinisation**: This can be seen when we toast bread. Long polysaccharides become shorter dextrins and change the colour of food.

Principles of Cooking Food

There are three principles to remember when cooking food: conduction, convection and radiation.

Conduction

✱ The transfer of heat from one molecule to the next until all the substance heated, e.g. the heat transferred in a saucepan which eventually heats up all the contents.

Convection

✱ This is the transfer of heat in a cyclical movement in a gas or a liquid, e. g. boiling water in a kettle.

Radiation

✱ This is the transfer of heat in direct lines from the heat source, e.g. grilling sausages.

Fig 27.1: Conduction.

Fig 27.2: Convection.

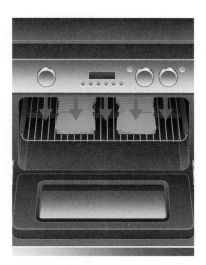

Fig 27.3: Radiation.

Methods of Cooking

There are three methods of cooking: moist, dry and frying.

Cooking Method	Example	Changes to Nutritive Value	Palatability
Moist	• Boiling • Steaming. • Poaching. • Stewing. • Braising. • Pressure cooking.	• Boiling inactivates the enzyme oxidase, which is known to destroy vitamin C. • Loss of water-soluble vitamins: B group and C. • Evaporation of water, causing food to shrink.	• Collagen in meat changes to gelatine. • Cellulose softens and the food becomes more digestible. • This method improves the palatability of the food, but overcooking causes food to become mushy.
Dry	• Roasting. • Baking. • Grilling. • Barbecuing.	• Loss of water-soluble vitamins: B group and C. • Fat melts. • Evaporation of water – shrinkage of food.	• Food becomes crisp. • When cooked accurately, food becomes more palatable.
Frying	• Shallow. • Deep. • Stir. • Dry.	• Increased calorie content. • Dry and stir frying are healthier options. • Vitamin A is lost due to high temperature.	• Extra flavour. • Greasy texture as a result of frying.

Moist Cooking Methods

	Boiling	Poaching	Steaming	Stewing	Braising
Principle	• Conduction and convection. • Food is cooked in water that boils at 100°C. • Food simmers at 90°C with lid on.	• Conduction and convection. • Food is cooked in water (below simmering – 85°C).	• Food is cooked as a result of steam rising from boiling water. • The food does not touch the water.	• Conduction and convection. • Long, slow method of cooking. • Food is cooked slowly in liquid at 80°–90°C.	• Combination of stewing and steaming. • Food is cooked in a small amount of liquid with diced vegetables called a mirepoix.
Advantages	• Quick. • Easy. • Drained liquid can be used for soups and sauces.	• Food can be poached in various liquids for more flavour, e.g. pears poached in red wine. • Quick method. • Good method for high protein foods.	• Little loss of nutrients. • Suitable for a wide variety of foods. • Little attention needed.	• All the nutrients are retained as the liquid is also consumed. • A complete meal can be cooked. • Suitable for tough cuts of meat.	• A complete meal can be cooked. • Suitable for tough cuts of meat.
Disadvantages	• A lot of nutrients are dissolved into the cooking liquid. • Can result in overcooking.	• Only suitable for some types of food. • Food must be monitored closely to prevent overcooking.	• Food can sometimes lack flavour and be bland. • Slow method of cooking.	• Slow method of cooking. • Can lead to overcooking very easily if left for too long. • Can dry out if not covered.	• Often needs browning under the grill before serving to give colour. • Slow method of cooking – loss of some nutrients.
Suitable Foods	• Vegetables. • Meat. • Pasta. • Rice. • Eggs.	• Fish. • Eggs. • Fruit, e.g. pears.	• Fish. • Chicken. • Christmas puddings. • Vegetables.	• Tough cuts of meat. • Vegetables. • Fruit.	• Meat. • Vegetables.

Dry Cooking Methods

	Baking	Grilling/Barbecuing	Roasting	Pot Roasting
Principle	• Takes place in an oven. • Convection currents. • In conventional and gas ovens, the top shelf is the hottest, as hot air rises. • A fan oven distributes the heat evenly.	• Cooked by radiation. • Fast method of cooking. • Heat from the grill seals the surface of the food.	• Cooked in the oven. • Food is basted with fat throughout to prevent it from drying out.	• Similar to roasting. • Cooked in a pot on the hob. • Food needs to be basted with fat to prevent it from drying out.
Advantages	• A wide range of foods can be baked. • Results in a crisp, attractive finish.	• Food cooks quickly. • Suitable for a wide range of dishes.	• Requires little attention except for basting. • A complete meal can be made.	• Useful if an oven isn't available. • Allows flavours to develop.
Disadvantages	• Opening and closing the oven door too often can result in a low-risen or inferior product. • The arrangement of food on shelves can result in different cooking times, leading to under- or over-cooking.	• Constant attention is needed. • Suitable for tender cuts of meat. • Overcooking can occur very easily.	• Meat can dry out if it's not basted. • If oven temperature is too high, meat can become tough.	• Can burn easily if not monitored. • This method of cooking requires a lot of attention.
Suitable Foods	• Breads. • Cakes. • Fruit tarts. • Vegetables. • Fish.	• Burgers. • Chops. • Sausages. • Rashers. • Fish. • Tomatoes.	• Meat: beef, lamb, chicken, pork. • Vegetables: potatoes, carrots, parsnips, peppers.	• Meat. • Vegetables (same as roasting).

Frying Methods of Cooking

	Shallow Frying	Deep Frying	Dry Frying	Stir Frying
Principle	• Food is cooked in fat in a shallow pan.	• Food is immersed in hot fat or oil. • Deep-fried foods are generally coated in a batter or breadcrumbs.	• Food is cooked without adding any extra fat or oil. • This is because some meats contain enough fat marbled throughout.	• Food is cooked by being tossed in a small amount of oil, usually in a wok.
Advantages	• Quick method of cooking. • Easy, little skill required.	• Gives food extra flavour. • Quick method of cooking.	• Healthy alternative as no extra oil/fat is added.	• Quick method of cooking. • Healthy method of cooking, as little oil is used.
Disadvantages	• Spattering can occur. • Constant attention needed because fats and oils overheat easily. • Increase in kilocalories.	• Increase in kilocalories. • Food can be quite greasy.	• Food can stick if not stirred. • Only suitable for meat with high fat content.	• Food will stick to the sides of the wok, if not stirred.
Suitable Foods	• Meat. • Eggs. • Vegetables.	• Onions. • Potatoes • Doughnuts. • Fish. • Meat.	• Minced meat. • Rashers.	• Meat. • Vegetables.

Factors in Choosing a Cooking Method

✳ Time available.
✳ The type of food.
✳ Personal tastes.
✳ Nutritional benefits.
✳ The equipment available.

Other Methods of Cooking

Pressure Cooking

This is cooking food with water at a temperature higher than 100°C (boiling point).

✳ Water boils at 100°C, but it can boil at a higher temperature if pressure is applied, which results in a faster cooking time.
✳ The build-up of steam inside the pressure cooker increases the boiling temperature.
✳ Suitable foods are meat, soups, Christmas puddings, vegetables, jams.

Structure of a Pressure Cooker

✳ A heavy saucepan with a locking lid.
✳ A rubber seal between lid and saucepan prevents steam escaping.
✳ The basket sits on a trivet, keeping the food out of the water.

* A vent in the lid lets out a small amount of steam.
* Different weights are put on the vent, which increases the amount of steam inside.

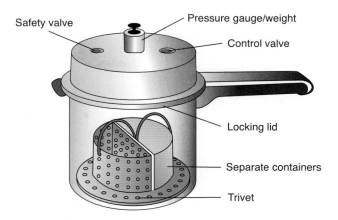

Fig 27.4: Cross-section of a pressure cooker.

Guidelines for Use

* Always follow manufacturer's instructions.
* Don't overfill the saucepan. A general rule is no more than two-thirds for solids and half for liquids.
* Make sure steam is escaping in a steady stream before putting on the weights.
* Time cooking correctly.
* Be careful when removing the lid for safety reasons because of the pressure build-up.

Weights Used

Weights/Pressure	Temperature of Water
5lbs (2.25kg)/Low	108°C
10lbs (4.50kg)/Medium	115°C
15lbs (6.75kg)/High	122°C

Advantages of Pressure Cooking	Disadvantages of Pressure Cooking
• Fast method of cooking. • Complete meals can be made in one pan. • Little to no nutrient loss. • No change to colour, flavour and texture of foods.	• A large storage area is needed to store it. • If not timed correctly, overcooking can happen very easily. • Accidents can easily happen if safety guidelines are not adhered to. • Only suitable for moist methods of cooking.

Microwave Cooking

* The transformer increases domestic voltage to a higher frequency.
* The magnetron converts electric energy to electromagnetic waves.
* These waves are guided into the metal-lined cabinet and:
  * **Reflect** off the walls of the microwave
  * **Transmit** through the container.
  * Are **absorbed** through the food.
* The molecules in the food create friction, so the food begins to cook.
* The centre of the food is cooked by conduction.
* Suitable for: reheating meals, cooking vegetables, melting chocolate, defrosting, etc.
* Unsuitable for: foods with a high fat content, thick foods that would take too long to cook.

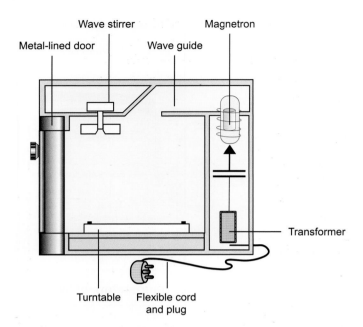

Wave stirrer
Magnetron
Metal-lined door
Wave guide
Transformer
Turntable
Flexible cord and plug

Fig 27.5: Cross-section of a microwave.

Guidelines for Use

✳ Always follow manufacturer's instructions.
✳ Allow standing time to finish off the cooking process.
✳ Time food accurately.
✳ Cooking time is affected by:
  ● The type of food.
  ● The thickness of the food – thicker foods will take longer to cook.
  ● The composition of the food – foods with fat and sugar cook very quickly.
  ● The amount of food – larger amounts of food will take longer to cook.

Advantages of Microwave Cooking	Disadvantages of Microwave Cooking
● Quick and easy. ● Retains nutritional value. ● No change to colour and flavour. ● Complete meals can be cooked.	● If not watched carefully, overcooking can occur. ● Extra space required for microwave in the kitchen. ● Restrictions apply to cooking some foods, e.g. pastry.

Soups, Sauces, Pastry and Raising Agents

Soups

Reasons for Including Soup in the Diet

✳ To stimulate the appetite.
✳ To give nourishment.
✳ To give warmth.
✳ It adds variety to a diet.
✳ It can be served as a starter, for lunch, or a light snack.
✳ It can be served hot or cold (e.g. gazpacho).

What is Stock?

✳ The flavoured liquid of meat, bones and vegetables that have been simmered.

✳ The meat, bones and vegetables are removed after this time and used for soups and sauces.
✳ Commercial stock cubes can also be bought, however, these have a higher salt content. It may be better to use half a stock cube or not to add any extra salt during cooking.

Making Home-Made Stock

✳ Use a heavy saucepan with a well-fitting lid.
✳ Use good quality ingredients. Inferior quality meat or bones will give an unpleasant flavour and cause the stock to deteriorate quickly.
✳ Scum should be removed, otherwise it will boil into the stock and spoil the colour and flavour.

* Fat should be skimmed, otherwise the stock will taste greasy.
* Stock should always simmer gently. If allowed to boil, it will evaporate and go cloudy.
* Salt should not be added to the stock.
* If stock is to be kept, strain, reboil, cool it quickly and place in the refrigerator.
* If stock is to be frozen, label and date it.

Classification of Soup

There are two main types of soup: thick soups and thin soups.

Thick Soups	Thin Soups
Puréed soups: Soups that are blended or liquidised to give the soup its consistency, e.g. mixed vegetable soup.	**Clear soups**: Soups made from a well-flavoured stock, which is then clarified (becomes clear) by adding egg white, e.g. consommé.
Thickened soups: Soups that are thickened with flour or cornflour, e.g. mushroom soup.  Fig 27.7: Consommé.
 Fig 27.6: Thick soup.	**Broths**: Soups made from a well-flavoured stock, which is not clarified. Contain small pieces of meat, vegetables, e.g. chicken broth.

Characteristics of a Well-Made Soup

* Has a good flavour and colour.
* Is the correct consistency – not too thick and not too thin.
* Well seasoned with salt, pepper and bouquet garni.
* Not too greasy.

How to Thicken Soups Using a Liaison:

A liaison is an ingredient used to thicken soups. It can be:
* Flour.
* Cornflour.
* Roux (equal quantities of fat and flour).
* Arrowroot.
* Cereals.
* Eggs and cream.
* Beurre manié (creamed fat and flour).

Preparing and Cooking Soup

* Always use good-quality, fresh ingredients.
* Prepare the ingredients carefully.
* Sauté the vegetables to allow the release of flavours.
* Add the required amount of stock. Home-made stock ensures a better-flavoured soup.

- ✳ Allow the mixture to come to the boil, then simmer gently.
- ✳ When seasoning, limit the amount of salt and use a bouquet garni.
- ✳ Blend the soup thoroughly to ensure the correct consistency and, if necessary, add more stock.
- ✳ Serve piping hot (or chilled if it is a cold soup).

Serving Soup

- ✳ **Garnishes**: Chopped parsley, chives, mint, cream, crème fraîche, grated orange rind, croûtons, crispy bacon pieces, grated cheese.
- ✳ **Accompaniments**: Bread rolls, bread, Melba toast, garlic bread, crackers.

Advantages of Commercial Soups	Disadvantages of Commercial Soups
• Quick to make. • Easy to make, little skill needed. • Useful in an emergency. • Wide varieties of flavours are available. • Available in packets, canned, frozen or chilled.	• Can be quite expensive. • Often high in salt and additives.

Sauces

Reasons for Using Sauces

- ✳ To add flavour to food.
- ✳ To moisten food.
- ✳ To add colour to a dish.
- ✳ For nutritive value.
- ✳ To coat food, e.g. cauliflower with cheese sauce.
- ✳ As part of the main dish, e.g. the sauce in a stew.

Classification of Sauces

Fruit Sauces	Sweet Sauces	Roux Sauces	Egg Sauces	Cold Sauces
• Apple sauce • Cranberry sauce	• Chocolate sauce • Butterscotch sauce • Caramel sauce	• Cheese sauce • White sauce • Mushroom sauce • Pepper sauce	• Custard • Mayonnaise • Hollandaise sauce	• Mint sauce • French dressing

Making a Roux Sauce

A roux sauce is equal quantities of fat and flour with varying amounts of liquid.

1. Melt fat.
2. Add flour.
3. Cook for one minute (to cook out the starchy taste).
4. Add liquid (milk/stock) gradually, stirring all the time to prevent lumps forming.
5. Bring to the boil and allow to simmer for a few minutes.
6. Season accordingly.

Composition of Sauces

Binding Sauce (panard)	Coating Sauce	Stewing Sauce	Pouring Sauce
25g fat	25g fat	25g fat	25g fat
25g flour	25g flour	25g flour	25g flour
125ml	250ml	375ml	500ml

Cooking Sauces

- Use correct amounts of ingredients.
- Follow the recipe.
- Make sure the sauce is of the correct consistency.

Serving Sauces

- Serve appropriately, e.g. hot sauces should be piping hot.
- Taste before serving to see if seasoning is necessary.
- Serve beside food or in a sauceboat.

Different Sauces for Different Foods

Food	Sauce
Pork	Apple sauce
Chicken	Bread sauce
Turkey	Cranberry sauce
Lamb	Mint sauce
Beef	Horseradish sauce
Duck	Orange sauce

Pastry

* Pastry is a mixture of fat, flour and water.
* Richer pastries can be made by adding eggs or sugar.
* The main difference between different types of pastries is how the fat is introduced to the mixture.

Classification of Pastry

Type	Use
Shortcrust pastry - Half fat to flour. - Variations include cheese pastry, wholemeal pastry.	- Apple tarts. - Quiches. - Sausage rolls. - Bakewell tarts.
Rich shortcrust pastry	- Mince pies. - Lemon meringue pies.

Type	Use
Rough puff pastry	• Cream slices. • Sausage rolls. • Vol-au-vents.  **Fig 27.8:** Vol-au-vents.
Puff/flaky pastry	• Sausage rolls. • Steak and kidney pies. • Cream horns.
Filo pastry	• Spring rolls. • Strudel. • Baklava.  **Fig 27.9:** Baklava.
Choux pastry	• Eclairs. • Profiteroles.
Suet crust pastry	• Dumplings. • Steamed puddings.  **Fig 27.10:** Steamed dumplings.

Making Pastry

✳ Make sure all ingredients and utensils are absolutely cold.

✳ Weigh ingredients accurately.

✳ Make sure the oven is pre-heated to a high temperature.

✳ Introduce air into the recipe by sieving.

✳ Make sure the water is cold and add it gradually.

✳ Handle pastry lightly.

✳ Knead gently.

✳ Roll out gently; always roll away from you and in one direction only.

* Chill pastry in the fridge before putting into the oven. Chilling prevents the pastry shrinking.
* Cook in a hot oven at 200°C at the start. This enables the starch grains to swell, burst and absorb the fat.
* After the first ten minutes, turn down the heat (190°C) to prevent burning.

Baking Blind

This means baking the pastry without any filling.
* Place greaseproof paper over the pastry.
* Lay rice/dried beans on top to prevent the pastry rising during cooking.
* Remove paper and beans for the last five minutes.

Preparing and Cooking Pastry

* Follow guidelines for making pastry to ensure successful results.
* Pastry needs to be cooked in a hot oven (200°C) for the first ten minutes to allow the starch grains to burst and absorb the fat.
* Too low an oven temperature would result in a heavy, greasy pastry.

Serving Pastry

* Pastry can be served either hot or cold.
* Sweet dishes, e.g. Bakewell tart, can be dredged with icing sugar.
* Savoury dishes, e.g. quiche, can be garnished with some parsley.

Raising Agents

A raising agent makes bread and cakes rise.

Classification of Raising Agents

There are three types of raising agents: natural/mechanical, chemical and biological.

Natural/Mechanical	Chemical	Biological
• Air	• Baking powder • Bread soda	• Yeast

Natural/Mechanical Raising Agents

Air can be introduced into a recipe by:
* Sieving.
* Rubbing-in.
* Kneading.
* Rolling.
* Whisking.

(1) Bowl with all ingredients

(2) Gas bubbles forming

(3) Mixture in cake tin

(4) Gas bubbles expand and rise. Gluten in flour allows mixture to rise

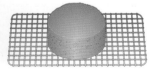
(5) Well risen cake with a crust

Fig 27.11: How a raising agent works.

Chemical Raising Agents

Chemical raising agents work on a scientific equation:

$$\text{Acid} + \text{Alkali} + \text{Liquid} \implies CO_2$$
(when CO_2 is heated it rises)

Baking Powder

$$\text{Acid} + \text{Alkali} + \text{Liquid} \implies CO_2$$

$$\text{Baking Powder} + \text{Milk/Eggs} \implies CO_2$$

Bread Soda

$$\text{Acid} + \text{Alkali} + \text{Liquid} \implies CO_2$$

$$\text{Buttermilk} + \text{Bread Soda} + \text{Buttermilk} \implies CO_2$$

Fig 27.12: Chemical raising agents.

Biological Raising Agents

The main biological raising agent is yeast.

* It is a living organism that produces carbon dioxide.
* It is put into the cooking mixture.
* It needs warmth, moisture and food in order to grow.
* When the bread/cake is put into the oven, the yeast cells are killed.

Types of Yeast Available:

There are three types of yeast available: fresh, dried and fast action.

Type of Yeast	Appearance/Use
Fresh Yeast  **Fig 27.13:** Fresh yeast.	• Creamy/beige colour. • Crumbly texture, breaks apart easily. • Can be stored in fridge for three to four days or in freezer for up to three months. • Blended with warm liquid before adding to the mixture.
Dried Yeast  **Fig 27.14:** Dried yeast.	• Available in a granular form. • Only half the quantity is needed compared to fresh yeast as dried yeast is more concentrated. • One packet of yeast is mixed with one teaspoon of sugar and is placed in 150ml of water to become frothy. (This usually takes 10–15 minutes in a warm place.) • Keep sealed in packets when not in use. • Will keep in sealed packet for six months.

Type	Use
Fast Action Yeast  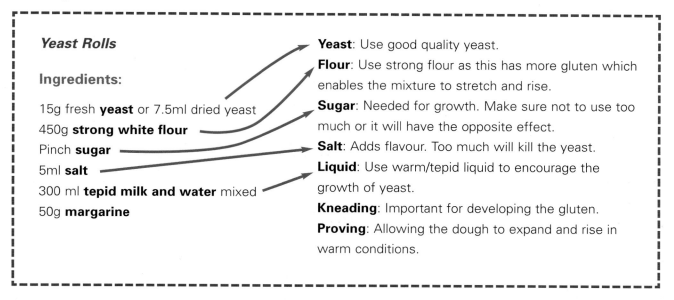 **Fig 27.15:** Fast action yeast.	• This is added directly to the mixture. • No rehydration is necessary prior to use. • It is a blend of dried yeast and flour improvers (these contain ascorbic acid and enzymes). • One sachet (7g) will raise 450g flour.

Cooking with Yeast

Yeast Rolls

Ingredients:

15g fresh **yeast** or 7.5ml dried yeast

450g **strong white flour**

Pinch **sugar**

5ml **salt**

300 ml **tepid milk and water** mixed

50g **margarine**

Yeast: Use good quality yeast.

Flour: Use strong flour as this has more gluten which enables the mixture to stretch and rise.

Sugar: Needed for growth. Make sure not to use too much or it will have the opposite effect.

Salt: Adds flavour. Too much will kill the yeast.

Liquid: Use warm/tepid liquid to encourage the growth of yeast.

Kneading: Important for developing the gluten.

Proving: Allowing the dough to expand and rise in warm conditions.

Fermentation

* Fermentation is the breakdown of sugar by micro-organisms (yeast and bacteria) to produce alcohol and carbon dioxide.
* Fermentation works on the action of enzymes.
* The enzyme diastase in flour changes starch to maltose.

* The enzyme maltase in yeast changes maltose to glucose.
* The enzyme invertase in yeast changes sucrose to glucose and fructose.
* The enzyme zymase in yeast ferments the glucose and fructose to CO_2 and alcohol.

$$C_6H_{12}O_6 + yeast + warmth \implies 2C_2H_5OH + 2CO_2 + energy$$

$$glucose + yeast + warmth \implies alcohol + carbon\ dioxide + energy$$

Fig 27.16: The effect of fermentation on the action of enzymes.

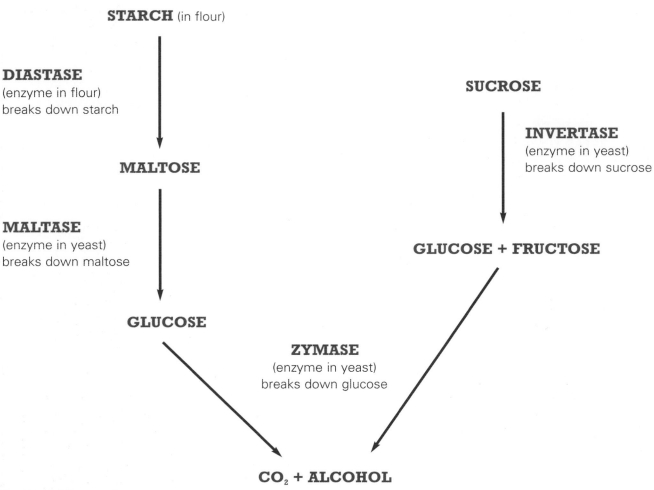

Fig 27.17: Fermentation.

Exam Questions
Higher Level (2007)

Questions

1. Outline the ways in which soup can contribute to the diet. (12)

2. List three liaisons used to thicken soup that you are familiar with. (9)

3. (a) Give an account of the classifications of sauces and give one example of each class.

(b) Describe four characteristics of a well-made sauce. (20)

4. List the general guidelines which should be followed when making home-made stock. (9)

Answers

1. Outline the ways in which soup can contribute to the diet. (12)

4 points x 3 marks each = 12.

- To give nourishment. Soups are made from fresh ingredients and are a source of vitamins, minerals and fibre. They are free from artificial colours, flavours and preservatives.
- To provide warmth on cold days. Soups can be served as a starter, for lunch or a light snack.
- They stimulate the appetite and aid digestion when used as a starter.
- They add variety to a diet. Vegetable soups made without fat and/or thickening agents are useful to add bulk to low-cholesterol or slimming diets.

2. List three liaisons used to thicken soup that you are familiar with. (9)

3 x 3 marks each = 9.

- Flour.
- Cornflour.
- Arrowroot.

3. (a) Give an account of the classifications of sauces and give one example of each class.

3 classes x 4 marks each = 12.
Classification = 1 mark.
Description = 2 marks.
Example = 1 mark.

Classification	Fruit Sauces	Sweet Sauces	Roux Sauces
Description	<ul><li>Usually made from mainly fruit and sugar.</li><li>This type of sauce is used on desserts.</li><li>It can also be used as an accompaniment to main courses.</li></ul>	<ul><li>These are dessert sauces.</li><li>They are usually sugar-based.</li><li>They make desserts more interesting.</li></ul>	<ul><li>This sauce is made from equal quantities of fat and flour, with varying amounts of liquid.</li><li>The amount of liquid used determines the consistency.</li><li>Examples include pouring sauce, stewing sauce, coating sauce.</li></ul>
Example	Apple sauce	Butterscotch sauce	Cheese sauce

3. **(b)** Describe four characteristics of a well-made sauce. (20)

4 points x 2 marks each = 8.

- Has a good flavour. It should not be overpowering so as to disguise the flavour of the food.
- Is the correct consistency, not too thick and not too thin and with no lumps.
- Well seasoned with salt, pepper and bouquet garni. It should be possible to taste the main ingredient, e.g. tomatoes.
- Not too greasy – too much fat will result in an inferior end product.

4. List the general guidelines which should be followed when making home-made stock. (9)

3 points x 3 marks each = 9.

- Use a heavy saucepan with a well-fitting lid. Use good quality ingredients.
- Scum should be removed, otherwise it will boil into the stock and spoil the colour and flavour.
- Fat should be skimmed, otherwise the stock will taste greasy. Stock should always simmer gently. If allowed to boil it will evaporate and go cloudy.

Food Preparation and Cooking Equipment

In most kitchens, you will find some or all of these pieces of equipment.

Food Preparation Equipment	Cooking Equipment
• Sharp knives.	• Cooker.
• Chopping board.	• Microwave oven.
• Food mixer.	• Sandwich toaster.
• Food processor.	• Deep fat fryer.
• Hand blender.	• Bread maker.

Selecting Food Preparation and Cooking Equipment

✳ **Cost:** How much is it? Can you afford the piece of equipment?

✳ **Brand name:** Is it a reliable brand?

✳ **Energy rating:** Does it have a good energy rating? Is it going to be energy efficient?

✳ **Need:** Do you actually need the piece of equipment? Will it cut down on work and be labour- and time-saving?

✳ **Size:** How big is the piece of equipment? How much space do you need for it? Does it need to be stored?

✳ **Guarantee:** This is an undertaking that the manufacturer will make good any fault that occurs in the product during the lifetime of the guarantee.

✳ **Personal taste:** Consideration should be given to likes and dislikes (e.g. colour) when choosing equipment.

Guidelines for Safe Use of Equipment

✳ Always follow manufacturer's instructions.
✳ Unplug before cleaning.
✳ Be careful of sharp blades when washing.
✳ Be careful of wet hands when operating electrical equipment.
✳ Don't overfill or underfill appliances.
✳ Make sure attachments are inserted correctly.
✳ Make sure all appliances are in good working order.
✳ Be careful not to over-run appliances and wear out the motor.

Caring for Equipment

✳ Always follow manufacturer's instructions.
✳ Unplug before cleaning.
✳ Wipe down the outside with a damp cloth and polish with a dry cloth.
✳ Don't immerse electric motors in water.
✳ Be careful of sharp blades/attachments.
✳ Store in a cool, dry place.

29   Recipe Modification

Reasons for Modifying a Recipe

✳   To make the dish more nutritious.

✳   For special dietary needs, e.g. using gluten-free flour for a coeliac diet, using soya products for a vegan, removing peanuts from a recipe because someone is allergic to nuts.

✳   In keeping with current healthy eating guidelines.

Eating less salt:

●   Not putting salt in the dish.

●   Not using commercially prepared stocks and packet soups.

●   Cutting down on convenience foods.

●   Adding flavour to dishes by using herbs and spices.

Eating less sugar:

●   Using artificial sweeteners.

●   Cutting down on the amount of sugar in a recipe.

●   Using tinned fruit where the fruit is in its own juice.

Eating less fat:

●   Cutting off visible fat from meat, e.g. the rinds of rashers.

●   Dry frying meat where possible, e.g. minced meat has invisible fat marbled throughout and does not need any extra oil added when cooking.

●   Using polyunsaturated spreads, e.g. Flora pro.activ contains plant sterols, which are thought to help reduce cholesterol build-up in the arteries.

●   Using low-fat products instead of full fat, e.g. low-fat milk, low-fat cheese.

Eating more fibre:

●   Using wholemeal flour in a recipe to increase fibre content, e.g. making wholemeal pastry for a quiche.

●   Using wholemeal products where possible, e.g. wholemeal pasta, brown rice, wholemeal bread instead of regular pasta, white rice and white bread.

●   Eating fruit and vegetables with the skins on where possible.

✳   To change the quantity or number of servings, e.g. doubling the ingredients in a recipe to go from four to eight servings.

✳   To add variety to a dish, e.g. by adding different ingredients to a stir fry.

✳   To make a dish more economical, e.g. using cheaper cuts of meat.

A Modified Recipe

Bacon and Leek Wholemeal Quiche

150g plain flour	2 eggs
50g margarine	150ml milk
Cold water	1 tablespoon natural yoghurt
4 rashers	Salt and pepper
25g butter	75g grated cheese
1 leek	

✳   **Flour:** Use wholemeal flour.

✳   **Rashers:** Trim off visible fat; grill instead of frying, cut down on the number of rashers used.

✳   **Milk:** Use low-fat milk.

✳   **Salt:** Omit salt; use herbs for flavour.

✳   **Cheese:** Use a low-fat variety.

Aesthetic Awareness of Food

30

Aesthetic Awareness in Food Choice

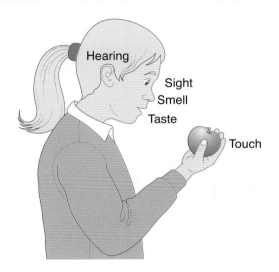

Fig 30.1: Human senses.

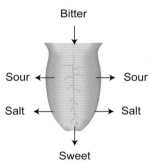

Fig 30.2: Taste buds.

Sight (Colour)

Colour is often a good indication of freshness in food, e.g. think of colour changes in a banana.

* Consumers expect certain colours for certain products, e.g. red for tomato ketchup, green for peas.

Hearing (Sound)

Food can sound crisp, e.g. breaking a cracker.

Taste (Flavour)

Different foods can bring out different flavours and affect our taste buds. This might affect the choice of food we purchase.

Smell (Aroma)

Our smell receptors are located in our nasal cavity.

* Smells coming from food can help us to identify the type of food that it is, its freshness or staleness.

Touch (Texture)

Texture refers to the 'feel' of the food.

* The texture of a food indicates if the food has gone off, e.g. a limp carrot.
* Additives are often used to improve the 'mouth feel' of food, e.g. gums add creaminess to dried soups, modified starch increases smoothness of foods.

Aesthetic Awareness in Food Preparation

Sight (Colour)

The phrase 'we eat with our eyes' is often used when discussing the appearance of a dish.

* A vibrant colour of food on a plate makes the food look appetising.

* We use our eyes and our sense of sight when preparing, cooking and eating food.
* Overcooking can result in an inferior end product.

Hearing (Sound)

Hearing the sizzle of food on the pan can stimulate our appetite and inform us that someone is cooking.
* We can hear popcorn 'popping'.
* We can hear a bottle of sparkling water being opened and its fizz as it's poured into a glass.

Taste (Flavour)

Different foods can bring out different flavours and affect our taste buds.
* An apple tart has a sweet taste, while a curry might taste spicy.
* Flavour enhancers are additives used to improve the flavour of food. They have no flavour themselves.
* Flavours should complement each other.
* Clever use of garnishes can alter the flavour of a dish.

Smell (Aroma)

Cooking food and the aromas it produces stimulate our appetite.
* Herbs and spices are often used to improve the aroma of a dish.
* Overcooking can create an unpleasant smell.
* Odours are lost when food is left to stand for a long time.

Touch (Texture)

When we eat food, we register its texture in our mouths.
* A fruit salad with apples in it would have a crunchy texture.
* A cheesecake or mousse would have a smooth texture.
* A chocolate chip cookie would feel chewy and nutty in your mouth.
* The combination of a variety of textures can affect the overall appeal of a meal.

Aesthetic Awareness in Food Presentation

Sight (Colour)

If a certain dish looks bland, it can be brightened up by the addition of colourful garnishes, e.g. lemon twists, cherry tomatoes, basil leaves.
* **Words for evaluating colour:** Bright, colourful, fresh, pale, overcooked, undercooked, greasy, shiny, cloudy, watery.

Hearing (Sound)

When food is placed on a plate, it may still be emitting noises; these stimulate our appetite and our other senses.
* **Words for evaluating sound:** Sizzling, fizzy, grating, crackling, popping.

Taste (Flavour)

The addition of lemon to a salad dressing would give it a sour taste.
* **Words for evaluating flavour:** Salty, spicy, sweet, sour, bitter, bland, tasteless.

Smell (Aroma)

Overcooked/burnt dishes give off an unpleasant smell. Undercooked dishes don't give off much aroma.
* **Words for evaluating aroma:** Strong, mild, sweet, sour, spicy, smoky, fresh, burnt.

Touch (Texture)

An ideal meal would contain different textures that contrast with each other, e.g. chicken curry would have chewy meat, soft rice, crunchy vegetables and a smooth sauce.
* Overcooking can affect the texture of foods, e.g. overcooking vegetables can change them from being *al dente* (having a bite) to being soggy and soft.
* **Words for evaluating texture:** Crisp, crunchy, hard, soft, chewy, nutty, flaky, lumpy, brittle, spongy.

Sensory Analysis

31

Sensory analysis is used to measure, analyse and interpret the characteristics of food by evaluating the sight, touch, smell, taste and sound of the food.

Uses of Sensory Analysis

* To develop new products.
* To modify products, e.g. reduce salt or sugar content, add omega 3 fatty acids.
* To evaluate food products in the classroom for the purpose of food assignments.

Types of Sensory Analysis Tests

Preference Tests

These are used to determine which product is preferred or if products are acceptable.

* **Paired Preference Tests:** Two samples are presented and the taster is asked to identify which one he/she prefers.
* **Hedonic Ranking Tests:** One or more samples are ranked on a five-point or nine-point verbal or facial scale which identifies the degree of liking for a product.

Five-point verbal hedonic scale
• Like a lot.
• Like a little.
• Neither like or dislike.
• Dislike a little.
• Dislike a lot.

Difference Tests

These are used to detect small differences between samples.

* **Simple Paired Test:** Two samples are presented and the taster must state whether they are the same or different.
* **Paired Comparison Test:** Pairs of samples are presented. The taster must state the difference between the samples based on a particular characteristic, e.g. saltiness, toughness, sweetness.
* **Triangle Test:** Three samples are presented. Two are exactly the same. The taster must identify which one is different. This is used to find out if people can tell the difference between foods. Often used when comparing two brands of the same food or comparing small differences in foods, e.g. the amount of sugar.

Grading or Quality Tests

These are used to rank specific organoleptic (flavour, texture, odour) characteristics of foods.

* **Ranking Test:** Used to sort a choice of foods in order (usually between two and twelve samples). They can be ranked:
  • According to the food that is preferred (hedonic ranking).
  • According to one specific characteristic, e.g. colour or flavour.
* **Rating Test:** Used to find out:
  • How much a person likes or dislikes a food (hedonic ranking).
  • To compare different aspects of quality of two or more foods (five-, seven- or nine-point scales).

Presentation of Results

The results of tasting sessions can be presented as:

* A pie chart.

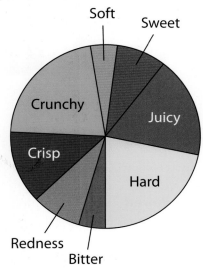

Fig 31.1: A pie chart.

* A histogram.

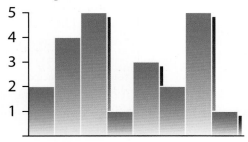

Fig 31.2: A histogram.

* A star diagram.

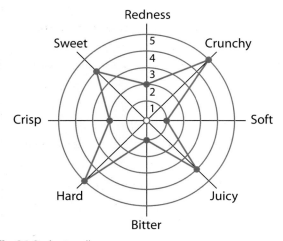

Fig 31.3: A star diagram.

Star Diagrams

* These are used by the food industry to describe the appearance and taste of food.
* Differences between products are easily observed using a star diagram.
* Several factors can be compared at once, e.g. the crunchiness and juiciness of an apple.
* A written description of the product can then be drawn up detailing how the product tastes and looks.

To use a star diagram:
1. Draw a circular graph with eight lines.
2. Label each line with a descriptor (a word that describes the food or product), e.g. soft, smooth.
3. Mark each line on the graph with a scale of 0 to 5.
4. Taste the food and give each description a score out of 5.
5. Mark each score on the graph, and join the scores to form a star diagram showing the product profile.

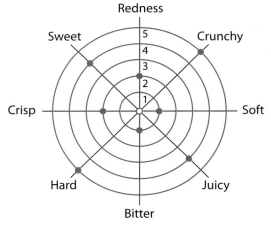

Fig 31.4: Product profile of an apple.

Product Profile of an Apple: The apple is very crunchy and hard; quite sweet and juicy; a little red and crisp, and not particularly soft or bitter.

Controlling the Testing Conditions for Sensory Analysis

* Mid-morning or mid-afternoon are the best times to conduct tests, as tasters will have less sensitivity.

* Tasters should not eat strongly flavoured food for at least thirty minutes before tests.
* Provide water for each taster to rinse out their mouth.
* All foods should be at the same temperature.
* The same amount of food should be served up to all the tasters.
* All the containers used should be the same size, shape and colour.
* Coding of samples shouldn't give any information or clues about the test, for example don't use A, B, C or 1, 2, 3.
* Samples can be sequenced:
  * Randomly (useful for large number of samples).
  * Balanced (useful for triangle tests) – every possible order occurs an equal number of times: AAB ABA ABB BAA BAB BBA (A = control; B = sample).
  * Using a combination of random and balanced.

Exam Questions
Higher Level (2007)

Questions

'Sensory analysis is a scientific discipline used to evoke, measure, analyse and interpret reactions to those characteristics of foods as they are perceived by the senses of sight, smell, taste and hearing.'

(*Institute of Food Technologists, 1981*)

1. Discuss the influence of any three of the senses in choosing, buying or eating food. (15)

2. Name three categories of sensory analysis tests and list one test from each category. (15)

3. Set out the conditions necesary for conducting sensory analysis tests to ensure accurate results. (20)

Sample Answers

1. Discuss the influence of any three of the senses in choosing, buying or eating food. (15)

   3 points x 5 marks each = 15.

   Hearing (Sound):
   * We use our ears and our sense of hearing when preparing, cooking and eating food. Hearing the sizzle of food on the pan can stimulate our appetite and inform us that someone is cooking.
   * We can hear popcorn 'popping'. We can hear a bottle of sparkling water being opened and its fizz as it is poured into a glass.
   * All of these sounds and more stimulate the appetite and our other senses.
   * **Words for evaluating sound**: Sizzling, fizzy, grating, crackling, popping.

   Smell (Aroma):
   * Our smell receptors are located in our nasal cavity. Smells coming from food can help us to identify the type of food that it is, its freshness or staleness.
   * Cooking food and the aromas it produces stimulate our appetite. Herbs and spices are often used to improve the aroma of a dish.
   * Overcooked/burnt dishes give off an unpleasant smell. Undercooked dishes don't give off much aroma.
   * **Words for evaluating aroma**: Strong, mild, sweet, sour, spicy, smoky, fresh, burnt.

Touch (Texture):

- This refers to the mouth feel of a food, i.e. what it feels like in your mouth. It also determined by touch, sight and hearing.
- When we eat food we register its texture in our mouth. A fruit salad with apples in it would have a crunchy texture. A cheesecake or mousse would have a smooth texture. An ideal meal would contain different textures that contrast with each other, e.g. chicken curry might have chewy meat, soft rice, crunchy vegetables and a smooth sauce.
- Overcooking can affect the texture of foods, e.g. overcooking vegetables can change them from being *al dente* (having a bite) to being soggy and soft. The texture of a food can also tell you if the food has gone off, e.g. if a carrot has become limp.
- **Words for evaluating texture**: Crisp, crunchy, hard, soft, chewy, nutty, flaky, lumpy, brittle, spongy.

2. Name three categories of sensory analysis tests and list one test from each category. (15)

3 tests x 2 marks each = 6 = total 15.

Categories of Sensory Analysis	Example of Test
Preference tests	Paired preference tests
Difference tests	Simple paired test
Grading or quality tests	Ranking test

3. Set out the conditions necessary for conducting sensory analysis tests to ensure accurate results. (20).

5 conditions x 4 marks each = 20.

- Mid-morning or mid-afternoon are the best times to conduct tests, as tasters will have less sensitivity.
- Tasters should not eat strongly flavoured food for at least thirty minutes before carrying out these tests.
- Provide water for each taster to rinse out their mouth. All foods should be at the same temperature.
- The same amount of food should be served up to all the tasters. All the containers used should be the same size, shape and colour.
- Coding of samples shouldn't give any information or clues about the test, for example don't use A, B, C or 1, 2, 3.
- Samples can be sequenced:
  - Randomly (useful for large number of samples).
  - Balanced (useful for triangle tests) – every possible order occurs an equal number of times: AAB ABA ABB BAA BAB BBA.
- Using a combination of random and balanced.

The Irish Diet

32

Irish Eating Patterns

Information on the eating patterns of Irish people can be obtained from:

* The National Nutritional Surveillance Centre, established in 1992.
* The Slán Surveys of Lifestyle, Attitudes and Nutrition in 1998, 2002, 2007.

Changes in the Irish diet have occurred because of:

* Improvement in transport systems.
* Improvement in water and electrical supplies.
* Better dietary guidelines.
* Improved agricultural practices.
* The impact of foreign cultures on Irish society.
* Improvements in the food processing industry.
* Consumers are widely travelled.

Changes in the Irish Diet in the Twentieth Century

Early 1900s	1950s	Present day
• Home-made bread and porridge were staple foods. • Meat was only eaten on special occasions. • Adequate supply of dairy products. • Little or no processed foods. • First World War saw an increase in food prices. • Second World War saw food shortages and rationing. • Bananas and oranges became more available.	• White bread and tea became a major part of the Irish diet. • Bacon and eggs popular among the middle classes. • Increase in meat and dairy products. • Introduction of a variety of cultural foods. • Foods could now be refrigerated. • Growing demand for convenience foods.	• Increase in convenience (over-processed) foods. • Increase in takeaway foods. • People eating out more. • More variety of foods available, e.g. meats: salami, Parma ham, prosciutto. • Increase in confectionery, sweets and biscuits. • More and more people are becoming health conscious and aware of current nutritional guidelines.
Nutritional significance		
• High carbohydrate. • Low iron intake. • Low intake of saturated fat. • Calcium from milk.	• Decrease in fibre. • Increase in saturated fats. • Increase in salt and food additives.	• Increase in salt. • Increase in additives. • Decrease in fibre. • Increase in HBV protein and iron. • Increase in sugar and saturated fat. • More people trying to follow nutritional guidelines.

Comparison of the Irish Diet 1998 and 2007

The table below shows the results from two Slán surveys, taken in 1998 and 2007.

Food Group	Slán survey 1998	Slán Survey 2007
• Cereal, bread and potato group	40% of all respondents consumed the recommended number of servings from this group.	26% (one in four respondents) were consuming the recommended six plus daily servings.
• Fruit and vegetables group	61% of those surveyed consumed the recommended amount from this group.	65% of those surveyed consumed the recommended amount from this group.
• Milk, cheese yoghurt group	22% of all respondents consumed the recommended number of servings from this group.	20% of respondents consumed the recommended number of servings from this group. Men were more likely than women to consume more than three servings (25% for men compared to 14% for women).
• Meat, fish and eggs group	38% of all respondents consumed the recommended number of servings from this group.	39% of respondents consumed the recommended number of servings from this group. Women were more likely than men to consume more than two servings (23% for women compared to 16% for men).
• Others	14% of all respondents consumed the recommended number of servings from this group.	18% of respondents consumed the recommended number of servings from this group. The majority of respondents (86%) consumed more than three daily servings of foods from the top shelf of the food pyramid.

Other Eating Habits

✳ Almost a third of respondents (30 per cent) either always or usually added salt to food while cooking while 32 per cent of respondents added salt to food at the table.

✳ Half (48 per cent) snacked between meals, most commonly on biscuits and cakes.

✳ Overall, 10 per cent of respondents did not eat breakfast on the day prior to the survey.

✳ Over one-fifth of respondents (22 per cent) reported being physically inactive.

Comparison of Current Nutritional Guidelines and Slán Survey 2007

Current Nutritional Guidelines State:	Slán Survey 2007 Findings
1. Eat less salt.	People are eating more salt than the recommended daily allowance of 6g.
2. East less sugar.	Sugar consumption in Ireland is higher than current healthy eating guidelines. There has been a definite increase in the consumption of sugar. The Irish population is one of the highest consumers of sugar in Europe.
3. Eat less fat.	The consumption of saturated fat has decreased in recent years. There has been an increase in the number and use of polyunsaturated fat and functional foods.

Current Nutritional Guidelines State:	Slán Survey 2007 Findings
4. Eat more fibre.	The recommended daily allowance of fibre is 25-35g a day. Slán 2007 shows individuals are not meeting this RDA.
5. Eat five portions of fruit and vegetables a day.	65% of respondents consumed at least five or more servings of fruit and vegetables a day.
6. Eat three portions of milk, cheese and yoghurt group a day	61% of respondents consumed less than three portions from this group a day as recommended in the food pyramid.

Aspects of Malnutrition Currently Identified

Nutrient	Causes	Effects	Corrective measures
Low dietary fibre	• Insufficient fibre intake. • Increase in the amount of processed foods eaten.	• Bowel disorders: constipation, diverticulitis, irritable bowel syndrome, piles, colon cancer.	• Increase dietary fibre. • Increase water intake. • Increase intake of fruit and vegetables (skin on where possible). • Reduce intake of processed foods.
High saturated fat	• Increased intake of animal fats. • Increase in takeaway meals eaten. • Increase in convenience foods eaten.	• High cholesterol. • Coronary heart disease. • Obesity. • Diabetes.	• Reduce saturated fats. • Increase polyunsaturated fats, especially omega 3 and omega 6. • Reduce intake of convenience foods.
Low iron intake	• Insufficient intake of haem iron. • Insufficient intake of non-haem iron. • Insufficient intake of vitamin C (for absorption of iron). • Menstruation.	• Anaemia. • Fatigue. • Breathlessness. • Feeling of 'being run down'.	• Increase intake of haem and non-haem sources of iron. • Increase intake of vitamin C.
Low calcium intake	• Insufficient intake of calcium-rich foods. • Insufficient intake of vitamin D, needed for absorption of calcium. • Increase in fibre, phytic acid and oxalic acid (factors that inhibit calcium absorption).	• Rickets. • Osteomalacia. • Osteoporosis. • Dental decay.	• Increase intake of calcium-rich foods. • Increase intake of vitamin D. • Increase intake of protein-rich foods.

33 The Irish Food Industry

The Structure of the Irish Food Industry

The Department of Food and Agriculture is primarily responsible for the Irish food industry. Other government departments and agencies are involved in the agri-food sector.

Agency	Function
Department of Agriculture and Food	• Monitors and control aspects of food safety. • Develops and implements national and EU schemes in support of agriculture. • Monitors and controls animal/plant health and animal welfare. • Provides support services to agriculture and food industry.
Department of Health and Children	• Monitors the Food Safety Authority of Ireland. • Implements food safety policies in conjunction with the health boards.
An Bord Bia **Bord Bia** Irish Food Board www.foodisland.com	• Promotes Irish food both nationally and internationally. • Provides information to consumers through leaflets regarding meat, eggs and cheese.
An Bord Iascaigh Mhara **BIM** Bord Iascaigh Mhara **Irish Sea Fisheries Board**	• Promotes Irish seafood nationally and internationally. • Provides information on the health benefits of fish to consumers.
Teagasc **Teagasc** AGRICULTURE AND FOOD DEVELOPMENT AUTHORITY	• Offers training to Irish farmers on all aspects of farming and undertakes research in food and agriculture.

Agency	Function
Enterprise Ireland ENTERPRISE IRELAND	• Provides support and finance for the development of indigenous (Irish-owned) food industries.
The Food Safety Authority of Ireland Food Safety AUTHORITY OF IRELAND	• Concerned with all aspects of food safety and hygiene. • Controls standards of food hygiene by establishing hygiene standards at stages of food production, supply and sale.

Major Food Export Sectors

Sectors	Percentage	Explanation
• Dairy and ingredients	26 per cent	• This category includes cheese, butter and ice cream.
• Beef	21 per cent	• This includes beef and live cattle.
• Lamb	2 per cent	• France is the chief market for Irish lamb.
• Pigmeat	7 per cent	• The UK is the main export market. The EU, US and Japan account for a large portion of Irish exports.
• Poultry	6 per cent	• Market share for chicken exports is on the increase. • Relatively small quantities are exported.
• Edible horticulture	3 per cent	• The UK is the major export market for Irish mushrooms. • Other foods exported include potatoes, soft fruit and cereals.
• Mariculture/seafood	5 per cent	• Ireland exports oysters, mussels, salmon and smoked salmon.
• Beverages	14 per cent	• The major beverage exports include whiskey, crème liqueur and spring water.
• Prepared consumer foods	22 per cent	• This is the fastest growing food export sector.

Food Exports

* Exports to the UK accounted for 43 per cent of all food and drinks exports, with 31 per cent going to the EU market and 26 per cent to the world market.

* While there have been fluctuations in this pattern of exports, the overall destination profile has not changed dramatically and this highlights the exposure of the sector to changes in euro/sterling and euro/dollar exchange rates.

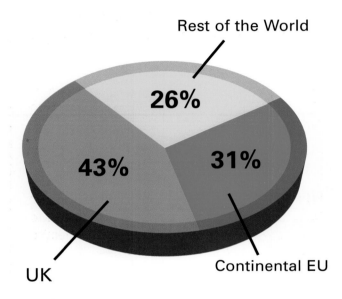

Fig 33.1: Destination of Irish food exports (An Bord Bia export review 2005–6).

Role of Small Businesses and Home Enterprises in the Irish Food Industry

* The agri-food industry has seen a growth in the speciality food sector.

* Speciality foods include: relishes, chutneys, jams, biscuits, chocolates and prawns.

* These foods are produced by small businesses or home enterprises.

* Many of these are family run. They employ people from the surrounding areas and bring a skilled workforce to the market.

* These businesses implement very high standards of hygiene in the production of their foods.

* These home enterprises promote the local area and Ireland's reputation.

Food Imports

Fig 33.2: Foods imported into Ireland.

Food	Country of origin
Fruit:	
• Oranges.	• Spain.
• Grapes.	• Mexico.
• Kiwi.	• Chile.
Vegetables:	
• Peppers.	• Spain.
• Chillies.	• Zambia.
• Green beans.	• Egypt.
Herbs:	
• Basil.	• Israel.
• Coriander.	• Israel.
Other:	
• Tea.	• Sri Lanka/Kenya.
• Coffee.	• Colombia/Costa Rica.
• Dried pasta.	• Italy.
• Cheeses.	• France/ Netherlands/ Denmark.

Investigation of a Local Food Industry

> It is recommended that each Home Economics class undertakes an investigation into a local food industry.

The following questions will help in your investigation. These questions were taken from the Home Economics guidelines for teachers.

1. When was it set up?
2. Why did it set up in the area?
3. Are the suppliers local?
4. Does this contribute to the area?
5. How many people does it employ?

6. Do they have plans for expansion?
7. Do they have plans to increase employment?
8. What types of aid or grants were and are available to them?
9. Have there been changes in any areas since the industry was established?
10. What type of research was needed to set up the industry?
11. What is their largest market?
12. How do they market their product/s?
13. What type of quality control do they use?

Investigation of a Local Food Industry

Name of Food Industry: H. J. Nolan (Dublin) Ltd.

Are the suppliers local? At Killybegs, 67 boats land their catch to Nolan's. Fish auctions are held three times a week at Nolan's depot in Howth, Killybegs and Kilkeel. Twice a day salmon caught in the West is brought to Dublin.

Does this contribute to the area? In the west and northwest of Ireland and in Howth many fishermen and their families have benefited from the Nolan business.

How many people does it employ? The company has 80 permanent workers.

Do they have plans for expansion? They continue to seek out new, convenient and tasty offerings that can be enjoyed by everyone.

Do they have plans to increase employment? Yes.

Have there been changes in any areas since they have been established? In 1998 they launched HJ Nolan Prawn Cocktail. This was one of the highest-growth chilled products in the Irish market. They were one of the first companies to change from wooden fish boxes to plastic fish boxes. They also moved from using chimney kilns to automatically controlled smokers.

Where is their market? Their market includes Europe, the Middle East, USA, Canada, South Africa, Australia and New Zealand.

How do they market their products? In-store marketing and marketing to the retailer.

What type of quality control do they use? Nolan products are produced under strict hygiene controls of HACCP in accordance with EU Directive 493/91.

Career Opportunities in Food and Related Industries

Within the food sector, there are a number of different areas in which people work.

∗ Certificates, diplomas and degree courses are available in many different areas of the food sector. Some of these are:

- **Agricultural college:**
  - Gurteen in Tipperary.
  - Warrenstown, Co. Meath.
- **Teagasc:**
  - Farm management courses (for green certificate).
  - Skill training, e.g. cheese-making.

- **Universities and institutes of technology:**
  Food science:
  - Food technology. – Microbiology.
  - Human nutrition. – Hotel management.
  - Dietetics.

Teacher training:
  - Home Economics teaching in St Angela's, Sligo.
- **Fáilte Ireland:**
  - Receptionists. – Bar skills.
  - Chefs. – Hotel management.

Career Opportunities in the Agri-Food Sector

Suppliers	• Farmer. • Butcher. • Fisherman.	Catering	• Chef. • Waiter.
Marketing	• Food demonstrator, e.g. An Bord Bia. • Advertising.	Food safety	• Environmental health officer. • Microbiologist.
Retailing	• Food promotion. Demonstrator in supermarkets.	Food technology	• Food technologist. • Food technician.
		Food research	• Dietician. • Nutritionist.

Sample Exam Questions

Questions

1. Outline why small businesses and home enterprises play a key role in the Irish food industry. (12)

2. Name two small Irish food businesses and give examples of the range of foods produced by each. (10)

Sample Answers

1. Outline why small businesses and home enterprises play a key role in the Irish food industry. (12)

   4 points x 3 marks each = 12.

   - The role of small businesses in the Irish food industry is to produce speciality foods. The agri-food industry has seen a growth in the speciality food sector. Speciality foods include: relishes, chutneys, jams, biscuits, chocolates and prawns. These foods are produced by small businesses or home enterprises.

   - Many of these are family run. They employ people from the surrounding areas and bring a skilled workforce to the market.

   - These businesses implement very high standards of hygiene in the production of their foods.

   - These home enterprises promote the local area and Ireland's reputation.

2. Name two small Irish food businesses and give examples of the range of foods produced by each. (10)

   2 industries x 5 marks each = 10.

Ballymaloe Foods
Foods produced include: relish, chutneys, ice cream.
H. J. Nolan (Dublin) Ltd
Foods produced include: smoked fish, seafood in brine, smoked salmon, farmed and wild seafood cocktail dishes.

FOOD PROCESSING AND PACKAGING

34 Food Processing

35 Food Packaging

36 Food Labelling

37 Food Additives

38 Microbiology

39 Food Spoilage

40 Food Preservation

41 Food Hygiene and Safety

42 National Food Safety Agencies

43 Food Laws

Section

4 5 6

34 Food Processing

Why is Food Processed?

✳ To extend its shelf life.
✳ To make the food more nutritious.
✳ To make the food safe to eat.
✳ To give consumers access to a variety of foods all year round.
✳ To create new products.

A range of processed foods is available. These include: dairy products, breakfast cereals, convenience foods, pasta and rice.

Profiles of Foods

There are three types of processing that you need to know in detail:

✳ A food that undergoes extensive processing, e.g. flour (see pages 131–2).
✳ A food that is processed to extend its shelf life, e.g. (see pages 102–3).
✳ A food that is an added value food (a product of higher economic value), e.g. the manufacture of cheese from milk (see pages 113–4).

Convenience Foods

> A convenience food is one that has been prepared so that cooking or serving is easier for the consumer.

Classification of Convenience Foods

Type	Frozen Foods	Cook-Chill Foods	Dried Foods	Canned/ Bottled Foods	Instant Foods/ Ready to Serve
Examples	• Frozen meals. • Vegetables. • Fish.	• Cartons of soup. • Portions of cottage pie. • Lasagne. • Fresh pastas.	• Packet soups. • Sauces. • Stock cubes. • Cake mixes. • Pancake mixes.	• Beans. • Peas. • Jams. • Beetroot. • Pickles.	• Salad bars. • Takeaway foods. • Delicatessen foods. • Cakes and pastries.
Preparation	• No preparation involved.	• No preparation involved.	• Preparation time reduced. • Add liquid (water, milk, eggs – see packet for instructions).	• No preparation involved.	• No preparation involved.

Type	Frozen Foods	Cook-Chill Foods	Dried Foods	Canned/ Bottled Foods	Instant Foods/ Ready to Serve
Cooking	• Cook from frozen.	• Reheat until piping hot.	• Cook as normal.	• Some need to be heated; others can be used directly when opened. • Quick and saves time.	• No cooking involved. • Only needs to be served.

Advantages and Disadvantages of Convenience Foods

Advantages	Disadvantages
• Saves time. • Reduces workload. Labour-saving. • Little skill needed. • Hardly any waste. • Many convenience foods are fortified with vitamins and minerals. • Low-fat varieties are available for health-conscious consumers. • Wide variety of products available for consumers to try out new things. • Easy to store. • Many have a long shelf life, which means they will keep for a long time unopened.	• Can be expensive. • Many are high in additives, e.g. artificial colours, flavourings and preservatives. • Many are high in sugar, salt and fat. • Products tend to be low in fibre. • Many have inferior texture, taste and colour in comparison to a home-made variety.

Cook–Chill Foods

There are two methods involved in the preparation of this type of food: cook–chill and cook–pasteurise-chill. Examples of cook–chill foods are a carton of vegetable soup and sliced ham.

Cook-Chill Method

✳ Food is divided into portions.
✳ Food is cooled to 3°C within thirty minutes of cooking.
✳ It is completely chilled within ninety minutes of cooking.
✳ Food is stored at 1–3°C.
✳ Food is stored in chilled cabinets after being transported.
✳ Shelf life is five days.

Cook-Pasteurise-Chill Method

✳ Cooked portion of food is put into a container.
✳ Container is heat sealed (partial vacuum is formed).
✳ Pasteurised at 80°C for ten minutes.
✳ Food is rapidly chilled to 3°C.
✳ Food is stored at –1°C to –3°C.
✳ Food is stored in chilled cabinets after being transported.
✳ Shelf life is two to three weeks.

Functional Foods

A functional food contains an ingredient that gives increased health benefits above the food's nutritive value.

Example of Functional Foods	Added Ingredient	Health Benefits
Yoghurt drinks, e.g. Actimel, Yakult.	Probiotics	Improve the functioning of the digestive system.
• Benecol • Flora pro-activ	Plant sterols	Reduce cholesterol build-up and the risk of coronary heart disease.
• Milk, e.g. Super milk. • Margarine, e.g. Dairygold Omega 3	Omega–3 fatty acids.	Thought to reduce the build-up of cholesterol in the arteries and thus prevent coronary heart disease.
• Breakfast cereals	Folic acid	Help prevent neural tube defects in foetuses.

Genetically Modified Foods

✳ Plant DNA is made up of four basic building blocks and the order of these building blocks in a gene results in the creation of different characteristics in a plant.

A genetically modified food is one in which the DNA structure of the food has been altered in some way.

Fig 34.1: The label indicates that this food has been genetically modified..

✱ By altering these genes or transferring them to another plant, scientists can 'engineer' the genetic make-up of the plants.

✱ This technology has the potential to produce foods which could be of great consumer benefit, such as:
- Tomatoes with increased vitamin content.
- Foods such as peanuts with reduced or no allergenicity.
- Wheat with increased levels of folic acid to prevent spina bifida.

✱ None of these genetically modified foods is currently on the market in the EU, including Ireland.

✱ A number of concerns about the use of this technology have been expressed, such as:
- Food safety.
- Potential damage to the environment.
- Ethical and moral objections.

✱ A wide variety of GM plant food is available in the US and Canada, including maize, soya beans, tomatoes and potatoes.

✱ Ingredients derived from four types of GM crops may be found in foods on the Irish market:
- Soya beans that are resistant to herbicide.
- Maize that is resistant to pest attack and/or herbicide.
- Oil from rapeseed that is resistant to herbicide.
- Oil from cotton seed that is resistant to pest attack and/or herbicide.

✱ Under current EU legislation, if more than 0.9 per cent of a food or ingredient is derived from a GM source, it must be labelled accordingly.

✱ A food labelled to indicate that no GM ingredients are present, e.g. it is GM free, must not contain any level of GM ingredients.

✱ The Food Safety Authority of Ireland (FSAI) carry out routine surveys on the food supply to monitor GM ingredients.

✱ Other government departments and agencies involved include the Department of Health and Children, the Department of Agriculture and Food, the Department of the Environment, the Department of Heritage and Local Government, the Environmental Protection Agency and the Irish Medicines Board.

Information: A survey carried out in 2000 by the FSAI focused on two maize-based products, tortilla chips and taco shells. The results of this survey, published in May 2001, revealed that 19 out of the 26 samples tested were found to contain GM ingredients.

35 Food Packaging

Why is Food Packaged?

* To give protection – to prevent the product becoming damaged.
* Food is easier to transport and store when it has been packaged.
* Labelling on the packaging gives information to the consumer about the product.
* Ensures the product is fresh and free from any germs.
* Acts as a form of advertising in terms of promoting the product.
* Easy for consumers to identify a product because of the packaging.

Fig 35.1: Different types of packaging.

What Should Good Packaging Be?

* Safe.
* Hygienic.
* Reasonably strong.
* Easy to open and reseal.

* Odourless.
* Attractive.
* Economical to produce.

Materials Used in Packaging

Glass

Examples of Where It's Used	Suitability	
	Advantages	**Disadvantages**
• Jam. • Salad cream. • Beetroot. • Mayonnaise. • Pickles. • Ready-made • Coffee. sauces.	• Clean and hygienic. • Lids are tight, so food is free from contamination. • Reusable.	• Fragile, easily broken. • Expensive to produce. • Expensive to transport as it's heavy.

Paper

Examples of Where It's Used	Suitability	
	Advantages	**Disadvantages**
• Bags of flour. • Cereal boxes. • Eggboxes. • Bread. • Orange juice cartons. • Packets of soups and sauces.	• Cheap to produce. • Lots of different forms (waxed, cardboard, laminated). • Can be used for a wide variety of products. • Biodegradable. • Wax-coated containers are strong and durable. • Some are heat-resistant. (A coating of polypropylene means the cardboard can be heated to 140°C.) • Information can be printed on it.	• Fragile, can tear easily. • Paper can fall apart when wet. • Doesn't reseal very well.

Metal

Examples of Where It's Used	Suitability	
	Advantages	**Disadvantages**
• Cans of soft drinks. • Tins of peas, beans, etc. • Bags of frozen vegetables. • Blocks of butter. • Takeaway containers.	• Easy to transport. • Easy to store. • Foods can be sterilised in the container itself. • Tins are lacquered to prevent reaction with the food.	• Expensive to produce. • Expensive to transport, as cans etc. are heavy. • Can get dented easily. • If not sealed properly, micro-organisms can cause food poisoning, (e.g. Clostridium botulinum).

Plastic

Examples of Where It's Used	Suitability	
	Advantages	**Disadvantages**
• Bottles of soft drinks. • Cartons of yoghurt. • Tubs of butter and margarine. • Packets of pasta and rice.	• Strong and durable. • Cheap to produce. • Cheap to transport. • Information can be printed on it. • Different forms of plastic available. • Can be used for a wide variety of products. • Lightweight and flexible.	• Some plastics may contaminate food. • Not biodegradable. • Lack of recycling plants. • Produced from crude oil – a non-renewable resource.

PS   **Polystyrene**: Used for takeaway trays and burger boxes.

PET   **Polyethylene terphthalate**: Used for soft drinks bottles.

LDPE   **Low density polyethylene**: Used for packets of pasta, rice, etc.

Learning Links Learning Links Learning Links

The Impact of Packaging on the Environment

Glass	Paper	Metals	Plastic
• Each Irish family uses an average of 500 glass bottles annually. • Glass is 100% recyclable and can be used many times. • Glass that is thrown away and not recycled will end up in landfills and never be used again.	• Paper can be recycled and when this is done, using paper can be environmentally friendly. • The average person in Ireland uses 30kg of magazines and newspapers per year.	• 52,000 tonnes of aluminium cans are used as packaging in Ireland. • Aluminium can be recycled and ready to use in just four to six weeks.	• 200,000 tonnes of plastic is used each year in Ireland, which is approximately 10 million bottles per week. • Plastic can take up to 500 years to decompose.

Glass	Paper	Metals	Plastic
• Glass recycling is energy efficient and reduces production costs.	• It takes 20 trees to make two tonnes of newspapers.	• Non-biodegradable.	• Manufactured from crude oil, a non-renewable resource.

Source: http://www.recycling.ie

Recycling Packaging

Households in Ireland produced 10 million tonnes of waste in 2005, of which 18 per cent was collected for recycling. This figure is comparatively low when compared to some other EU countries that recycle over 55 per cent of their waste.

Reducing the Impact of Packaging on the Environment

✳ By looking at the weekly waste collection, we can assume a reduction of at least 40 per cent when we **reduce**, **reuse** and **recycle**.

✳ Buy all fruit and vegetables loose and when shopping in the supermarket leave behind any unnecessary packaging. Where possible, buy products that have minimal packaging or refillable containers.

✳ Say no to plastic bags and use a cloth bag instead.

✳ Bring all bottles and jars to bottle banks.

✳ Ask at the local school and youth groups if they need paper for projects. Sell all old books to bookshops, including schoolbooks and paperbacks.

✳ Old clothes and shoes can also be recycled by bringing them to a local charity shop.

✳ Make use of a compost bin for food waste.

Action Speaks Louder Than Words

On average every householder generates over a tonne of waste each year. That is 400kg of waste per head of population and it is growing at a rate of 3 per cent per year.

A recent survey has shown that the composition of household waste is approximately:

✳ **34 per cent** food and garden waste.
✳ **25 per cent** paper and packaging waste.
✳ **12 per cent** plastic waste.
✳ **6 per cent** glass waste.
✳ **7 per cent** textile waste.
✳ **4 per cent** metal waste.
✳ **12 per cent** other – unclassified waste/ special waste.

At present, 92 per cent of this waste is taken to landfills; only 8 per cent is recycled.

Source: http://www.cultivate.ie/toolkit/environment/ recycling_in_ireland.html

Amount Per Serving	
Calories 260	Calories from Fat 120
	% Daily Value*
Total Fat 13g	**20%**
Saturated Fat 5g	**25%**
Trans Fat 2g	
Cholesterol 30mg	**10%**
Sodium 660mg	**28%**
Total Carbohydrate 31g	**10%**
Dietary Fiber 0g	**0%**
Sugars 5g	

36
Food Labelling

Purpose of Food Labelling

There are four main reasons for labelling food:

* To inform the consumer about the food item.
* To provide nutritional information about the product.
* To provide cooking instructions.
* To provide information on storage and use.

Good labelling should be:

* Clear.
* Legible.
* Truthful.
* Written in the language of the country it is to be sold in.

> The Food Safety Authority of Ireland (FSAI) is responsible for EU legislation on food labelling being adhered to.

Information found on Packaged and Non-Packaged Foods

Packaged Foods	Non-Packaged Foods
• The name of the product.	• Name of the food either on the food or near the product (shelf sticker or a chalk board).
• List of ingredients in descending order of quantity.	
• The net quantity.	• Fruit and vegetables must indicate their origin, variety and class near the product.
• Country of origin.	
• Name and address of manufacturer, packer or seller within the EU.	• The metric price – price per kilo.
• Instructions for storage and use.	
• Cooking instructions.	
• A date of minimum durability.	
• Alcoholic strength – if a beverage contains more than 1.2 per cent alcohol.	

Nutritional Labelling

* Gives information on a food's energy value (measured in kcals/kJs).
* Gives information about the nutritive value of the food.

* The nutrient information is given per 100g/100ml of the product.
* A minimum/maximum content of a particular ingredient must be given, e.g. low-fat yoghurt – maximum 10 per cent fat.

WHOLE WHEAT CEREAL WITH ADDED VITAMINS & IRON. 12 BISCUITS

Ingredients:

Wholegrain Wheat (95%), Malted Barley Extract, Sugar, Salt, Niacin, Iron, Thiamin (B1), Riboflavin (B2), Folic Acid.

Allergy Advice

This product contains wheat & barley.

For Best Before, see bottom flap.

Nutrition: Typical Average Values

	Per 37.5g serving	Per 100g
Energy	537kJ/ 127kcal	1432kJ/ 338kcal
Protein	4.3g	11.5g
Carbohydrate	25.7g	68.4g
(of which sugars	1.7g	4.4g)
Fat	0.8g	2.0g
(of which saturates	0.2g	0.6g)
Fibre	3.8g	10.0g
(of which soluble	0.9g	2.3g)
(of which insoluble	2.9g	7.7g)
Sodium*	0.10g	0.26g
*Equivalent as Salt	0.24g	0.65g
Vitamins & Iron		
Thiamin (B1)	0.4mg	1.2mg
Riboflavin (B2)	0.5mg	1.4mg
Niacin	5.7mg	15.3mg
Folic Acid	64.0µg	170.0µg
Iron	4.5mg	11.9mg

A 37.5g serving of Weetabix (2 biscuits) provides 32% of the Recommended Daily Allowance (RDA) of the vitamins & iron listed. 100g of Weetabix provides 85% of the RDA of the vitamins & iron listed.

Guideline Daily Amounts (GDA)

	Adult	Per 37.5g Serving
Calories	2000	127
Fat	70g	0.8g
Saturates	20g	0.2g
Total Sugars	90g	1.7g
Fibre	24g	3.8g
Salt	6g	0.24g

GDA's are recommended by Nutrition Professionals for average weight adults. You should adjust your intake according to your own age, weight, build and lifestyle.

This pack contains six 2-biscuit servings.

Fig 36.1: Weetabix label.

Claims made on labels must not be false or misleading.
- Medicinal claims, such as that a food prevents or cures diseases, are not allowed.

Bar Codes

✳ A barcode is a series of lines and spaces which are scanned and read by a scanner.

✳ The price, product name and brand of the item are obtained when the bar code is scanned.

✳ This information is printed on the customer's receipt.

✳ The shop's stock record is reduced accordingly.

Fig 36.2: A bar code.

Price Labelling

✳ It is a legal requirement for all food to have the price on or nearby the good.

✳ Pre-packed foods, e.g. meat, cheese, rashers, must show the selling price and the unit price on the label.

37

Food Additives

Additives are substances added to food to improve the colour, flavour, taste, texture or keeping quality of the food.

Advantages of Additives	Disadvantages of Additives
• The colour of the food is improved. • The flavour of the food is improved. • Preservatives extend the shelf life of foods. • The nutritive value of foods is improved. • The risk of food poisoning is reduced. • They enable an increase in the variety of foods available to consumers.	• Consumers may be deceived by the colour, flavour, texture of food that contains additives. • Some people have unfavourable reactions to some additives, e.g. rashes, migraine, nausea, hyperactivity, etc. • Little is known about the cumulative 'cocktail' effect on people's health of a combination of additives. • Research studies show a possible link between additives and cancer.

Classification of Additives

Additives are classified in six ways:

✱ Colourings (E100–E199).
✱ Preservatives (E200–E299).
✱ Anti-oxidants (E300–399).
✱ Physical conditioning agents (E400–E499).
✱ Flavourings (no E number).
✱ Sweeteners (E900–E999).
✱ Nutritional supplements.

E numbers prefixed by the letter 'E' are awarded when they have been tested and accepted by the EU.

Certain = Colourings
People = Preservatives
Actually = Anti-oxidants
Prefer = Physical Conditioning Agents
Friday to = Flavourings
Saturday = Sweeteners
Nights = Nutritional Supplements

Learning Links Learning Links Learning Links Learning Links

Colourings (E100–E199)

Function	Natural	Uses	Artificial	Uses
• To improve the colour of a food. • To replace colour lost in processing. • To add colour to colourless foods. • To satisfy consumer demands, e.g. tomato ketchup should be red.	Chlorophyll (green) found in plants.	In canned vegetables.	Tartrazine (yellow).	In soft drinks.
	Caramel (brown) formed by heating carbohydrates.	In sauces and gravies.	Amaranth (purple).	In blackcurrant products.
	Carotene (yellow/orange) found in yellow/orange fruit and vegetables.	In soft drinks.	All artificial colourings are chemically synthesised.	

Note: The following food products do not have colourings: bottled water, pasta and bread.

- This is used to give a yellow colour to fizzy drinks, ice cream, sweets and custard powder.
- It is thought to cause headaches and migraine, increased attacks of asthma and sleeplessness in small children.
- This colouring is banned in Australia and Norway.

Preservatives (E200–E299)

Function	Natural	Uses	Artificial	Uses
• To prevent the growth of micro-organisms. • To extend the shelf life of the product. • To make food available that would otherwise be 'out of season'. • To prevent food poisoning.	Sugar (from beets and cane).	In jams and sweets.	Sulphur dioxide.	In sausages and fruit juices.
	Salt (sodium chloride).	In pickles and bacon.	Sorbic acid.	In processed cheese and fruit yoghurt.
	Alcohol (produced by the fermentation of yeast).	In cakes.	Benzoic acid.	In coffee and flour.
	Vinegar (from yeast fermentation).	In pickles and beetroot.		
	Smoke (from wood burning).	In meat (ham) and fish (salmon).		

Note: Preservatives and anti-oxidants are not permitted in baby food.

- Sorbic acid inhibits the growth of yeasts and moulds.

Anti-Oxidants (E300–E399)

Function	Natural	Uses	Artificial	Uses
• To prevent oxidative rancidity (see 'Properties of Lipids' p. 30). • To reduce waste of food.	Vitamin A (beta-carotene).	In fruit products.	Butylated hydroxyanisole (BHA).	In stock cubes.
	Vitamin C (ascorbic acid).	In fruit drinks and jams.	Butylated hydroxytoluene (BHT).	In chewing gum.
	Vitamin E (tocopherols).	In vegetable oils.		

Think **ACE** for natural anti-oxidants vitamins A, C, E

Learning Links Learning Links Learning Links

Flavourings (No E Numbers)

Function	Natural	Uses	Artificial	Uses
• To add flavour to food. • To enhance the flavour of the food. • To replace any flavour lost in processing.	Sugar (from beets and cane).	In breakfast cereals, jams and tinned beans.	Esters • Amyl acetate. • Ethyl acetate.	• Pear flavouring. • Rum flavouring.
	Salt (sodium chloride).	In cheese, butter and sauces.	Aldehydes • Benzaldehyde • Maltol.	• Almond/cherry flavouring. • Adds a freshly baked smell to bread and cakes.
	Herbs (from plants).	In stock cubes.		
	Spices (from plants).	In sauces.		

Flavour Enhancers (E620–E640)

These are substances that have no flavour themsleves, but intensify the flavour of food to which they are added, e.g. monosodium glutamate (MSG). Uses: Chinese food, packet soups and sauces, crisps.

Monosodium Glutamate (MSG)

✳ This is the sodium salt of glutamic acid (an amino acid).

✳ Consuming large amounts of MSG can bring about unfavourable reactions in people.

✳ These reactions are often referred to as 'Chinese restaurant syndrome'.

✳ Symptoms include dizziness, chest or neck pain and palpitations. They are usually short-lived.

Physical Conditioning Agents (E400–E499)

Type	Function	Examples	Use
Humectants	• To prevent food drying out.	• Sweeteners, e.g. sorbitol and mannitol.	• Sweets • Confectionery
Polyphosphates	• To prevent lumping.	• Magnesium carbonate.	• Cake mixes.
Buffers	• To control the pH level of the food.		
Anti-caking agents	• To prevent lumps forming in dehydrated products.		• Flour and baking powder.
Stabilisers	• To assist emulsifiers by preventing the emulsion from separating.	• Carrageenan. • Guar gum.	• Ice cream. • Confectionery.
Emulsifiers (see Properties of Lipids' p. 30).	• To force oil and water to mix without separating.	**Natural:** • Lecithin in egg yolk. • Alginates in seaweed. • Pectin in fruits. **Artificial:** • Glycerol monostearate (GMS).	• Mayonnaise and hollandaise sauces. • Ice cream. • Jams. • Ice cream.

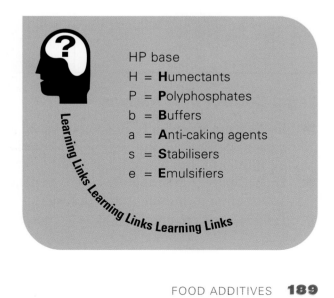

HP base
H = **H**umectants
P = **P**olyphosphates
b = **B**uffers
a = **A**nti-caking agents
s = **S**tabilisers
e = **E**mulsifiers

Learning Links Learning Links Learning Links Learning Links

Sweeteners (E900–E999)

Function	Natural	Uses	Artificial	Uses
• To sweeten food. • Artificial sweeteners are used in low-calorie products. • Some artificial sweeteners are used in products for diabetics.	Sugar.	In biscuits, cakes and tinned fruit.	**Intense Sweeteners:** Aspartame (Nutrasweet, Canderel).	In soft drinks and sweetening tablets.
	Fructose.	In tinned peas.		
	Glucose.	In jelly and tinned fruit.	Saccharin (Hermesetas).	In soft drinks and cider.
			Bulk Sweeteners: Sorbitol. Mannitol. Xylitol.	In sugar-free confectionery and jams. In sugar-free chewing gum.

Note: The difference between **intense** and **bulk** sweeteners.

Bulk Sweeteners

- Same sweetening power as sugar.
- Used in large amounts.
- High in kilocalories.

Intense Sweeteners

- Many times sweeter than sugar.
- Used in small amounts.
- Low in kilocalories.

Nutritional Supplements

Function	Natural	Uses
• To replace nutrients lost in processing. • To add to the nutritive value of the food. • To meet consumer demands for healthier food products.	**Vitamins:** • A, D • B group • C	• Margarine and low-fat milk. • Breakfast cereals and TVP. • Fruit drinks
	Minerals: • Iron • Calcium	• Breakfast cereals • Milk and flour.

Legal Control of Additives

✱ In 1989, the European Community adopted a framework directive that set out the criteria by which additives would be assessed.

✱ Food additives can be approved if they present no hazard to the health of the consumer.

✱ Food additives must not mislead the consumer.

✱ The use of food additives must demonstrate advantages that benefit the consumer.

✱ Food additives must preserve the nutritional quality of the food.

✱ Food additives must enhance the keeping quality or stability of a food.

* The anti-oxidants BHA and BHT cannot be used in baby foods.
* Food additives must be subjected to appropriate toxological testing and evaluation.
* All food additives must be kept under continuous observation.

* Additives must at all times comply with the approved criteria of purity.
* Approval for food additives must be limited to the lowest levels of use necessary to achieve the desired effect.

  Source: Food Safety Authority of Ireland.

Contaminants

Contaminants are substances that can enter the food chain at any time and have the potential to cause damage to the body.

Classification of Contaminants

* Industrial residues.
* Radioactive residues.
* Metal residues.
* Agricultural residues.
* Other contaminants: micro-organisms and foreign bodies.

Maximum Residue Levels (MRL)

- The European Commission has set maximum residue levels (MRL).
- These are indicators of the maximum amount of a residue permitted in a food fit for human consumption.
- Acceptable daily intake (ADI) is the amount of residue which is permitted daily over long periods of time with no ill effects to the body.

The Effects of Contaminants

Type of Contaminant	Effects
Industrial Residues: **Dioxins**: Formed by burning hydrocarbon fuels in industries.	• Believed to be cancer-causing.
Radioactive Residues: **Radiation** from nuclear explosions and from nuclear power stations.	• Can cause cancers, leukaemia and thyroid disease.
Other Contaminants: • **Micro-organisms**: Bacteria, fungi and viruses. • **Foreign bodies**: Poor hygiene practice results in hair, nails and jewellery contaminating food.	• Can cause food poisoning. • Can cause food poisoning.

Type of Contaminant	Effects
Metal Residues: • **Cadmium**: Plastics, batteries and burning fuels. • **Lead**: Used in copper pipes and added to paints.	• Damage to liver and kidneys. • Damage to liver and kidneys. • Affects the nervous system. • Affects the immune system.
Agricultural Residues: • **Pesticides**: Used to kill weeds, pests and fungi. • **Antibiotics**: Used to treat animal sickness.	• Poisonous. • Cause respiratory problems. • Cause heart and circulatory problems. • Cause birth defects. • Can contaminate the water supply. • Humans can have allergic reactions. • Resistant strains of bacteria may develop.

Sample Exam Questions

Questions

1. Classify food additives and give one example of each. (10)

2. Describe the advantages of additives. (8)

Answers

1. Classify food additives and give one example of each. (10)

   5 classes x 1 mark each + 5 examples x 1 mark each = 10.

   • Colourings (E100–E199), e.g. caramel.
   • Preservatives (E 200–E299), e.g. benzoic acid.
   • Physical conditioning agents, e.g. emulsifiers.
   • Flavourings (no E number), e.g. maltol.
   • Sweeteners (E900–E999), e.g. sorbitol.

2. Describe the advantages of additives. (8)

   4 functions x 2 marks each = 8.

   • The colour, flavour and nutritive value of the food is improved.
   • There is an increase in the variety of foods available to consumers.
   • Preservatives extend the shelf life of foods.
   • The risk of food poisoning is reduced.

Microbiology

Microbiology is the study of micro-organisms. Micro-organisms are minute living organisms that are located in the environment.

Classification of Micro-organisms

Micro-organisms are classified into three groups:
* Fungi.
* Bacteria.
* Viruses.

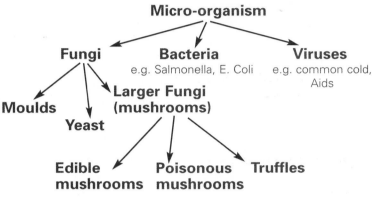

Fig 38.1: Elements of micro-organisms.

Factors Influencing Growth of Micro-Organisms

The environmental factors which influence the growth of micro-organisms are:
* Temperature.
* Food (nutrients).
* Oxygen.
* Correct pH level.
* Moisture.
* Time.

Temperature

All micro-organisms have an optimum temperature at which they grow best.
* **Psychrophiles:** These grow best at temperatures of -5°C to 20°C.
* **Mesophiles:** These have an optimum growth of 20°C to 45°C.
* **Thermophiles:** These grow best at temperatures above 45°C.

Most bacteria grow best in the **danger zone** (5°C to 65°C).

Nutrients

* Certain micro-organisms get their food from **dead matter**; these are known as **saprophytes**.
* Some micro-organisms get their food from **living matter**; these are known as **parasites**.
* Micro-organisms need food for energy and growth.
* Nitrogen compounds are necessary for growth so micro-organisms grow readily on protein foods, e.g. meat and fish.
* Yeast grows best on carbohydrate-rich foods, e.g. bread.

Oxygen

The availability of oxygen:
* **Aerobic:** These micro-organisms need oxygen to grow.
* **Anaerobic:** These micro-organisms grow in the absence of oxygen.

* **Facultative:** These micro-organisms grow with or without the presence of oxygen.
* **Microaerophilic:** These grow in a reduced oxygen environment.

Correct pH Level

* Each micro-organism has an optimum pH.
* Bacteria prefer a neutral pH of 7.
* Yeast and moulds prefer a slightly acidic pH.

Moisture

Micro-organisms grow best in a high water activity environment, which is necessary for their metabolism. Water activity (Aw) is measured on a scale of 0–1.

* 0 = Low-moisture foods.
* 1 = High-moisture foods.

Micro-organisms grow best in food of water activity higher than 0.61 Aw.

Competitive: Micro-organisms compete with each other for nutrients, moisture and air.

Symbiotic: Two micro-organisms grow together and benefit each other to grow.

Fungi

Fungi do not make their own food by photosynthesis, as they do not contain chlorophyll (green pigment found in plants). There are two types of fungi:

* Those that feed on dead matter (known as saprophytes).
* Those that feed on living matter (known as parasites).

There are three main types of fungi in relation to food. These are:

* Moulds.
* Larger fungi (mushrooms).
* Yeast.

Moulds

Moulds are multi-cellular fungi that are generally found on the surface of food. Food becomes contaminated by moulds when they release mycotoxins (a toxin produced from fungi).

Conditions Necessary for Growth of Moulds:

* **Temperature:** Most moulds tend to be mesophiles. Like most micro-organisms, moulds are inactivated by very low temperatures (freezing). Cooking destroys moulds in particular temperatures above 75°C.
* **Food:** The majority of moulds are saprophytes.

These grow on a variety of food, including bread and fruit.

* **Oxygen:** Moulds are aerobic – they need oxygen to grow.
* **pH level:** Moulds require a slightly acidic pH condition to grow.
* **Moisture:** Moulds need moisture in order to grow. They grow best in conditions of high humidity.
* **Time:** Time is necessary in order for moulds to grow.

How to Prevent Food Spoilage by Mould

* Always take care when handling food, in particular fruit and vegetables, to avoid bruising.
* Perishable food must be stored in a refrigerator.
* Vinegar can be used to preserve some foods, e.g. chutney.
* Always check the use-by date.
* Ensure food is cooked right through.
* Always make sure cupboards are clean and dry to prevent mould growth.

Structure of Moulds

* A spore is a single cell.
* When a spore lands on favourable conditions (those necessary for growth, correct nutrients, temperature, oxygen, etc.), a hypha (a thin thread-like filament) grows into the food.

* The hypha absorbs nutrients from the food which enables it to grow.

* The hypha grows into branching hyphae.
* These develop into a mass of intertwining filaments called mycelium.

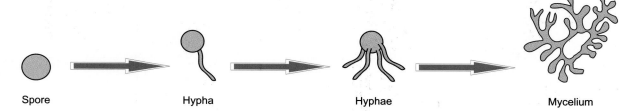

Spore   Hypha   Hyphae   Mycelium

Fig 38.2: Structure and growth of a mould.

Reproduction of Moulds

Moulds can reproduce **asexually** or **sexually**.

Asexual reproduction:

* This occurs when the mycelium is well established.
* A hypha will grow upwards.
* The head of the hypha can either be a sporangium (round) or a conidium (chains of spores).
* When ripe, the sporangium or conidium bursts, releasing spores which travel by wind or by water.
* If the spores land on favourable conditions, the cycle starts again.

Sporangium bursts releasing spores

Spores

Sporangium

Hypha grows upwards

Mycelium

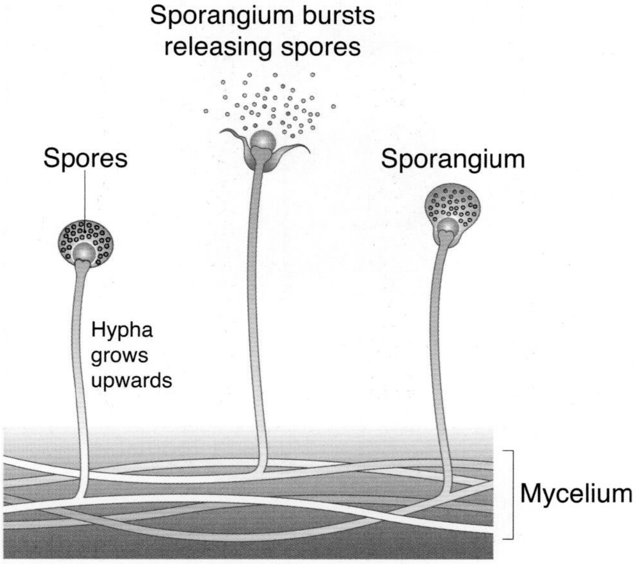

Fig 38.3: Asexual reproduction.

Sexual reproduction:

* This occurs when two hypha grow side by side.
* Each hypha sends out branching hyphae, which grow towards each other.
* These hyphae fuse to form a zygospore. The zygospore contains developing spores.
* The zygospore has a thick wall enabling it to survive long periods of time in unfavourable conditions.
* When conditions are favourable, the spores within the zygospore develop hyphae and these grow out of the zygospore.
* Sporangia or conidia develop.
* On ripening, spores are released. These spores are carried by wind or by water. If they land on favourable conditions, the cycle starts again.

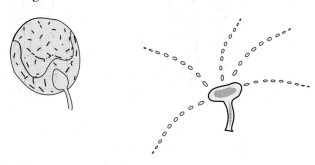

Fig 38.4: Sporangium (left); conidium (right).

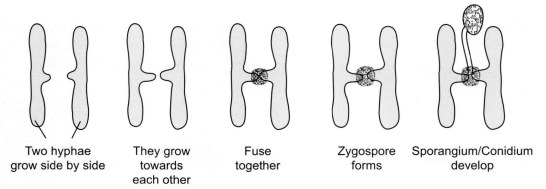

Two hyphae
grow side by side

They grow
towards
each other

Fuse
together

Zygospore
forms

Sporangium/Conidium
develop

Fig 38.5: Sexual reproduction.

Classification of Moulds

Moulds can be classified into two
main groups:

✱ Phycomycetes.
✱ Ascomycetes.

Phycomycetes:

✱ Optimum temperature 30°C.
✱ Non-septae (no cross walls).
✱ Produce a sporangium.
✱ Reproduce asexually or sexually.

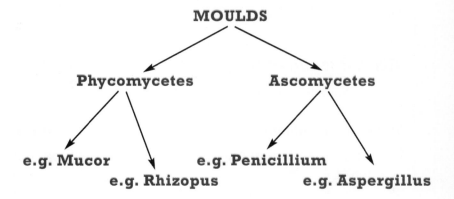

Fig 38.6: Classification of moulds.

Name of Mould	Description	Food Sources
Mucor	• Saprophyte. • Reproduces sexually or asexually. • White hyphae. • Greyish sporangium.	• Bread. • Cheese. • Common in soil. **Fig 38.7:** Bread mould, mucor.
Rhizopus	• Saprophytic mould. • Reproduces asexually. • Fluffy, white mycelium. • Black sporangium.	• Bread. • Rot on fruit and vegetables. • Common in soil.

Ascomycetes:

* Optimum temperature 25°C.
* Septae (have cross walls).
* Produce conidia.
* Reproduce asexually.

PASS:

Phycomycetes reproduce **A**sexually and **S**exually, produce **S**porangia.

Learning Links Learning Links Learning Links

Name of Mould	Description	Food Sources	
Penicillium	• Saprophyte. • Greenish-blue mould. • Used to produce penicillin. • Used to ripen blue vein cheeses.	 **Fig 38.8:** Penicillium mould.	• Bread. • Fruit. • Cheese.
Aspergillus	• Saprophyte. • Grey-greenish or black mould.	• Fruit. • Grain. • Black rot on fruit and vegetables.	

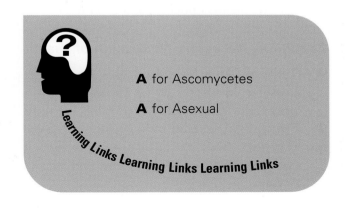

A for Ascomycetes

A for Asexual

Learning Links Learning Links Learning Links

Large Fungi

Three examples of large fungi are:

✳ Edible mushrooms.
✳ Poisonous fungi.
✳ Truffles.

Edible Mushrooms (Basidiomycetes)

Mushrooms are large-bodied fungi, which begin as a spore growing on suitable conditions, e.g. soil or a tree. A mushroom is made of millions of hyphae, which grow upwards but are tightly packed together.

Examples of edible mushrooms include: Agaricus campestris (field mushroom) and Agaricus bisporus (button mushroom, commercially grown).

Reproduction of Mushrooms:

✳ The mushroom cap opens as the mushroom matures.
✳ It is the gills that produce the basidia, which produce the spores.
✳ The spores are released and dispersed through the air.
✳ If the spores land in favourable conditions, the cycle starts again.

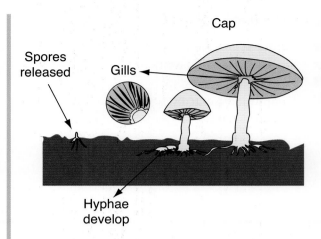

Fig 38.9: Button mushrooms.

Poisonous Fungi	Truffles
• Inedible. • Contain poison. • Example: amanita.	• Food delicacy. • Grow underground. • Strong, pungent flavour. • Expensive.

Yeast

Yeast (saccharomycetes) is a single-cell fungus. Yeast causes spoilage of food such as fruit, fruit juices and jam. It is used in the manufacture of food, such as bread, beer and vinegar. Yeast can be oval, rod-shaped or spherical. It has: a thin outer wall; a granular cytoplasm; a nucleus; and food reserves.

Conditions Necessary for Growth of Yeast

✳ **Temperature:** Yeast requires a temperature between 25°C and 30°C. Therefore, it is a mesophile. Temperatures above 60°C kill yeast.
✳ **Food:** Yeast feeds on carbohydrate-rich food.
✳ **Oxygen:** Yeast is facultative, therefore it can grow with or without the presence of oxygen.
✳ **pH level:** Yeast requires an acidic environment in order to grow.
✳ **Moisture:** Yeast requires moisture.
✳ **Time:** Yeast requires time.

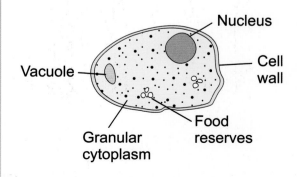

Fig 38.10: Structure of yeast.

Reproduction of Yeast:

Yeast reproduction occurs asexually by budding.

✳ Under favourable conditions, the cell wall develops a small bulge.

✳ The nucleus moves towards the bulge and divides in two.

✳ As the bulge develops, a wall forms.

✳ This wall separates the bud from the parent cell.

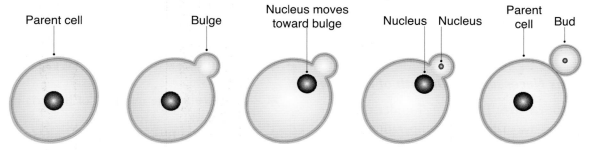

Fig 38.11: Reproduction of yeast.

Preventing Food Spoilage by Yeast:

✳ Handle food with care.

✳ When making jam, ensure sugar is weighed accurately.

✳ Always store preserves correctly.

Advantages and Disadvantages of Fungi, Mould and Yeast

Advantages of Fungi	Disadvantages of Fungi
• Fungi help decompose organic matter. • Fungi are used to decompose sewage. • Many fungi are edible. • Fungi are used in the production of novel proteins (Quorn).	• Fungi cause food spoilage. • Fungi destroy certain products, e.g. potatoes and cereals. • Fungi cause human diseases such as ringworm and athlete's foot. • Some fungi are poisonous and cause sickness, e.g. amanita.
Advantages of Mould	**Disadvantages of Mould**
• Moulds are used to produce cheeses. • Some moulds are used to produce antibiotics, e.g. penicillin.	
Advantages of Yeast	**Disadvantages of Yeast**
• Yeast is used in the making of bread and of alcohol. • Yeast is a rich source of B group vitamins.	

Bacteria

✱ Bacteria are unicellular (a micro-organism made up of one cell).

✱ Bacteria are present in soil, air, water, in the intestines of animals and are found on plants and humans.

✱ Some bacteria are non-pathenogenic (do not cause disease), whereas others are pathenogenic (cause disease).

Conditions Necessary for Growth of Bacteria

✱ **Temperature:** Bacteria fall under the three headings associated with temperature:

• Psychrophiles: Optimum temperature range for growth is -5°C–20°C.

• Mesophiles: Optimum temperature range for growth is 20°C–45°C.

• Thermophiles: Optimum temperature range for growth is above 45°C.

✱ **Food:** There are two forms of bacteria: saprophytic and parasitic.

• **Saprophytic bacteria**: feed on dead matter (food and soil).

• **Parasitic bacteria**: feed on living matter, e.g. plants and animals.

✱ **Oxygen:** Bacteria are aerobic, anaerobic and facultative.

✱ **pH levels:** The majority of bacteria prefer a neutral pH.

✱ **Moisture:** Bacteria require moisture in order to grow.

✱ **Time:** Bacteria can double in number every 20 minutes.

Structure of Bacteria

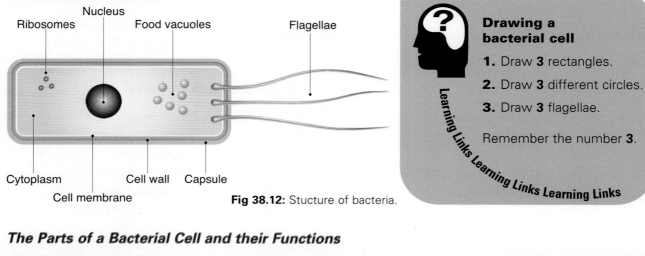

Ribosomes Nucleus Food vacuoles Flagellae

Cytoplasm Cell membrane Cell wall Capsule

Fig 38.12: Stucture of bacteria.

Drawing a bacterial cell

1. Draw **3** rectangles.

2. Draw **3** different circles.

3. Draw **3** flagellae.

Remember the number **3**.

Learning Links Learning Links Learning Links

The Parts of a Bacterial Cell and their Functions

Part of Cell	Function
Capsule	• A jelly-like protective layer.
Cell wall	• A rigid, permeable structure that gives the cell shape.
Cell membrane	• A semi-permeable membrane.
Cytoplasm	• This is where nuclear material can be found.
Nuclear material	• This distinguishes one bacterium from another.
Ribosome	• This is used to make proteins.
Flagellae	• Long, thread-like structures that allow the cell to move.

Reproduction of Bacteria

Bacteria reproduce asexually by a method called **binary fission**.

* The cell increases in length and the nuclear material divides in two.
* A membrane forms between the sets of nuclear material.

* The cell wall forms, dividing the cell into two daughter cells.
* The cells separate.
* Bacteria reproduce very rapidly.

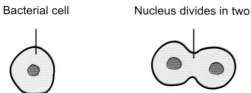

Bacterial cell   Nucleus divides in two

Cell wall separates two daughter cells   Two separate cells

Fig 38.13: Reproduction of bacteria.

Spore Formation in Bacteria

* When conditions become unfavorable for the growth of bacteria, endospores develop within a bacterium.
* Endospores are tough dormant cells produced by bacilli and clostridia (both rod-shaped bacteria) when conditions are unsuitable for growth.
* The spore forms inside the cell. Spores are resistant to cold, heat and some chemicals.
* A tough protein wall surrounds the endospore.
* The parent cell disintegrates.
* The spore can remain dormant for long periods of time, and when conditions are favourable the spore is released and will germinate.

Conditions Necessary for Destroying Endospores

* Moist heat: 121°C for fifteen minutes.
* Dry heat: 150°C for one hour.

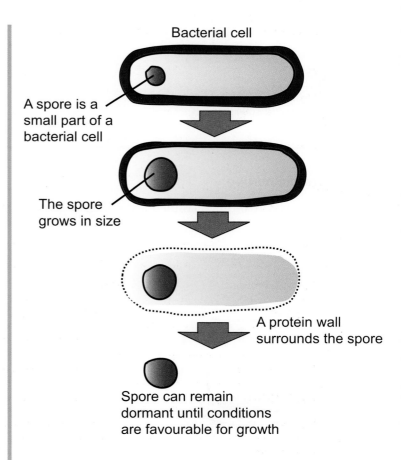

Bacterial cell

A spore is a small part of a bacterial cell

The spore grows in size

A protein wall surrounds the spore

Spore can remain dormant until conditions are favourable for growth

Fig 38.14: Spores being released.

Classification of Bacteria

Bacteria are classified according to their shape:

* **Coccus**: Spherical.
* **Bacillus**: Rod-shaped.
* **Spirals/Vibrio**: Short, curved.
* **Spirillum**: Long, coiled threads.

Type of Bacteria		Examples
Coccus **Fig 38.15:** Coccus bacteria.	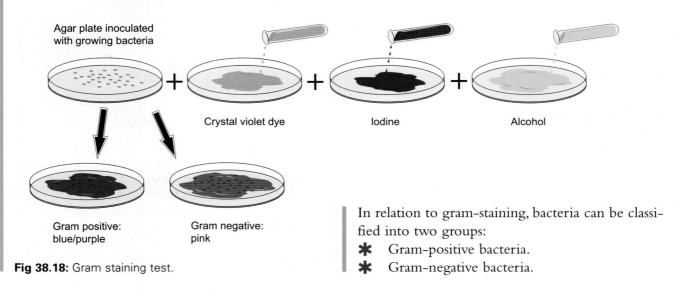	• **Single**: coccus, e.g. meningitis. • **In pairs**: diplococci, e.g. pneumonia. • **In chains**: streptococci, e.g. tonsilitis. • **In clusters**: staphylococci, e.g. food poisoning.
Bacillus **Fig 38.16:** Bacillus bacteria.		**Two types:** • Bacilli, e.g. salmonella, E.coli and listeria. • Clostridia, e.g. Clostridium botulinum.
Vibrio and Spirillum **Fig 38.17:** Vibrio and spirillum bacteria.		**Two types:** • Vibrios (comma), e.g. cholera. • Spirilla (spiral), e.g. syphilis.

Gram Staining

Bacteria can also be classified according to gram staining.

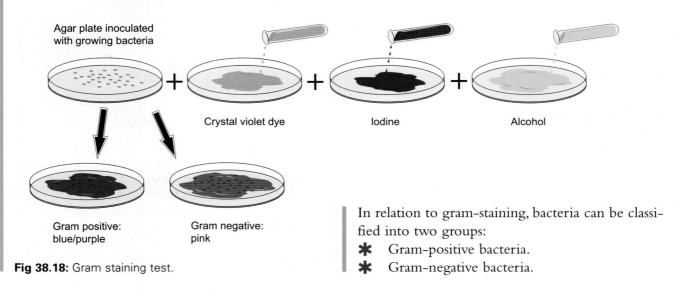

Agar plate inoculated with growing bacteria

Crystal violet dye

Iodine

Alcohol

Gram positive: blue/purple

Gram negative: pink

Fig 38.18: Gram staining test.

In relation to gram-staining, bacteria can be classified into two groups:

* Gram-positive bacteria.
* Gram-negative bacteria.

Gram staining is carried out in a laboratory when:

* An agar plate is inoculated with a strain of bacteria.
* Crystal violet dye (blue colour) is poured over the bacteria.
* Iodine solution (blue-black colour) is poured over the bacteria.
* Acetone (alcohol) is poured over the bacterial cells.

Results:

* If the bacteria are blue-purple, the bacteria present are gram-positive.
* If the bacteria are pink, the bacteria present are gram-negative.

Gram Positive	Gram Negative
• Form spores. • No flagella present. • Not resistant to antibiotics. • The cell wall is a thick, single layer. • Examples include: clostridium and lactobacillus.	• No spores formed. • Flagella present. • More resistant to antibiotics. • The cell wall is two thin layers. • Examples include: Salmonella and E.coli.

Growth of Bacteria

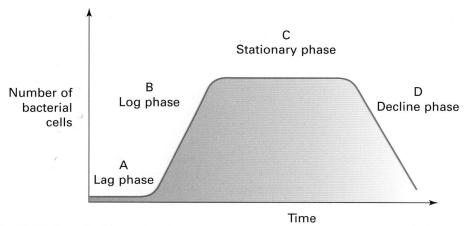

A = **Lag phase:** Bacteria adjust to their surroundings. There is little increase, if any, in the numbers in this phase.
B = **Log phase:** Bacteria multiply quickly.
C = **Stationary phase:** Bacteria run low in nutrients and growth is stationary.
D = **Decline phase:** Lack of nutrients and build-up of waste cause death.

Fig 38.19: Growth of bacteria.

Death of Bacteria

There are three factors causing the death of bacteria:
* Depletion of nutrients.
* Micro-organisms produce toxins that eventually pollute their own environment.
* Overcrowding of cells occurs, which leads to competition for food, air and moisture.

Toxins

Some bacteria produce toxins that are poisonous. Two types of toxins are: endotoxins and exotoxins. These toxins often cause food poisoning.

Endotoxins:

* They are made inside the bacteria cells.
* They are released when the bacterial cell dies.

* This toxin only affects the part of the body where the bacterium was living.
* Endotoxins cause infectious food poisoning.
* An example of a bacterium that produces an endotoxin is salmonella.

Exotoxins:

* The bacteria secrete these from the outside of the cell onto the food.
* These toxins are produced before and after the consumption of food.

* They can be carried by the blood stream all over the body.
* Exotoxins cause toxic food poisoning.
* An example of a bacterium that produces exotoxin is Clostridium botulinum.

Mycotoxin:

* This is a toxin produced from fungi.
* Examples include: aflatoxin produced from the Aspergillus mould and patulin produced from the Penicillium mould.

Advantages of Bacteria	Disadvantages of Bacteria
• Some bacteria produce vitamins B and K. • Some bacteria are used as starter cultures in the manufacture of yoghurt and cheese. • Bacteria break down waste matter into simpler substances.	• Cause food spoilage, e.g. milk souring. • Pathogenic bacteria cause food poisoning. • Some bacteria can cause diseases, e.g. cholera.

Viruses

* Viruses are non-cellular structures.
* They are tiny parasites that consist of either RNA or DNA (genetic material).
* Viruses are responsible for causing a wide range of human diseases, including the common cold, influenza, polio, rabies, hepatitis, Aids and cancer.

Uses of Micro-Organisms

Micro-organisms are used in food production to make:
* Cheese.
* Yoghurt.
* Mycoprotein.
* Bread.
* Alcohol.
* Vinegar.

Food	Micro-Organism
• Cheese (see p. 112)	• Lactic acid bacteria.
• Yoghurt (see p. 110)	• Lactobacillus bulgaricus. • Streptococcus thermophillus.
• Mycoprotein (see p. 117)	• Fusarium gramin.
• Bread	• Yeast.
• Alcohol	• Yeast.
• Vinegar	• Yeast. • Acetic acid bacteria.

Part Sample Exam Questions

Questions

1. Explain how yeast reproduces. (12)

2. What are the environmental factors that affect the growth of yeast? (12)

Answers

1. Explain how yeast reproduces. (12)

   4 points x 3 marks each = 12.

   Yeast reproduction occurs asexually by budding:
   - Under favourable conditions, the cell wall develops a small bulge.
   - The nucleus moves towards the bulge and divides in two.
   - As the bulge develops, a wall forms.
   - This wall separates the bud from the parent cell.

2. What are the environmental factors that affect the growth of yeast? (12)

   4 points x 3 marks each = 12.

   - **Temperature**: Yeast requires a temperature between 25°C and 30°C, therefore it is a mesophile. Temperatures above 60°C kill yeast.
   - **Food**: Yeast feeds on carbohydrate-rich foods.
   - **Oxygen**: Yeast is facultative, therefore it can grow with or without the presence of oxygen.
   - **pH levels**: Yeast requires an acidic environment in order to grow.

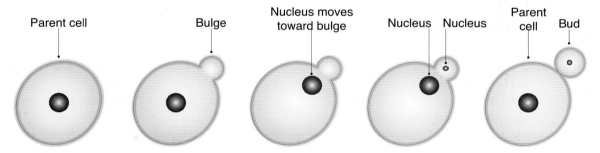

Fig 38.11: Reproduction of yeast.

39 Food Spoilage

Causes of Food Spoilage

There are three main causes of food spoilage:
✳ Moisture loss. ✳ Enzymes. ✳ Micro–organisms.

Moisture Loss

✳ This occurs naturally in fruit and vegetables.
✳ This occurs after harvesting as fruit and vegetables no longer absorb water from the soil through the roots.
✳ Fruit and vegetables appear limp and have a wrinkled skin.
✳ Other foods, such as high-protein foods like fish and cheese, lose moisture from their surface when they are exposed to the air.

Enzymes

✳ An enzyme is a biological catalyst which speeds up or slows down a reaction, without taking part in the reaction itself.
✳ Enzymes are naturally present in foods.
✳ They are protein in nature.
✳ They are present in animals and plants.
✳ Enzymes bring about the ripening of food, eventually leading to the food's decay and browning.

Ripening

- Enzymes present in fruit and vegetables bring about their ripening.
- Fruit and vegetables go from a state of being under-ripe to ripe to over-ripe. For example a banana changes from green to yellow to, eventually, black (decay).
- Starch in under-ripe fruit changes to sugar in ripe fruit.
- The texture (mouth feel) of the fruit/vegetable changes as it ripens from hard to soft, e.g. an unripe pear goes from being hard to soft as it ripens.

Fig 39.1: Banana going from green to yellow to black.

Browning

- This is also known as **enzymic browning**.
- Some fruit and vegetables become brown in colour when the cut surface is exposed to the air.
- An enzyme, oxidase, is released when the fruit/vegetable is cut and interacts with the air (oxidation). For example, the cut surface of an apple becomes brown in colour when it's exposed to the air.

Fig 39.2: Apple going brown.

Control/Prevention of Enzymatic Spoilage of Food

* **Heat:** Enzymes become inactivated at high temperatures. The browning and ripening of food is prevented.
* **Cold:** Enzymes are slowed down. By placing food in the fridge (4°C), enzyme activity is slowed down.

Fig 39.3: Blanching vegetables.

* **Blanching before freezing:** Freezing does not fully inactivate enzymes. Blanching food before freezing inactivates enzymes. Blanching involves immersing the food in boiling water for a set period of time and then plunging the food into ice cold water for the same amount of time.
* **Acids:** Enzymes work best in a neutral pH level. When the pH level is altered by the addition of acids, enzymes become inactivated. An example of this is adding lemon juice to a fruit salad to prevent the fruit (apples and bananas) going brown.
* **Additives:** The preservative sulphur dioxide is used to prevent enzyme action in dried fruit, fruit juices and vegetables.

Micro-Organisms

* Micro-organisms need an optimum temperature, food, oxygen, a suitable pH level, moisture and time in order to grow.
* The main micro-organisms that bring about the spoilage of food are yeasts, moulds and bacteria.

Yeasts	Moulds	Bacteria
• Spoilage is visible. • Spoil the exterior of food. • Examples include the spoilage of fruits. • Not responsible for food poisoning.	• Spoilage is visible. • Spoil the exterior of food. • Examples include mould growth on bread and cheese. • Not responsible for food poisoning.	• Spoilage is not visible. • Spoil the interior of food. • Toxins are produced inside the food. • Some foods become soured, e.g. milk and yoghurt. • Responsible for food poisoning.

Note: The mould Aspergillus flavus (found on nuts and grains) produces an aflatoxin that has been associated with cancer of the liver.

Food Poisoning

Food poisoning is caused by eating foods that contain harmful substances. There are three types of food poisoning: chemical, biological and bacterial.

Chemical food poisoning:

* This involves chemicals from pesticides, antibiotics, metal residues entering the food chain.

Biological food poisoning:

* This involves natural substances in foods that are poisonous, e.g. green potatoes contain solanine, which can cause nausea; and amanita mushrooms are poisonous and cause illness.

Bacterial Food Poisoning:

✳ Bacterial food poisoning is classified in two ways: toxic and infectious.

✳ High-risk foods include eggs, poultry, milk, cream, meat and reheated dishes.

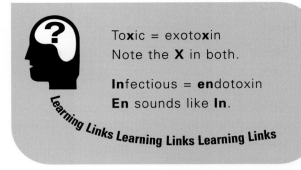

Toxic = exoto**x**in
Note the **X** in both.

Infectious = **en**dotoxin
En sounds like **In**.

Learning Links Learning Links Learning Links

Toxic Food Poisoning	Infectious Food Poisoning
• Bacteria produce and release toxins outside their bacterial cells.	• Bacteria produce and release toxins inside their bacterial cells.
• These toxins are known as exotoxins.	• These toxins are known as endotoxins.
• They have a short incubation period.	• They have a long incubation period.
• Symptoms occur quickly – within two hours of eating food.	• Symptoms don't appear quickly – normally twelve hours after eating food.
• Exotoxins are not easily destroyed.	• Endotoxins are easily destroyed.
• Thirty minutes' boiling is necessary to destroy exotoxins.	• Heating food destroys endotoxins.
• Examples of toxic food poisoning bacteria are Staphylococcus aureus and Clostridium botulinum.	• Examples of infectious food poisoning bacteria are salmonella, Listeria monocytogenes and E. coli.

Examples of Toxic Food Poisoning

Clostridium botulinum

Description	Environmental Factors	Food Sources	Habitat	Incubation Period	Duration	Symptoms
• Rod-shaped. • Gram-positive. • Spore-forming.	• Anaerobic. • Acidic pH.	• Canned foods. • Vacuum-packed foods. • Sausages. • Cheese.	• Soil. • Vegetables. • Intestines of pigs.	• 12–36 hours.	• 1–8 days.	• Headache. • Double vision. • Dizziness. • Swallowing difficulties. • Slurred speech. • Diarrhoea.

Staphylococcus aureus

Description	Environmental Factors	Food Sources	Habitat	Incubation Period	Duration	Symptoms
• Spherical shape. • Gram-positive. • Non-spore-forming.	• Facultative. • Tolerant to salt.	• Unpasteurised milk. • Cold meat.	• Nose. • Throat. • Unwashed hands. • Skin of humans.	• 2–6 hours.	• 24 hours.	• Vomiting. • Diarrhoea. • Stomach cramps.

Examples of Infectious Food Poisoning

Salmonella

Description	Environmental Factors	Food Sources	Habitat	Incubation Period	Duration	Symptoms
• Rod-shaped. • Bacilli. • Gram-negative. • Non-spore-forming.	• Facultative. • Survives best at temperatures of 37°C (this is why salmonella bacteria grow very well in the body).	• Poultry. • Eggs. • Fish.	• Unwashed hands. • Intestines of humans and animals. • Rodents.	• 12–36 hours.	• 1–7 days.	• Vomiting. • Diarrhoea. • Nausea. • Cramps. • Fever.

Listeria monocytogenes

Description	Environmental Factors	Food Sources	Habitat	Incubation Period	Duration	Symptoms
• Rod-shaped. • Gram-positive. • Spore-forming.	• Facultative. • Grow best at 30°C (mesophile). • Slightly acidic pH level.	• Raw meat (chicken). • Coleslaw. • Soft cheeses. • Pâté. • Cook-chill foods.	• Human and animal waste. • Soil.	• 1–70 days.	• Several days.	• Diarrhoea. • Fever. • Possible miscarriage. • Premature births. • Meningitis in newborn babies.

E. coli 0157

Description	Environmental Factors	Food Sources	Habitat	Incubation Period	Duration	Symptoms
• Rod-shaped. • Gram-negative.	• Aerobic. • Grow best at temperatures between 30–40°C.	• Undercooked beefburgers and minced meat products. • Unpasteurised milk. • Raw meat.	• Unwashed hands. • Excreta. • Intestine of human and animals. • Polluted water.	• 12–24 hours.	• 1–5 days.	• Cramps. • Vomiting. • Diarrhoea. • Kidney failure. • Death.

Exam Questions
Higher Level (2004)

Questions

In Ireland during 1998 and 1999, almost 2,000 people became ill from infectious gastroenteritis, a form of food poisoning. The commonest sources of infections were restaurants, hotels and takeaways. Some outbreaks also occurred in private homes.

(Food Safety Authority of Ireland)

1. Differentiate between:
   (a) infectious food poisoning
   (b) toxic food poisoning. (8)

2. Name and give a detailed account of any **one** type of food poisoning bacteria.

Refer to:

- Sources of infection.
- High-risk foods.
- Symptoms. (20)

Sample Answers

1. Differentiate between:
   (a) infectious food poisoning
   (b) toxic food poisoning. (8)

4 marks for infectious food poisoning + 4 marks for toxic food poisoning = 8.

Toxic Food Poisoning	Infectious Food Poisoning
• Bacteria produce and release toxins outside their bacterial cells. • These toxins are known as exotoxins. • They have a short incubation period. • Symptoms occur quickly, within two hours of eating food. • Exotoxins are not easily destroyed. • Thirty minutes' boiling is needed to destroy exotoxins. • Examples of toxic food poisoning: Staphylococcus aureus and Clostridium botulinum.	• Bacteria produce and release toxins inside their bacterial cells. • These toxins are known as endotoxins. • They have a long incubation period. • Symptoms don't appear quickly – 12 hours after eating food. • Endotoxins are easily destroyed. • Heating food destroys endotoxins. • Examples of infectious food poisoning: salmonella, Listeria monocytogenes and E. coli.

2. Name and give a detailed account of any **one** type of food poisoning bacteria.

Refer to:

- Sources of infection.
- High-risk foods.
- Symptoms. (20)

name of food poisoning bacteria = 5 marks
5 marks for each criterion = 15

Salmonella

Description	Environmental Factors	Food Sources	Habitat	Incubation Period	Duration	Symptoms
• Rod-shaped. • Bacilli. • Gram-negative. • Non-spore-forming.	• Facultative. • Survives best at temperatures of 37°C (this is why salmonella bacteria grow very well in the body).	• Poultry. • Eggs. • Fish.	• Unwashed hands. • Intestines of humans and animals. • Rodents.	• 12–36 hours.	• 1–7 days.	• Vomiting. • Diarrhoea. • Nausea. • Cramps. • Fever.

40 Food Preservation

Principles of Food Preservation

Food preservation is the act of making food last longer and preventing food spoilage.

✱ To **prevent** enzyme activity.
✱ To **prevent** the growth of micro-organisms.
✱ To **prevent** micro-organisms re-entering foods by sealing the food.
✱ To **maintain** colour, taste, texture, flavour and nutritive value of the food as much as possible.

Reasons for Preserving Food

✱ **To avoid waste:** Preserving food reduces the amount of food that is thrown away when there is a lot of it available, e.g. a glut of fruit and vegetables.

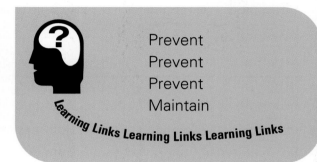

Prevent
Prevent
Prevent
Maintain

Learning Links Learning Links Learning Links

✱ **Useful in emergencies:** Canned, bottled and frozen foods can be quickly and easily prepared and served in an emergency.
✱ **Availability:** Makes out-of-season foods available all year around.
✱ **Variety:** Introducing chutneys, etc. to meals adds flavour and taste.
✱ **Cost:** Preserving food at home is cheaper than buying foods commercially preserved, therefore it saves money.

Methods of Preservation

Home Preservation Methods	Commercial Preservation Methods
• Freezing. • Heat treatments (jam-making, chutney-making, bottling). • Dehydration (home drying) • Chemical preservation (jam, chutney, pickling).	• Freezing. • Heat treatments (canning/bottling, pasteurisation, sterilisation, ultra heat treatment [UHT]). • Dehydration (spray drying, roller drying, fluidised bed drying, accelerated freeze-drying, sun drying). • Chemical preservation (use of sugar, salt, acids, anti-oxidants, nitrates and nitrites, and sulphur dioxide). • Fermentation. • Irradiation.

Freezing

Principles of Freezing

* Very low temperatures are used to freeze food. This prevents the growth of micro-organisms and inactivates enzymes, if food is blanched first.
* When moisture is converted into ice, micro-organisms cannot multiply.
* When food is wrapped, it prevents the re-entry of micro-organisms.

Quick Freezing	Slow Freezing
• -25°C • Fast-freeze section of the freezer. • Small ice crystals. • No damage to cell wall. • No loss of nutrients, colour, flavour or texture. **Fig 40.1:** Quick freezing. 	• 0 to -24°C • Ice box of a fridge. • Large ice crystals. • Damage to cell wall. • Loss of nutrients, colour, flavour and texture. **Fig 40.2:** Slow freezing. 

Foods Suitable for Freezing:

* Most fruit and vegetables.
* Meat.
* Fish.
* Soups and sauces.
* Bread and cakes.
* Pastry.
* Pizza.
* Lasagne.

Foods Unsuitable for Freezing:

* **Whole eggs:** They will crack. Egg whites and yolks can be frozen separately.
* **Bananas and avocados:** They blacken due to enzyme activity.
* **Lettuce, cucumber and peppers:** They have a high water content. They become limp on thawing. They also become discoloured.
* **Mayonnaise:** It will separate.

Advantages of Home Freezing	Disadvantages of Home Freezing
• Bulk freezing saves time and money. • Frozen food is handy in a hurry. • Simple and safe method. • Wide variety of foods can be frozen. • Colour, flavour, texture and nutrients are not lost. • Enables you to bulk buy foods. • Out-of-season foods are available.	• Bulk freezing takes time as you have to bulk cook large quantities of food. • The initial cost of buying a freezer can be expensive. • Packaging material used for freezing goods can be expensive. • Too much frozen convenience foods are not good for a healthy lifestyle.

General Rules for Freezing Food

Preparation:

* Freeze only the best quality foods.
* Set freezer at -25°C (fast freeze), 3–4 hours beforehand.
* Freeze only one-tenth of the capacity of the freezer in any 24 hours.
* Freeze foods in usable amounts.
* Never place hot or warm foods in the freezer.

Packaging:

✳ Use suitable freezer packaging: waterproof, vapour-proof, moisture-proof and strong.

✳ If freezing liquids, e.g. soups and sauces, allow room for expansion of liquids on freezing.

✳ Seal packaging well.

✳ Remove as much air as possible when sealing.

✳ Label packaging with date of freezing, name of product and quantity.

Freezing:

✳ Freeze foods in fast-freeze section of freezer.

✳ Make sure food to be frozen is in contact with the sides or the base of the freezer.

✳ Open-freeze foods that stick together, e.g. strawberries. These can easily be put into a container after freezing.

✳ Never refreeze foods that have already been thawed.

✳ Once frozen, remove from fast-freeze section and return freezer to normal temperature of –18°C.

Storage:

✳ Similar foods should be stored together.

✳ Use foods within the recommended time.

✳ Foods should be used in rotation.

✳ Keep a freezer filled; this reduces running costs.

✳ Don't keep the freezer open for long periods of time.

Thawing:

✳ Frozen food should be thawed out in the refrigerator.

✳ Any foods that could drip should be placed in a bowl or on a plate to prevent cross-contamination. (Remember: in a fridge, put cooked meats on the top shelf and uncooked meats on the bottom shelf.)

Fig 40.3: Blanching method.

✳ Use up thawed food quickly as micro-organisms become active again.

✳ Vegetables should be cooked from frozen. This retains colour, flavour, texture and nutritive value.

✳ Ensure you read labels on commercial frozen products; many do not require thawing and can be cooked from frozen.

Example of How to Blanch and Freeze Vegetables

Ingredients
500g carrots
5 litres of boiling water
Ice cold water

Equipment
Vegetable peeler, sharp knife, chopping board, large saucepan, wire basket, colander, large bowl, freezer bags.

Method

1. Bring the water to the boil.
2. Wash, peel and chop carrots.
3. Place the carrots in the wire basket and put into boiling water for four minutes.
4. Remove from boiling water and plunge into ice cold water for four minutes.
5. Drain using a colander.
6. Place in freezer bags and remove air using a straw.
7. Label.
8. Place in fast-freeze section of freezer.

Heat Treatments

There are three ways of preserving food through heat:

* Jam–making.
* Chutney–making.
* Bottling.

Jam-Making

Principles of Jam-making

* Micro-organisms are destroyed as fruit is heated to 100°C.
* Sixty-five per cent sugar is added, which acts as a preservative and prevents microbial growth of the fruit.
* Pectin and acids help the jam set.
* Sealing prevents the re-entry of micro-organisms.
* The ingredients used in jam-making are fruit, sugar, pectin and acid.

Fig 40.4: Pots of home-made marmalade.

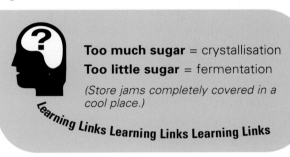

Too much sugar = crystallisation
Too little sugar = fermentation
(Store jams completely covered in a cool place.)

Learning Links Learning Links Learning Links

Fruit	Sugar	Pectin	Acid
• Use ripe fruit. • Fruit high in pectin. • Acidic fruit. • Examples include blackcurrants and cooking apples.	• Needs to be accurately weighed. Too much causes crystallisation. • Warmed sugar will dissolve quickly. • Granulated sugar is generally used. • Sure-Set sugar is ideal for jam-making.	• This is a polysaccharide. • It is found in the cell walls of ripe fruit. • Pectin affects the setting quality of the jam.	• Releases pectin from the cell walls of the fruit as the fruit softens. • Gives a good colour and flavour to jam. • Acid prevents crystals forming. • Lemon juice is commonly added.

A closer look at pectin:

Under-ripe Fruit	Ripe Fruit	Over-ripe Fruit
• Pectose (protopectin). • Poor setting quality.	• Pectin. • Good setting quality.	• Pectic acid. • Poor setting quality.

Levels of pectin in different fruits:

Good level of pectin	Medium level of pectin	Poor level of pectin
• Apples. • Oranges. • Blackcurrants.	• Plums. • Apricots. • Raspberries.	• Strawberries. • Cherries. • Pears.

Testing for pectin in fruit:

✱ Place one teaspoon of fruit juice into a small glass.

✱ Add three teaspoons of methylated spirits.

✱ Mix together and leave for one minute.

✱ Pour from one glass into another glass.

Results:

✱ One firm clot = high in pectin.

✱ Three/four smaller clots = medium amount of pectin.

✱ Lots of smaller clots = poor amount of pectin.

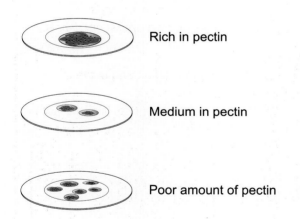

Rich in pectin

Medium in pectin

Poor amount of pectin

Fig 40.5: Different amounts of pectin.

Pectin content can be improved by:

✱ Mixing a fruit low in pectin with a fruit high in pectin, e.g. strawberry and apple.

✱ Using Sure-Set sugar, in which each granule is coated with a mixture of apple pectin and fruit acid.

✱ Using commercial liquid pectin.

Method for Making Strawberry Jam

Fig 40.6: Home-made strawberry jam.

Ingredients

1 kg strawberries   lemon juice
1 kg sugar   water

Equipment

Sharp knife, chopping board, pot, pot stand, small plate, wooden spoon, large plate, baking tray, jam jars, cellophane covers, wax discs, elastic bands, labels.

Method

1. Weigh out ingredients.
2. Wash and sterilise the jars (place jars on a baking tray and put in the oven at 100°C for half an hour).
3. Wash and chop fruit.
4. Allow fruit to soften and to release the pectin over a low heat.
5. Place sugar onto a large plate and warm in the oven (this helps the sugar dissolve more quickly).
6. Add sugar to fruit and allow to dissolve.
7. Bring mixture to the boil and boil rapidly.
8. Check to see if the jam has reached its setting point.
9. Pour jam into the sterilised jars, leaving 1.5cm head space, and wipe clean.
10. Cover with waxed discs and cellophane covers, and label. Store in a cool, dry place.

To test for setting:

The wrinkle test/cold plate test

✱ Put a teaspoon of jam onto a cold plate.

✱ Allow it to cool for a minute.

✱ Push the jam with your finger – if it wrinkles it's ready.

Wrinkle forms

Fig 40.7: The wrinkle test.

The flake test

✱ Lift out some jam with a wooden spoon.

✱ Allow it to cool for a minute.

✱ If the jam falls off the spoon in one flake, it's ready.

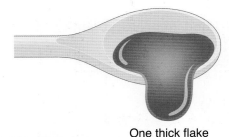

One thick flake

Fig 40.8: The flake test.

The thermometer test

1. Place a thermometer into a saucepan of jam.
2. Read the temperature gauge.
3. If it reads 104°C, it's ready.

Fig 40.9: The thermometer test.

Chutney-Making

Principles of Chutney-making

✱ Acid (vinegar) lowers the pH level and inhibits the growth of micro-organisms.

✱ Sugar dehydrates the micro-organisms and inhibits their growth.

✱ High temperatures destroy micro-organisms.

Method for Making Chutney

Ingredients

500g cooking apples	250g sugar
1 onion	1 teaspoon salt
300ml white vinegar	1 teaspoon allspice
200g raisins	

Equipment

Sharp knife, chopping board, pot, pot stand, small plate, wooden spoon (a metal spoon gives a metallic taste and reacts with the vinegar), jars, plastic screw-on tops (cellophane covers allow evaporation), labels.

Method

1. Simmer chopped onion and apple in vinegar for ten minutes.
2. Place remaining ingredients into the pot.
3. Bring to the boil and allow to simmer uncovered.
4. When the mixture reaches a jam-like consistency, spoon into jars.
5. Put on plastic screw-on tops.
6. Label.
7. Store in a cool, dry place.

Dehydration (Home Drying)

This method of preservation was used more in the past than it is today.

✱ Herbs are the most commonly home-dried food. These are dried in the hot press.

✱ Dehydration removes moisture, so that micro-organisms cannot grow.

Commercial Preservation

* Commercial freezing.
* Commercial heat treatments:
  * Canning/bottling.
  * Pasteurisation.
  * Sterilisation.
  * Ultra heat treatment (UHT).
* Commercial dehydration:
  * Spray drying.
  * Roller drying.
  * Fluidised bed drying.
  * Accelerated freeze-drying (AFD).
  * Sun drying.

* Commercial chemical preservation uses:
  * Sugar.
  * Salt.
  * Acids.
  * Anti-oxidants.
  * Nitrates and nitrites.
  * Sulphur dioxide.
* Fermentation.
* Irradiation.

Commercial Freezing

Principles of Commercial Freezing

* Extremely low temperatures: prevents growth of micro-organisms.

* Moisture is converted to ice: micro-organisms cannot multiply.

Blast Freezing	Plate/Contact Freezing	Fluidised Bed Freezing/ Flow freezing	Cryogenic Freezing
• Food is passed through a tunnel on a conveyor belt. • Cold air (-30°C to -40°C) is blasted through. • Examples of food: meat and vegetables.	• Food is placed between two cold metal surfaces. • Cold air (-30°C to -40°C) is blasted through. • Examples of food: burgers, fish, flat food products.	• Similar to blast freezing. Food is passed through a tunnel on a conveyor belt. • Cold air is blasted up from underneath the conveyor belt, so food looks like it is flowing. • Cold air (-30°C to -40°C) is blasted through. • Examples of food: small foods, such as peas, sweetcorn.	• Food is sprayed with liquid nitrogen. This is the most expensive form of freezing. • Cold air (-200°C) is blasted through. • Examples of food: prawns and strawberries.

Commercial Heat Treatments

Principles of Canning/Bottling

✳ High temperatures destroy micro-organisms and enzymes.

✳ Airtight containers prevent the re-entry of micro-organisms.

Types of Canning	Method	Uses
• Aseptic canning. • Canning high-acid foods. • Canning low-acid foods.	• Food is prepared. • Vegetables are blanched; meat/fish is cooked. • Cans are filled with syrup, brine or oil. • Air is removed. • Cans are sealed hermetically (airtight). • Cans and food are sterilised. • Cans are allowed to cool and are labelled.	• Fruit. • Vegetables. • Soup. • Fish. • Meat. • Milk.

Aseptic canning:

✳ Food and can are sterilised separately.

✳ Food is heated to 120°C–150°C.

✳ Food is put into the can and sealed hermetically.

✳ The cans are then cooled and labelled.

✳ **Advantage:** A short processing time means there is little loss of quality and nutritive value of food.

High-Acid Foods	Low-Acid Foods
• Heated to 100°C for less than thirty minutes. • High-acid foods have a pH of less than 4.5, which is enough to destroy pathogenic bacteria.	• Heated to 115°C for more than thirty minutes. • This temperature and time is needed to destroy bacterial spores.

Pasteurisation:

✳ Heated to 72°C for twenty-five seconds.

Sterilisation:

✳ Heated to 110°C for thirty minutes.

Ultra heat treated (UHT):

✳ Heated to 132°C for one second.

Commercial Dehydration

Principles of Commercial Dehydration

✳ Removing moisture inhibits microbial growth.

✳ Water is needed by micro-organisms in order to grow.

✳ Dehydration does not kill micro-organisms but it stops their growth.

Type	Use	Method
Spray drying	• Milk.	• Milk is sprayed into a chamber heated to 165°C. • The dried particles are collected at the bottom of the chamber. • The cooled, dried milk is packed into airtight containers.

Type	Use	Method
Roller drying	• Milk products. • Baby foods. • Breakfast cereals.	• Food is poured over heated, revolving rollers. • The food is scraped off, cooled and packed into airtight containers.
Fluidised bed drying	• Vegetables.	• Hot air is circulated around the food. • The food doesn't stick together, as it's constantly moving. • The food is packed and labelled.
Accelerated freeze-drying (AFD)	• Coffee. • Fruit. • Vegetables. • Meat.	• The food is frozen. • The food is then gradually heated. • Sublimation of ice occurs: the ice crystals are converted to water vapour without becoming a liquid. • The water vapour is then removed.
Sun drying	• Tomatoes. • Figs. • Grapes.	• Food is exposed to sunlight in hot climates and is dehydrated.

Fig 40.10: Sun drying tomatoes.

Commercial Chemical Preservation

Principles of Chemical Preservation

✱ Preservatives are added to foods.

✱ The chemical preservative dissolves in the water of the food.

✱ The micro-organisms become dehydrated.

✱ Acids lower the pH level and thereby prevent enzymatic action and inactivate micro-organisms.

✱ Alcohol denatures protein in bacterial cells.

Type of Preservation	Use
• Sugar	• Jam, fruit (canned or bottled in syrup).
• Salt	• Bacon, sausages, cheese, foods canned in brine.
• Acids	• Pickles, chutney.
• Anti-oxidants	• Fats and oils, fruit, dried food products, baked products.
• Nitrates and nitrites	• Meat.
• Sulphur dioxide	• Flour, fruit juices.

Fermentation

Principles of Fermentation

✳ Fermentation is the breakdown of sugar by micro-organisms (yeast and bacteria) to produce alcohol and carbon dioxide.

✳ The enzyme zymase in yeast ferments the glucose and fructose to CO_2 and alcohol.

Foods formed from yeast fermentation include beer, bread, vinegar and wine.

✳ **Bread:** When bread is made, it is the carbon dioxide that is used to make the end product.

✳ **Wine and beer:** In this case, it is the alcohol that is used to make the end product.

✳ **Vinegar:** This is formed by the fermentation of yeast on an alcohol and by acetobacter bacteria.

✳ **Wine and malt vinegars:** When the bacteria grow on wine, the end product is wine vinegar. When they grow on beer, the end product is malt vinegar.

✳ **Yoghurt:** This is formed when the starter cultures (Lactobacillus bulgaricus and Streptococcus thermophillus) are added to pasteurised milk. These bacteria cause the fermentation of lactose (milk sugar) into lactic acid.

$$C_6H_{12}O_6 + yeast \longrightarrow 2C_2H_5O_4 + 2CO_2 + energy$$

$$glucose + yeast \longrightarrow alcohol + carbon\ dioxide + energy$$

Fig 40.11: Equation for fermentation.

Irradiation

Principle of Irradiation

✳ Food is exposed to radiation.
✳ The radiation destroys micro-organisms.
✳ Examples of food that is irradiated include dried herbs and spices, fruit and vegetables.

Fig 40.12: Radura symbol.

Advantages of Irradiation	Disadvantages of Irradiation
• Pathogenic bacteria are destroyed. • Shelf life is increased. • Ripening and sprouting of fruit and vegetables are slowed down. • No need to use chemical preservatives.	• Greater levels of radiation are often used than are actually needed. • Vitamins can be destroyed. • There are fears over the development of free radicals and the levels of radioactivity. • The use of irradiation on inferior foods by manufacturers.

Effects of Preservation on Food

Freezing

✱ Micro-organisms are inhibited.
✱ Enzymes are inactivated.
✱ There is a loss of water-soluble vitamins (B group and C) when food is thawed.
✱ Freezer burn can occur on protein foods that are not covered properly.
✱ Freezing is the best method of preservation, as there is little loss of nutritive value.

Canning

✱ Micro-organisms are inhibited.
✱ Enzymes are inactivated.
✱ There is a loss of water-soluble vitamins (B group and C) due to high temperatures.
✱ There is a loss of colour, flavour and texture.
✱ There may be an increase in sugar and salt content due to the preserving chemicals that are added.

Dehydration/Drying

✱ Micro-organisms are inhibited.
✱ Enzymes are inactivated.
✱ There is a loss of water-soluble vitamins (B group and C) due to water loss.
✱ There is a loss of colour, flavour and texture.

Analysis of Different Methods of Preservation

This involves examining a particular type of food (peas) and comparing the different methods of preservation under set criteria.

	Frozen Peas	Canned Peas
Ingredients used	• Peas	• Peas. • Water additives. • Colouring (tartrazine and green S).
Shelf life	• When frozen correctly, they last for up to one year.	• Have a very long shelf life. • Can be stored for up to three years. • Once opened, consume within two days.

	Frozen Peas	**Canned Peas**
Labelling	Information found on frozen peas packet: • Name of product. • Nutritional information. • RDA and GDA. • Cooking instructions. • Storage instructions (contains *star rating) • Customer care telephone number and address. • Weight. • Best-before date.	Information available on can label: • Name of product. • Ingredients. • Nutritional information. • Cooking instructions. • Storage instructions. • Customer care address. • Weight. • Best-before date.
Type of packaging	• Metal (foil bags).	• Metal (tin cans).
Effects of processing	• Micro-organisms are inhibited. • Enzymes are inactivated.	• Micro-organisms are inhibited. • Enzymes are inactivated. • Loss of water-soluble vitamins (B group and C) due to high temperatures. • Loss of colour, flavour and texture. • May be an increase in sugar and salt content due to preserving chemicals added.
Risk of spoilage	• Repeated defrosting and thawing can encourage rapid microbial growth and lead to food poisoning.	• If cans are dented, food could become spoiled due to the presence of Clostridium botulinum.
Cost	• €1.19 per 450g	• €0.68 per 225g
Use	• Frozen peas are easy to use. • Easy to open. • Quick cooking time.	• Canned peas are easy to use. • Pull rings on cans can break easily. • Quick cooking time.

41

Food Hygiene and Safety

Hygiene Guidelines

Careful food handling and a hygienic work environment are crucial to prevent food poisoning.

Personal Hygiene

* Wash hands regularly with hot, soapy water.
* Always wash hands after handling pets, sneezing, smoking, handling rubbish, using the toilet.
* Protective clothing, such as hairnets and aprons, should be worn.
* Always cover cuts.
* Do not wear jewellery.
* Keep hair tied back.
* Keep nails short and clean.
* If a food handler is sick, they should not prepare food.

Kitchen Hygiene

* Kitchen work surfaces should be smooth and easy to clean.
* Floor and wall surfaces should be durable.
* Food should be covered at all times.
* Rubbish bins should be cleaned.
* Clean cloths and tea towels regularly.
* Keep pets out of the kitchen.
* Mop up spills immediately after they occur.

Food Hygiene/Preparation

* Keep all food covered.
* Handle food as little as possible.
* Avoid cross-contamination by ensuring that raw food does not come into contact with cooked food.

* Never wash hands in the sinks used for the preparation of food.
* Use disposable gloves when preparing high-risk foods (chicken, meat).

HACCP

HACCP is a preventative system of food control. It identifies and monitors where hazards can occur in food purchase, preparation, cooking, storage and transport in order to prevent problems.

Food Hygiene in Cooking

* When cooking poultry, always ensure that sufficiently high temperatures are reached to prevent the risk of food poisoning.
* Serve cooked food straight after cooking.
* Avoid reheating, where possible.
* If reheating food, make sure it reaches temperatures above 100°C.

Food Hygiene for Storage

* Maintain the fridge temperature below 5°C. This temperature will delay the growth of micro-organisms, as they grow best between 5°C and 65°C.
* Never refreeze frozen food that has thawed.
* Always ensure that containers used for storage are absolutely clean.
* Stored foods must be correctly covered.

Fig 41.1: HACCP signs.

> **H** = Hazard
> **A** = Analysis and
> **C** = Critical
> **C** = Control
> **P** = Point

Hazard

✳ A hazard in food is anything that may cause harm to the consumer. A hazard can be biological, chemical or physical.

- **Biological:** This is contamination of a food by pathogenic micro-organisms such as bacteria and fungi.
- **Chemical:** Chemical hazards include pesticides, chemicals in cleaning agents and toxic metals.
- **Physical:** Broken glass, crockery, metal, dirt or bits of packaging

> **Risk**
> - In food production, a risk refers to the possibility of a hazard occurring.
> - There are three main types of risk: high, medium and low.

Hazard Analysis

✳ This is the methodical assessment of the steps involved in the production of a food in a food premises.

✳ It begins with the purchase, delivery and storage of raw materials, and their preparation, cooking, assembly and sale.

A Critical Control Point

✳ A critical control point (CCP) is a stage in the food-making process where hazards must be controlled or restricted.

✳ A critical control point (CCP) can be a location, practice, process, raw material, or where controls can be applied to prevent or minimise hazards.

✳ Identifying critical control points guarantees that a potential hazard does not become a real hazard.

The HACCP System

> With each critical control point it is important to ensure everyone in the HACCP team knows:
> - What has to be done.
> - When it has to be done.
> - Who is doing it.

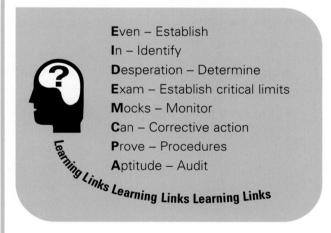

Even – Establish
In – Identify
Desperation – Determine
Exam – Establish critical limits
Mocks – Monitor
Can – Corrective action
Prove – Procedures
Aptitude – Audit

Learning Links Learning Links Learning Links

1. **Establish** a HACCP team.
2. **Identify** hazards and estimate the risks associated with the potential hazard.
3. **Determine** critical control points. These CCPs will reduce or eliminate hazards.
4. **Establish** critical limits.
5. Establish a system to **monitor** the control of CCPs.
6. Take **corrective action** whenever monitoring indicates critical limits are not met.
7. Establish **procedures** to verify that the HACCP system is working as planned.
8. **Audit** and review regularly.

Developing a HACCP System

1. Assemble the HACCP team. All team members should have an in-depth understanding of HACCP.
2. Describe the food and its distribution.
3. Describe the intended use and consumers of the food.
4. Develop a flow diagram to show the stages involved in the production of food.
5. Verify the flow diagram.

The Benefits of HACCP

✳ An effective HACCP system will identify hazards which could affect the safety of a product.

✳ CCPs are put in place where hazards have been identified, reducing the risk of difficulties arising.

✳ Workers involved in the stages of food production become more knowledgeable about the importance of HACCP.

✳ HACCP requires forward planning and therefore saves money.

✳ HACCP ensures that the legal requirements for safety are met.

✳ Records collected throughout the process produce a truthful picture of the operation that could not be achieved from one single inspection.

Implementing a HACCP System

Below are the stages that need to be considered in implementing a HACCP system in the production of **shepherd's pie**.

Stage of Food Production	Potential Hazards	Control Measure
• Purchase of ingredients	• The meat may be contaminated with bacteria. • Vegetables may be bruised or mouldy. • Perishables may not be stored at correct temperature. • Non-perishables may not be stored correctly.	• Buy all ingredients from a reliable supplier. • Check all vegetables to ensure that there is no bruising and no mould present. • Check use-by date on perishable and non-perishable goods and ensure all packaging is intact.
• Transport of raw materials	• Rise in temperature can enable the growth of micro-organisms. • Meat and vegetables transported together could lead to cross-contamination. • The packaging of non-perishables may be damaged.	• Store foods at the correct temperature. • All food should be wrapped separately. • Transport foods in suitable containers.

Stage of Food Production	Potential Hazards	Control Measure
• Storage of food before use	• Growth of micro-organisms. • Cross-contamination of food. • Damaged packaging.	• Store all food at correct temperature. • Cover all ingredients and store separately. • Check packaging of all foods.
• Preparation of shepherd's pie	• Growth of micro-organisms. • Contamination of meat. • Cross-contamination of food.	• Accurate addition of ingredients. • Implementation of good hygiene standards. • Clean equipment. Use separate equipment for preparing meat and vegetables. • Prepare quickly and efficiently.
• Cooking	• Growth of micro-organisms	• Ensure completely cooked, for full time. • Ensure oven is at correct temperature.
• Serving	• Growth of micro-organisms. • Contamination by food handlers. • Use of unclean equipment.	• Serve quickly. • Use clean equipment. • Ensure food handlers follow hygiene guidelines when serving food.

ISO 9000

The ISO 9000 series is a set of standards concerned with quality.

✱ Minimum requirements are set down to ensure that customer requirements are met.

✱ ISO is an international organisation.

✱ ISO standards are awarded by the National Standards Authority of Ireland.

✱ ISO 9001 is used to guarantee quality of design, development, production, installation and servicing.

✱ ISO 9001:2000 promotes the implementation of a process approach when developing, applying and improving the effectiveness of a quality management system.

✱ Food companies can be issued with ISO 343. This indicates that food has been prepared to high standards of hygiene.

Exam Questions

Higher Level (2004)

Questions

In Ireland during 1998 and 1999, almost 2,000 people became ill from infectious gastroenteritis, a form of food poisoning. The commonest sources of infections were restaurants, hotels and takeaways. Some outbreaks also occurred in private homes.

(Food Safety Authority of Ireland)

1. List five guidelines that should be followed to ensure the safe preparation and storage of food in the home. (10)

2. Explain how a Hazard Analysis Critical Control Point (HACCP) system can benefit a catering business in the prevention of food poisoning outbreaks. (12)

Sample Answers

1. List five guidelines that should be followed to ensure the safe preparation and storage of food in the home.

   5 guidelines x 2 marks each = 10.

   Preparation
   - Handle food as little as possible.
   - Avoid cross-contamination by ensuring that raw food does not come into contact with cooked food.

   Storage
   - Always maintain the fridge temperature below 5°C, as this temperature delays the growth of micro-organisms.
   - Never refreeze frozen food that has thawed.
   - Always ensure that containers used for storage are absolutely clean.

2. Explain how a Hazard Analysis Critical Control Point (HACCP) system can benefit a catering business in the prevention of food poisoning outbreaks.

   4 ways x 3 marks each = 12.

   - A properly implemented HACCP system will identify the hazards that could affect the safety of a product. Prevention is the key to HACCP and therefore fewer problems arise. HACCP requires forward planning and thus saves money.
   - The system which includes the identification of hazards and the determining of CCPs puts the focus on the important issues.
   - HACCP involves all aspects of food production and therefore food is safer.
   - HACCP ensures that the legal requirements for safety are met. Data collected throughout the process and over time produce a more complete and accurate picture of the total operation than could be achieved from one single inspection.

National Food Safety Agencies

42

Irish Agencies

There are a number of agencies in Ireland which monitor food legislation and ensure that all recommended procedures are correctly implemented. They are:

* The Department of Agriculture and Food.
* The Department of Health and Children.
* The Department of the Environment and Local Heritage.
* Local authorities.

* Local Health Service Executives (HSE).
* Public Analyst laboratories.
* The Food Safety Authority of Ireland.
* The Office of the Director of Consumer Affairs.

Department	Function
Department of Agriculture and Food Department of **Agriculture, Fisheries and Food** An Roinn **Talmhaíochta, Iascaigh agus Bia**	• Carries out testing of animals for disease such as TB, brucellosis. • Controls the use of antibiotics in animals. • Monitors the use of pesticides in the production of fruit and vegetables.
Department of Health and Children **Department of Health & Children** AN ROINN SLÁINTE AGUS LEANAÍ	• Educates consumers on food safety guidelines. • Involved in the development of new food safety policies. • Monitors food premises.

Department	Function
Department of the Environment, Heritage and Local Government. Comhshaol, Oidhreacht agus Rialtas Áitiúil **Environment, Heritage and Local Government**	• Examines and controls the public water supply (including bottled water).
Local authorities	• Involved in the licensing of farms, retail outlets that sell milk. • Checks abattoirs and butchers to ensure best practices are adhered to.
Local Health Service Executives	• Environmental health officers (EHOs) are employed by this service. • EHOs ensure that all food legislation is being adhered to in relation to nutritional information and labelling. • Carry out regular inspections of food premises.
Public Analyst laboratories	• These laboratories analyse drugs, food and water samples at a fee for the public. • They liaise with EHOs.

Food Safety Authority of Ireland
 	
 Food Safety
 AUTHORITY OF IRELAND
	• This is an independent body.
	 • It was established in 1996.
	 • It was set up because of food scares at the time, e.g. BSE.
	 • The role of the FSAI includes:
	   – Close monitoring of premises involved in food production from farm to fork.
	   – Ensuring that HACCP is being implemented.
	   – Ensuring that best practices are implemented.
	   – Giving advice on nutrition together with education on food-borne diseases.
	   – Investigating food poisoning outbreaks.
	   – Monitoring and controling of new foodstuffs such as GM foods.
	   – Establishing standards against which consumer can complain.

Director of Consumer Affairs (Food Safety Legislation)	• Ensures that food safety legislation is being upheld in relation to the labelling of food. • If food manufacturers fail to comply with this legislation, they can be prosecuted. • The Director of Consumer Affairs deals with any consumer complaint regarding advertising or package information.

Food Laws

The main purposes of food laws are:
* To protect human health.
* To prevent fraud and provide information.
* To inform the consumer.
* To facilitate trade.

National and European Legislation

Food Hygiene Regulations (1950–1989)

These regulations:
* Prohibit the sale of food, which is diseased, contaminated or unfit for human consumption.
* Require that precautions are taken at all stages of production to prevent food contamination.
* Enable unfit food to be seized and ensure that it is destroyed.
* Provide the annual licensing of food stalls.
* Ensure that food handlers on a food premises practise hygiene regulations.

Labelling Regulations, 1982, 1991

* In Ireland, food labelling is controlled by the regulations set out by the EU in 1982.
* They cover areas such as labelling, presentation and advertising of foodstuffs.
* The Liability for Defective Products Act 1991 holds the producer liable for damage caused fully or partially whether or not the producer was negligent.

Sale of Food and Drugs Acts, 1875, 1879, 1899, 1936

* These acts protect the consumer against fraud and tampering with the food.
* It is an offence to:
  * Mix, colour, powder, stain any article of food with an ingredient or material that may cause damage to health.
  * Sell any article of food that is not of the nature, substance and quality demanded by the purchaser.
* The Sale of Food and Drugs Acts give the consumer the right, on payment of a fee, to have food analysed by the Public Analyst laboratories.

Health (Official Control of Foodstuffs) Regulation, 1991

* This regulation gives control to the HSE to inspect all premises involved in food processing.
* This regulation incorporates the various areas of sampling and analysing food, inspection of food, premises and staff.
* The HSE is also committed to monitoring all food exports.

European Communities (Hygiene of Foodstuff) Regulations, 2000

* These regulations set down standards that food premises must adhere to.
* Hygiene regulations apply to:
  * Premises.
  * Preparation areas.
  * Storage areas.
  * Transportation.
  * Water supply.
  * Personal hygiene.
  * Staff training.

* All European countries are required to have an inspection programme.

Health Acts, 1947, 1953, 1970

* These regulations put in place measures to prevent danger to public health that may arise from the manufacture, importation, distribution or sale of food.

Section

FAMILY RESOURCE MANAGEMENT

44 Family Resource Management

45 Managing Household Financial
Resources

46 Housing Finance

47 Household Technology

48 Textiles

49 Consumer Studies

44 Family Resource Management

Management is the skilful handling or running of something.

Resources are anything that helps to achieve goals. Examples of resources include:

- Time.
- Energy.
- Money.
- Skills.
- People.
- Equipment.

Family resource management is running the family by using resources.

Purpose of Family Resource Management

✱ To understand the resources at hand.
✱ To use resources effectively to achieve the family's goals.
✱ To enable all family members to achieve their full potential.

Management Systems

There are two types of management system: the open system and the closed system.

Open System	Closed System
• The family utilises other systems to achieve its goals, e.g. the education system and the health system.	• The family does not utilise other systems to achieve its goals, e.g. the Amish community, which is self-sufficient.

The Family is a Managerial Unit

✱ All management skills are used in the home, including planning, organising, controlling, leading, motivating and communicating.

✱ Examples of situations where these skills are used in the family include: meal-planning, problem-solving, listening, making decisions, resolving conflicts, organising housework, anticipating problems or events.

Components of Management

✳ Management consists of three components: inputs, throughputs and outputs.

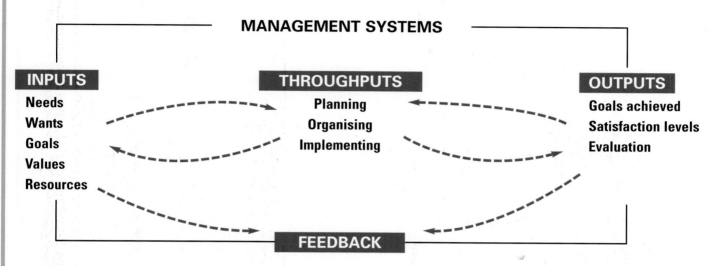

Fig 44.1: Management systems.

Inputs

Inputs are defined as anything brought into the management system.

✳ Inputs are made up of demands and resources.

Demands	Resources
Needs: • Are essential. • Examples include food, clothing, shelter, love and security.	**Human resources:** • Relates to all the things a person can offer to the management system. • Examples include a person's knowledge, intelligence, sense of honesty, trust, manners and skills, such as communication skills.
Wants: • Are desirable. • Examples include luxury cars, state-of-the-art mobile phones and designer clothes.	**Material resources:** • Relates to money and equipment.
Goals: • What a person in the family would like to achieve. • Goals can be short, medium or long term. • An example of a short-term goal would be passing a class test.	**Environmental resources:** • Physical resources relates to the earth, air, temperature and sound. • Social resources relate to social institutions, which can be either political or economic.

Demands	Resources
• An example of a medium-term goal would be getting a good Leaving Certificate. • An example of a long-term goal would be having a good job.	
Values: • Relates to what a person in the family believes to be right and wrong. • Examples include being a vegetarian, only using environmentally friendly materials, only buying Irish-owned goods, being an anti-fur campaigner.	

Throughputs

Throughputs involve the areas of planning, organising and implementing.

Planning	Organising	Implementing

• Involves creating a plan or 'to do' list in order to achieve a goal.
• Gathering information.
• Identifying resources.
• Considering alternatives.
• Types of plan include: directional plans, strategic plans and contingency plans.
	• Allocating tasks and resources to people.
	• There are two forms of organisation:
	  – **Job/Task-centred organisation**: Traditional form of organisation where the person carrying out the task has the necessary knowledge, skill and experience.
	  – **Person-centred organisation**: This involves an individual, who has no experience of carrying out the task, learning by doing.
	The best form of organisation involves a combination of both forms.
		• Putting the plan into action.
		• Taking control, if necessary, to make sure it all goes well.
		• Being flexible if something unforeseen comes up.

Outputs

Outputs are the results that are achieved at the end of the process.

* Have the needs been met?
* Were the wants fulfilled?
* Have the goals been reached?
* Did any values change?
* Satisfaction levels: Satisfaction or dissatisfaction is based on emotions.
* Were all resources used?

Evaluate the whole process and feedback this information so it can be used for the next management process.

Decision-Making

There are many steps involved in a decision-making process.

* Identify the decision to be made.
* Look at the possible solutions.
* Consider the alternatives.
* Consider the consequence of each alternative.
* Pick a solution.
* Establish a plan of action and draw up a list of resources.
* Carry out the decision.
* Evaluate the decision.

Types of Family Decision

There are three types of decision that families can reach:

* **Accommodation:** Agreement is reached as a result of accepting the dominant member's viewpoint.
* **Consensual:** Mutual agreement by all family members.
* **De facto:** No one really minds or cares about the decision.

Communication

* Communication is a two-way process.
* It involves the sharing of ideas, information and emotions.
* Good communication is essential for achieving goals.
* Communication will not be effective if there

are any obstacles in its way, e.g. insensitivity, being opposed to someone else's opinion, information being delivered in a demanding or threatening way.

* An example of communication being used in a family could be the preparation of the house for Christmas Day:
  * Deciding on the goals.
  * Sharing ideas.
  * Discussing solutions.
  * Allocating tasks.
  * Reviewing and evaluating.
* Communication is necessary in conflict resolution and talking and listening are two important aspects of communicating.
* A message or information cannot be heard or received if both parties are talking and nobody is listening.

Factors Affecting Family Management

There are nine factors that affect family management: composition of the family; stages in the life cycle; employment patterns; gender roles; values; standards; management of the dual role; socio-economic status; and culture.

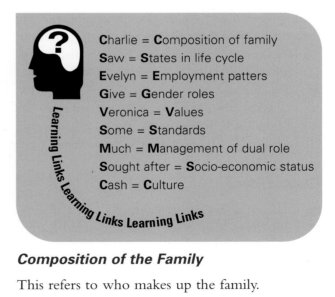

Charlie = **C**omposition of family
Saw = **S**tates in life cycle
Evelyn = **E**mployment patters
Give = **G**ender roles
Veronica = **V**alues
Some = **S**tandards
Much = **M**anagement of dual role
Sought after = **S**ocio-economic status
Cash = **C**ulture

Composition of the Family

This refers to who makes up the family.

* The number of people in a family can affect how it is managed: the more individuals there are in a family, the more needs there are to be met.

* Whether it is a one- or two-parent family will have an effect on management, for example on time and family resources.
* Family members with any mental or physical disabilities will require a special management approach to cater for their needs, e.g. wheelchair access for the physically disabled.

Stages in the Life Cycle

* This refers to the ages of the people in the family.
* A family with young children will have different needs from a family with grown-up children. Constant monitoring of younger children is essential.
* Teenagers in a family can affect its management by being involved in decisions, e.g. planning a family holiday.
* Elderly people have different management issues as they may not be as active as they once were, have less access to money and different interests.

Employment Patterns

* The job an individual does has an effect on the amount of money coming into a home.
* If there are dual earners in a home, more money will be available as both partners are working.
* Spouses doing job sharing, flexitime or taking career breaks can all affect the management of the home. Less income may be available than when both spouses are working full-time.
* The hours people work – 9 to 5, shift work, nights – can all affect the management of the household, from meal times to sleeping patterns to childminding arrangements.

Gender Roles

* The term 'gender' refers to male or female.
* The term 'role' relates to an expected pattern of behaviour.
* When the two words are put together, it refers to the roles or behaviour expected by men and women.
* Gender roles are changing today and it is evident in the management of families.

* There is equal partnership and shared roles, e.g. men are involved in child rearing while women are the main breadwinners.
* All jobs in a home are should be distributed equally with no great emphasis on gender.

Values

* The values people have can affect the management of a home.
* Values affect the decisions taken by families: for example, only buying organic products or installing solar panels in their homes to be more environmentally friendly.
* It is important to note that the values families and individuals have may change due to circumstances. If, for example, an elderly parent is unwell and has to be taken care of, family members may have to reprioritise the management of the home to include the needs of the elderly parent.

Standards

* The standards a family deem to be important would affect the management of the family.
* For example, the standard of expecting children to say 'please' and 'thank you'.

Management of the Dual Role

* The dual role can refer to the situation where both spouses work outside the home.
* Where this happens, extra care and planning needs to be done to ensure the smooth running of the home.
* Management of roles will be different if one partner works outside the home and the other is working inside the home.
* In single-parent families, there is the extra demand of being the earner and the parent. This will put extra constraints on the resources of time and money.

Fig 44.2: Managing the dual role.

Socio-Economic Status

✱ This relates to the job an individual has, the amount of money they earn and where they live.

✱ Families from different socio-economic backgrounds will generally have different priorities.

✱ The lower socio-economic groups have to place more emphasis on needs (food, clothing and shelter), whereas higher socio-economic groups can afford more of the wants (luxury cars, access to private leisure clubs and trips abroad).

Culture

✱ The culture of a country can affect the management of the family, for example, the way people dress, the foods people eat and how women are seen.

✱ Religious customs and practice are very evident in some cultures.

✱ There can be conflict within cultures when these cultures are questioned or being changed, e.g. the status of women changing by being allowed to vote, working outside the home.

Sample Exam Questions

Questions

1. Outline the advantages of a good management system. (12)

2. Explain the three components of management and give two examples of each. (12)

3. Discuss four factors that affect the management of family resources. (16)

Answers

1. Outline the advantages of a good management system. (12)

   4 points x 3 marks each = 12.

   • To understand the resources we have at hand. Using resources effectively to achieve the family's goals.

   • To allow all family members to achieve their full potential.

   • To utilise management skills such as planning, organising, controlling, leading, motivating and communicating.

   • Examples of situations where these skills are used in the family include: meal-planning, problem-solving, listening, making decisions, resolving conflicts, organising housework, anticipating problems or events.

2. Explain the three components of management and give two examples of each. (12)

   3 components x 2 marks each = 6.
   (2 examples x 1 mark each) x
   3 components = 6.

Inputs

• Inputs are made up of demands and resources.

Demands	Resources
Needs: • Are essential. • Examples include food, clothing, shelter, love and security.	**Human resources:** • Relates to all the things a person can offer to the management system. • Examples include a person's knowledge, intelligence, sense of honesty, trust, manners and skills, such as communication skills.

Throughputs

Throughputs involve the areas of planning, organising and implementing.

Planning	Organising	Implementing
• Involves creating a plan or 'to do' list in order to achieve a goal.	• Allocating tasks and resources to people.	• Putting the plan into action.

Outputs

Outputs are the results that have been achieved at the end of the process.

- Have the needs been met?
- Evaluate the whole process and feedback this information so it can be used for the next management process.

3. Discuss four factors that affect the management of family resources. (16)

   4 factors x 4 marks each = 16.

Composition of the family

- The number of people in a family can affect how it is managed: the more individuals there are in a family, the more needs there are to be met.
- Whether it is a one- or two-parent family will have an effect on management, for example on time and family resources.
- Family members with any mental or physical disabilities will require a special management approach to cater for their needs, e.g. wheelchair access for the physically disabled.

Stages in the life cycle

- This refers to the ages of the people in the family.
- A family with young children will have different needs from a family with grown-up children.
- Teenagers in a family can affect the management of a family by being involved in decisions.
- Elderly people have different management issues as they may not be as active as they once were, have less access to money and different interests.

Employment patterns

- The job an individual does has an effect the amount of money coming into a home.
- If there are dual earners in a home, more money will be available as both partners are working.
- Spouses doing job sharing, flexitime or taking career breaks can all affect the management of the home. Less income may be available than when both spouses are working full-time.
- The hours people work – 9 to 5, shift work, nights – can all effect the management of the household, from meal times to sleeping patterns to childminding arrangements.

Socio-economic status

- This relates to the job an individual has, the amount of money they earn and where they live.
- Families from different socio-economic backgrounds will generally have different priorities.
- Lower socio-economic groups have to place more emphasis on needs (food, clothing and shelter), whereas higher socio-economic groups can afford more of the wants (luxury cars, access to private leisure clubs and trips abroad).

Managing Household Financial Resources

45

The Household as a Financial Unit within the Economy

* Families contribute to the economy of the country in which they live.
* Family members who work earn wages, pay taxes and spend money, generating revenue for the Government.
* This contribution keeps the economy buoyant.
* Family income spent on goods and services generates employment and wealth in the country.
* Taxes paid by working family members are used for state services.
* Some households are dependent on the state to intervene in the family function of economy by providing state benefits.

Social Factors Affecting Household Income

Age	Sex	Social Class	Culture
• A person's income usually increases as they get older. • A teenager might take on a part-time job to have money for discretionary expenditure. • Older people on old-age pensions might have less money to spend on wants.	• Gender equality laws ensure equal pay for all. • However, research shows that there are more men than women in the workforce and that most managerial positions are filled by men.	• This refers to the family's socio-economic grouping. • Families in the lower socio-economic group will have less available income to spend on wants. • Higher socio-economic groups generally have better educational opportunities, which affects career advancement and income.	• Different cultures will value income differently. • Income may be spent on needs or wants, e.g. in developing cultures, income is used for needs. • Some cultures dictate whether a woman can work outside the home.

Household Income

* This is the amount of money coming into a house.
* Sources of income include wages, salaries, pensions, returns on investments and social welfare benefits and allowances.
* **Gross Income:** Income before deductions are made.
* **Net Income:** Income after deductions are made. This is often referred to as take-home pay.

Deductions

Deductions can be compulsory or voluntary.

Compulsory Deductions	Voluntary Deductions
These include: • PAYE. • PRSI. • Government health levy.	These include: • Pensions. • Union fees. • Private health insurance. • Savings schemes.

PAYE (Pay as You Earn)

* This is also known as income tax.
* This deduction is made by an individual's employer before the individual receives his/her pay.
* The money is forwarded to the Revenue Commissioners.
* The money is used by the Government for capital expenditure, e.g. paying teachers, nurses, gardaí, providing hospitals and schools, and constructing roads.
* Every employee has their own PPS (Personal Public Service) number.
* If people are self-employed, e.g. farmers, and own their own business, they must complete their own tax returns.

To calculate how much tax a person has to pay, there are currently two rates of tax liability:
* 20 per cent standard rate.
* 41 per cent high rate.
* An individual must pay tax at the standard rate up to a certain amount (known as the 'standard rate cut-off point') and then is taxed at the higher rate.
* A person's standard rate cut-off point varies depending on personal factors, such as being single, married, with or without children.

Tax Rates and Bands 2009

You are:	20% band	41% band
Single person	€36,400	Balance
Married couple One income	€45,400	Balance
Married couple Two incomes	€45,400 (with an increase of €27,400 max)	Balance
One-parent family	€40,400	Balance

Tax Rates and Bands 2008

You are:	20% band	41% band
Single person	€35,400	Balance
Married couple One income	€44,400	Balance
Married couple Two incomes	€44,400 (with an increase of €26,400 max)	Balance
One-parent family	€39,400	Balance

Tax credits

* Tax credits are used to lower the amount of tax that can be calculated on a person's gross pay.
* Tax credits may change from year to year depending on budgets set by the Minister for Finance.

* Each year every employee receives a tax certificate called 'Notification of determination of tax credits and standard cut-off point'. This enables individuals to be aware of their tax liability and tax credits.

Tax credit allowances

Personal Tax Credit	Tax Year 2008	Tax Year 2009
Single Person	€1,830	€1,830
Married Person	€3,660	€3,660
Widowed Person qualifying for One-Parent Family Tax Credit	€1,830	€1,830
Widowed Person without dependent children	€2,430	€2,430
Widowed Person in year of bereavement	€3,660	€3,660
One-Parent Family, Widowed, Deserted, Separated or Unmarried (with qualifying dependent children)	€1,830	€1,830
Widowed Parent Bereaved in 2008	—	€4,000
Widowed Parent Bereaved in 2007	€4,000	€3,500
Widowed Parent Bereaved in 2006	€3,500	€3,000
Widowed Parent Bereaved in 2005	€3,000	€2,500
Widowed Parent Bereaved in 2004	€2,500	€2,000
Widowed Parent Bereaved in 2003	€2,000	—
Home Carer (max.)	€ 900	€ 900
PAYE Tax Credit	€1,830	€1,830
Age Tax Credit if Single/Widowed	€ 325	€ 325
Age Tax Credit if Married	€ 650	€ 650
Incapacitated Child	€3,660	€3,660
Dependent Relative	€ 80	€ 80
Blind Tax Credit – Single	€1,830	€1,830
Blind Tax Credit – One Spouse Blind	€1,830	€1,830
Blind Tax Credit – Both Spouses Blind	€3,660	€3,660
Blind Tax Credit – Additional Allowance for Guide Dog	€ 825	€ 825
Incapacitated Person – Allowance for Employing a Carer	€50,000 max.	€50,000 max.

The Child's/Relative's Income Limits	Tax Year 2008	Tax Year 2009
One-Parent Family Tax Credit	0	0
Incapacitated Child Tax Credit	0	0
Dependent Relative Tax Credit	€13,473	€13,837

Exemption Limits/Personal Circumstances	Tax Year 2008	Tax Year 2009
Single/Widowed 65 years of age or over	€20,000	€20,000
Married 65 years of age or over	€40,000	€40,000

PRSI (Pay Related Social Insurance)

* This is a compulsory deduction.
* The majority of employees over the age of sixteen must pay PRSI.
* Employers and employees share the amount to be paid.
* It is based on a percentage of an employee's earnings.
* PRSI is used for claiming benefits, e.g. maternity benefit, unemployment benefit, disability benefit, etc.
* In order to claim benefits, a person must have made a minimum of thirty-nine contributions in the previous tax year.
* Certain groups are exempt from paying PRSI, including people with a medical card, those receiving a one-parent family benefit, etc.

Health Levy

* This is deducted at the rate of 2 per cent from an individual's gross income.
* This money is used for improving Ireland's health system.

Other Sources of Income (Social Welfare Payments)

Social Insurance Payments	Social Assistance Payments	Universal Payments
Payments based on an individual's PRSI contributions. - Maternity benefit. - Unemployment benefit. - Disability benefit. - Old age (contributory) pension. - Widow's/widower's (contributory) pension.	Payments based on a means test – non-contributory. - Supplementary welfare allowance. - Family income supplement. - One-parent family payment - Carer's allowance. - Old age (non-contributory) pension. - Widow's/widower's (non-contributory) pension.	Payments automatically given regardless of PRSI contributions or means testing. - Child benefit.

Supplementary Welfare Allowance

✱ A weekly allowance paid to individuals whose means are insufficient to meet their needs.

✱ This payment is administered by the Health Boards.

✱ It is means tested and individuals must be FAS-registered.

✱ Individuals may also be entitled to additional payments, such as fuel allowance, back-to-school clothing and footwear allowance, and rent/mortgage interest supplement.

Family Income Supplement

✱ A weekly payment to one-parent families or earners in low-paid jobs.

✱ To qualify for FIS, an individual must:
  - Be working for at least 19 hours a week in paid full-time employment.
  - Have at least one dependent child.
  - Have a maximum weekly income at a level set by the Government, which is based on family size.
  - The FIS payment is 60 per cent of the difference between the family's income limit and actual income i.e. 60 per cent of (income limit − actual income).

Example:	
A family with two children earns	€250 a week
Family FIS limit	€570
Difference	€320
60 per cent of the difference	€192

From January 2008, you can qualify for FIS if you have:	And your family income is less than:
One child	€490
Two children	€570
Three children	€655
Four children	€760
Five children	€870
Six children	€970
Seven children	€1,090
Eight children	€1,170

Child Benefit

✱ Paid monthly for each child.

✱ Payments stop when the child reaches sixteen, or nineteen if the child is in full-time education or has a disability.

Pensions

There are three types of pensions: personal/private, occupational and state pensions.

Personal/Private	Occupational	State	

• Individuals pay a set amount into a private pension fund.
• The amount of money that one receives is not guaranteed, so it could be more or less than what was anticipated.
	• Individuals pay a small amount of their wages into a pension fund set up by their employers.	**Old Age Contributory Pension**
		• Individuals over 65 years of age can apply for this pension.
		• Not means-tested.
		• PRSI contributions have been paid over a number of years.
		• Additional **benefits** include:
		  – Free travel.
		  – Medical card.
		  – Free electricity.
		  – Free TV licence.
		Additional **allowances** include:
		  – Over 80 allowance.
		  – Living alone allowance.
			Old Age Non-Contributory Pension
			• Individuals over 66 years of age can apply for this pension.
			• Means-tested (additional income, e.g. spouse's income, is taken into account during assessment)
			• No PRSI or less than the minimum amount of contributions have been paid.
			• Additional **benefits** include:
			  – Free travel, electricity, TV licence.
			  – Medical card.
			• Additional **allowances** include:
			  – Over 80 allowance.
			  – Living along allowance.

Household Expenditure

This is the money that we spend.

Essential Expenditure		Discretionary Expenditure
Fixed: This is at the same time for the same amount.	**Irregular:** This is at different times for varying amounts.	This occurs when all essential expenditure and savings have been made.
• Rent/mortgage. • Insurance. • Telephone.	• Food. • Clothes. • Doctor's bills. • School supplies.	• Holidays. • Entertainment. • Leisure. • Gardening supplies.

Planning a Budget

A budget is a plan for spending money over a particular period.

Reasons for Budgeting

* To control spending.
* Areas of overspending are highlighted.
* To control the use of credit.
* Gives a sense of financial security and peace of mind.
* Sets a good example to children in the family.
* Allows for savings.

Preparing a Budget

* Add up the total income (include all sources of income, e.g. wages, salaries, benefits.). Don't include bonuses as these are not guaranteed.
* Add up total expenditure (both fixed and discretionary).

Guideline for Planning a Household Budget	
Food	25%
Housing	25%
Household	15%
Clothing	10%
Travel	5%
Education	5%
Health	5%
Personal / Leisure	5%
Savings	5%

* Divide by 12 to get the monthly expenditure. Divide by 52 to get the weekly expenditure.
* Always incorporate an element of saving.
* Particular times of the year require extra money, e.g. Christmas, back to school.
* Keep a copy of all bills and receipts.
* Evaluate and review and make changes where needed.

Getting Help Making a Household Budget

The Money Advice and Budgeting Service (MABS):

* Was set up under the Department of Social and Family Affairs.
* Offers help to low-income families or those at risk of getting into debt.
* Helps families to develop money-management skills.
* Makes families aware of special schemes, such as Back to School Clothing and Footwear Policy, the National Fuel Scheme.
* Helps families to get cheaper sources of finance, e.g. from credit unions.

Paying for Goods and Services

There are many ways to pay for goods and services that don't involve credit: cash, cheque book, debit card (laser), credit transfer (giro slip), direct debit/standing order, Bill Pay and online banking.

Fig 45.1: Cheques and cash are non-credit methods of payment.

Cash

Advantages	Disadvantages
• Quick and easy method. • Doesn't incur extra costs (like credit). • Less chance of overspending. • This form of payment can be used for paying for household groceries.	• Risk in carrying large sums of cash around.

Cheque (with Cheque Guarantee Card)

Advantages	Disadvantages
• Safer to post than cash. • Convenient. • An overdraft can be organised. • This form of payment can be used for paying for household furniture.	• Charge for each cheque book. • Charge for each cheque used.

Debit Cards

Advantages	Disadvantages
• Safer than carrying cash. • Facility of getting cash back when paying for goods. • Can't overspend and get into debt (money is taken from the holder's current account). • Easy to use. • Wide range of retailers accepts them. • Card can also be used as an ATM card and a cheque guarantee card. • This form of payment can be used for paying electricity or phone bills.	• A charge may be made for each and every transaction. • There is a government charge for the card.

Credit Transfer/Bank Giro

Advantages	Disadvantages
• Very easy to use as all details regarding the bill (amount, name, address) are printed on the giro. • This form of payment can be used for making credit card payments.	• May be awkward for people as they have to go to the bank or post office to pay with it. • There is a charge for the transaction.

Direct Debit/Standing Order

Advantages	Disadvantages
• Bills are not forgotten because they are automatically paid out of the holder's account. • Easy to set up and convenient to use. • This form of payment can be used for paying gas bills.	• If there are too many of these accounts with too much money leaving the account, you could run into debt. • Charges may apply for these transactions. • May be a charge for the initial set-up.

Bill Pay

Advantages	Disadvantages
• Convenient as they are operated by An Post and there are many branches and outlets available nationwide. • This facility is also available online. • There is no charge for carrying out this service. • This form of payment can be used for Eircom or Bord Gáis bills.	• Not all transactions can be done online, therefore it can be awkward for people to try and get to the post office.

Telephone Banking

Advantages	Disadvantages
• Service offered by banks throughout the country, so very easy access for customers nationwide • Available 24 hours a day. • Easy to use.	• A charge is made for ringing this telephone banking number.

Online Banking

Advantages	Disadvantages
• Twenty-four-hour access, 365 days a year. • Worldwide accessibility. • Easy to use. • Convenient way of paying bills.	• A charge for transactions may apply. • Access to the internet may not be available. • If the PIN is disclosed to others, they have access to all account information.

Credit

Credit – Buy Now, Pay Later	
Advantages	**Disadvantages**
• You get the use of the goods without having to pay for them straight away. • It is very useful in emergencies. • It is safer than carrying large amounts of cash. • Expensive items can be bought on credit, as you wouldn't have all the necessary cash to pay for them, e.g. a car. • People can buy items straight away without wondering if they have the cash, e.g. in sales or impulse buying.	• It can encourage impulse buying, leading to debt. • High rates of interest means that you usually end up paying more for the item in the long run. • There is a temptation to take on too many credit agreements, which could easily lead to debt. • The customer does not own the goods until the last instalment has been paid – repossession could occur if instalments are not made.

Forms of Credit

Credit cards, overdrafts, term loans and hire purchase are all examples of forms of credit.

Fig 45.2: Credit cards.

Credit Cards

✳ Very quick and convenient form of credit.
✳ The cardholder can buy goods and has one month to repay at least a minimum amount.
✳ If the bill is not paid in full, interest is charged on the outstanding balance.
✳ The bank or building society offering the credit card sets a credit limit, which can be increased.
✳ Credit cards can be used to withdraw cash from ATM machines (the interest charged can be very high, and is charged from the day the money is withdrawn).

✳ Credit cards are widely used for booking flights, concerts and hotels online or over the telephone worldwide.
✳ Government stamp duty of €40 is charged annually.
✳ When opting to take on a credit card, it is important to check out the rate of interest charged and be aware that late payments and exceeding your credit limit will incur penalties.
✳ Interest rates can be as high as 18.65 per cent. Many lending institutions offer short-term special interest rates to attract customers, e.g. 0 per cent for the first six months.

Overdrafts

✳ This facility enables customers to withdraw money from their account even though they have no money left in the account.
✳ Interest is paid on the amount overdrawn.
✳ Interest rates can be from 7.46 to 11.47 per cent.
✳ No interest is charged if the consumer doesn't use the facility.
✳ A charge is added for setting up the overdraft.
✳ An overdraft is suitable for people with a short-term cash flow problem. It is not a good idea for people who often run into problems through erratic spending habits.

Term loans

* A consumer can look for a loan from a range of lending institutions.
* Term loans are often used to buy a holiday, house or car.
* When the consumer is granted the loan, the agreed amount is transferred to the consumer's nominated account.
* The amount is paid back in instalments over an agreed period of time.
* Interest is charged immediately and can be at a fixed or variable rate.
* It is worth shopping around different lending institutions, as different rates of interest are offered.
* Term loan interest can range from 11.73 per cent for less than one year to 11.43 per cent for more than one year.
* Note: It is worth noting that the Credit Union generally offers the lowest rates of interest. Members of a credit union can get loans of up to three times their savings.

Hire purchase

* A consumer hires and pays for goods over a set period of time and a set amount of money.
* This form of credit is used to buy large household appliances, e.g. a fridge or TV.
* The consumer has the use of the goods while paying for them but does not own the goods until the last instalment has been paid.
* If the consumer fails to meet the repayments, the goods can be repossessed.
* Hire purchase is an expensive form of credit as interest rates can be high.
* The consumer is protected by the Hire Purchase Acts, 1946 and 1960.
* Under a hire purchase agreement, the following must be stated:
  * The cash price and hire purchase price.
  * The amount and number of each instalment, and the date it's due.
  * The APR (annual percentage rate).
  * Description of the goods.
  * Details (including names, addresses) of all the parties involved.

* The rights of the consumer.
* Information about a 'cooling-off period'.

> A cooling-off period allows the consumer 10 days to opt out of this form of credit. Note: It does not apply to credit cards, overdrafts or housing loans.

The Consumer Credit Act, 1995

* This was introduced in 1995 and is one of the most important consumer laws.
* It looks at all areas of credit, from advertising to written agreements.
* Credit advertisements must show the APR, any deposits needed, if there are any extra charges involved or any other types of restriction.
* It protects consumer rights by stipulating that some practices are not allowed, e.g. lenders visiting consumers in their workplace.
* Protection for the consumer also comes in the form of being entitled to a 10-day 'cooling-off' period.
* This act is enforced by the Office of the Director of Consumer Affairs.

Savings

Reasons for Saving

* In case of emergencies.
* If planning something, e.g. a holiday.
* For peace of mind and a sense of security.
* In order to build a good financial reputation with a lending institution.
* To earn interest.

Choosing Where to Save

Before deciding on where you wish to save it is very important to look at the following factors.

* **Risk/Return:** How safe is the scheme? Do you know exactly much you will get back or is it risky?
* **Amount of Interest:** Different financial institutions offer different rates of interest. Shop around for the best one!

✳ **Tax:** Are your savings subject to DIRT (Deposit Interest Retention Tax) or will your saving be tax-free?

> **DIRT** = Tax paid on interest earned. Note: from 1 January 2009 DIRT stands at 23%.

✳ **Ease of access to funds:** How easy is it to get your money? Are you locked in for a certain length of time?

Choosing where to save:
Think of the word

RATE.

Learning Links Learning Links Learning Links

Banks and Building Societies

Type of account	Risk/Return	Amount of Interest	Tax	Ease of Access
Demand deposit account	No risk.	Rates are low percentage, e.g. 0.05–0.1%.	No tax to pay.	Easy to take out money from ATM machine.
Notice deposit account	No risk.	Higher rate of interest percentage, approx. 5.75%.	Subject to DIRT.	Fifteen days' notice needed.
Special term account	Funds are invested for a fixed term of three or five years – no risk.	Interest rate is fixed for the first year.	Interest is tax-free.	No withdrawals can be made in the time period.
Equity-based savings plan	Greater risk, as savings are based on the performance of the stock market.	Returns can be great. Note: The value of the investment may go down as well as up.	Interest is tax-free. Note: Any withdrawals before the agreed time is subject to 23% tax on the interest earned.	Penalties if money is taken out before agreed time. Minimum investment time is five years.

An Post

Type of account	Risk/Return	Amount of Interest	Tax	Ease of Access
Deposit account	No risk.	Low interest rate, 3% annual rate.	Subject to DIRT.	Very easy, at any post office, with a photo ID.
Instalment savings scheme	No risk – fixed amount saved over 12-month period and left for five years on deposit.	15% over five years	Interest is tax-free.	Seven to thirty days' notice needed.

Type of account	Risk/Return	Amount of Interest	Tax	Ease of Access
Saving Bonds	State-guaranteed investment of minimum €100 up to maximum of €80,000.	10% interest over three-year period.	Interest is tax-free.	Seven working days' notice needed.
Saving Certificates	State-guaranteed investment of a lump sum €50 to €80,000.	21% interest over 5½-year period.	Interest is tax-free.	Seven working days' notice needed.

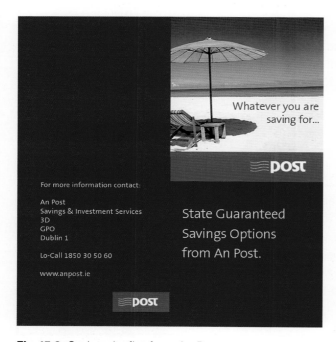

For more information contact:

An Post
Savings & Investment Services
3D
GPO
Dublin 1

Lo-Call 1850 30 50 60

www.anpost.ie

Whatever you are saving for...

State Guaranteed Savings Options from An Post.

Fig 45.3: Savings leaflet from An Post.

Insurance

Insurance provides protection against something detrimental that may happen. A fee, called a premium, is paid to the insurance company for this cover. This fee is paid annually.

Benefits of Insurance

* Insurance gives people protection against loss or damage.
* Life assurance can be a form of saving.
* A life assurance policy can be used as security for a loan.
* Life assurance provides lump sum payments to the assured's dependents on the death of the assured.
* Tax relief at source is available for some forms of insurance.
* In the event of illness and loss of income, financial support can be provided through income protection policies.
* Insurance provides peace of mind.

Large numbers of premiums → Insurance Company Fund → Compensation, Running Costs, Profits

Fig 45.4: How insurance companies work.

Types of Insurance

- **Insurance** is protection against something that **may** happen.
- **Assurance** is protection against something that **will** happen.

Life Assurance

Term Assurance

* Simplest and cheapest type of life assurance.
* Individual's life is insured for a set period.
* An agreed lump sum is paid out if the insured person dies within that time.
* No payment is made if the person survives the term.

Term assurance is generally taken out by people who have borrowed money to cover a loan and want the loan to be repaid if they die before the loan is fully repaid.

Whole of Life Assurance

* More expensive than term assurance.
* Covers an individual for their entire life – no time limit.
* Money is paid out to the insured person's family on the death of the insured person.

Endowment Assurance

* Most expensive type of cover.
* Has a savings element attached to the whole-life cover.
* An agreed premium is paid every month and it is invested in a fund by the insurance company.

Health Insurance

Income Protection Insurance	Critical Illness Cover	Private Medical Insurance
<ul><li>This provides a percentage (75%) of income for an individual until retirement in the event that they are unable to work.</li><li>Most people with permanent health insurance are covered for a limited period of time if they become ill or are unable to work due to some unforeseen circumstances, e.g. disability.</li><li>Self-employed people or people who want to have extra cover opt for this policy cover.</li></ul>	<ul><li>If a person is diagnosed with an illness on a stated list, such as cancer, this insurance provides a lump sum.</li><li>The money can be used for such things as medical expenses or to help with income loss.</li><li>This is an optional extra that some employees can take out.</li></ul>	<ul><li>VHI, Hibernian Health and Quinn Healthcare are examples of Irish private health insurance companies providing schemes that people can pay into.</li><li>There are different types of scheme available which provide for different cover.</li><li>Premiums are based on the type of cover required.</li><li>Private health insurance offers the benefits of medical treatment abroad, the option of a private room in hospital, etc.</li></ul>

Property Insurance

House and Building Insurance	Contents Insurance	All Risks
• Money is provided to rebuild or repair a house. • Walls, windows, roof, floors, outhouses are covered. • Building insurance can cover against fire, flooding, lightning and storm damage, other natural disasters and robbery. • It is very important to read the fine print of the policy as some disasters may not be covered. • House and building insurance must be taken out before a mortgage is approved.	• This policy covers contents, such as furniture, clothes, and appliances, from damage or theft. • Premiums vary depending on the contents to be insured and where the house is located. • It is very important to read the fine print of the policy as some contents may not be covered, e.g. glassware.	• Valuable and expensive items, such as jewellery, paintings, cameras, etc., can be given cover in this type of policy. • These items are covered both inside and outside the home.

Motor Insurance

Third Party	Third Party Fire and Theft	Fully Comprehensive
• Cheapest form of cover. • Covers injury to third parties or to their vehicle. • The insured doesn't get any compensation for themselves.	• Covers third party plus compensation to the insured if vehicle is damaged by fire or is stolen.	• Covers third party, fire, theft and also provides for the insured person and their vehicle.

Other Types of Insurance

✱ PRSI: See p. 244.

Part Sample Exam Questions

Questions

1. List the factors which should be considered when planning a household budget. (12)

2. Outline how borrowers are protected by the Consumer Credit Act, 1995. (12)

Sample Answers

1. List the factors which should be followed when planning a household budget. (12)

   4 points x 3 marks each = 12.

   - Add up the total income (include all sources of income, e.g. wages, salaries, benefits). Don't include bonuses as these are not guaranteed. Add up total expenditure (both fixed and discretionary).
   - Divide by 12 to get the monthly expenditure and divide by 52 to get the weekly expenditure.
   - Always incorporate an element of saving. Particular times of the year require extra money, e.g. Christmas, back to school.
   - Keep a copy of all bills and receipts. Evaluate and review and make changes where needed.

2. Outline how borrowers are protected by the Consumer Credit Act, 1995. (12)

   4 points x 3 marks each = 12.

   - Introduced in 1995 and is one of the most important consumer laws. This act looks at all areas of credit from advertising to written agreements.
   - Credit advertisements must show the APR, any deposits needed, if there are any extra charges involved or any other types of restriction.
   - It protects consumer rights by stipulating that some practices are not allowed, e.g. lenders visiting consumers in their workplace. Protection for the consumer also comes in the form of being entitled to a 10-day 'cooling-off' period.
   - This act is enforced by the Office of the Director of Consumer Affairs.

46 Housing Finance

Mortgages

* This is a loan from a lending agency taken out in order to buy a house. The loan is repaid over an agreed period of time by repayments.
* People can get mortgages from banks or building societies.

Considerations When Choosing a Mortgage

* Always consider the APR – variable or fixed.
* Some institutions offer incentives for first-time buyers.
* Find out if the loan can be paid off early.
* Find out if there is a fee for clearing the mortgage early.
* Find out if it is possible to take a break from the repayments.
* Find out if the mortgage can be moved from one property to another.

APR – Annual Percentage Rate: This is a rate of interest that incorporates the setting up and management costs for a credit option.

Conditions an Applicant Must Satisfy to Obtain a Mortgage

There are many factors to consider when applying for a mortgage.

Length of a Mortgage (Term):

* Mortgage repayments can be spread out over varying lengths of time from five to forty years.
* The term taken depends on the amount needed for the mortgage and the applicant's ability to make repayments.
* The applicant's age affects the length of the mortgage; an older person will only get a shorter mortgage period to make sure the repayments will be covered.

Amount to be Borrowed:

* The general rule is two to three times the main salary plus once the second salary.

A Person's Credit History:

* An individual's ability to show that they are regular savers and don't have much debt will prove their creditworthiness to the lending institution.

A Deposit:

* Ten per cent of the purchase price is generally required as a deposit.
* Most lending institutions offer mortgages of 80–90 per cent of the purchase price.
* Some lending institutions offered 100 per cent mortgages in recent times; however, due to the economic downturn this has changed.

The Type of Property:

✳ Lending institutions require a survey of the proposed property to be bought.

✳ The purpose of this is to give a true and fair view of the market price of the house at a given time.

Insurance:

✳ Buildings insurance is a statutory obligation. Mortgage holders must have insurance on the proposed property.

Interest Rate

There are three types of interest rates available with mortgages: fixed, variable and tracker.

Fixed	Variable	Tracker
• Fixed rate of interest for a set period of time. • Fixed for three to five years. • The borrower doesn't have to worry about increasing interest rates and can budget for the same payments each month. • A fixed interest rate tends to be higher than a variable one.	• This interest rate changes in line with the European Central Bank (ECB). • The borrower has to pay more if the interest rates are increased but pays less if the interest rates are lowered. • Lending institutions can also add on a percentage above the ECB's base rate. • The lending institution's percentage may increase as the ECB rate increases.	• This tracks the ECB rate. • The lending institution levies a margin on top of the ECB rate, which is charged to the borrower. • The lending institution's percentage on a tracker mortgage is fixed.

Types of Mortgage

There are three common types of mortgage: repayment/annuity, endowment and pension.

Repayment/Annuity Mortgage

✳ Most popular type of mortgage.

✳ Both capital and interest is payable each month over the duration of the loan.

✳ This ensures that at the end of the loan the whole mortgage is paid off (redeemed).

Mortgage Protection Policy

• Financial institutions insist on a mortgage protection policy before giving a mortgage.

• This policy ensures that if the insured person dies before the mortgage is paid off the mortgage is cleared.

• A mortgage protection policy does not have to be obtained from the mortgage lending institution.

✳ A mortgage protection policy (life assurance) is a compulsory requirement for this type of mortgage.

Endowment Mortgage

✳ Less popular option.

✳ The borrower borrows a fixed sum of money from a lending institution.

✳ The borrower pays the lending institution interest each month.

✳ The borrower also pays a sum of money each month to an insurance company for the duration of the loan. This payment is called a premium.

✳ When the mortgage is completed, the borrower must cash in/surrender the endowment policy with the insurance company.

✳ The sum of money received at that time may or may not cover the loan outstanding at the lending institution.

✳ It is because of this element of risk that an endowment mortgage is a less popular option.

Pension Mortgage

* Most popular with people who are self-employed.
* It is similar to an endowment mortgage.
* Two repayments are made – one to pay off the interest and the other into a pension fund.
* At the end of the loan time, enough money should have matured to pay off the outstanding amount as well as providing a lump sum for retirement.

Mortgage Interest Relief/Tax Relief at Source (TRS)

* This is given by the lending institution in the form of either a reduced mortgage payment or a lodgement to your bank account.
* The Revenue Commissioners will advise the lender of your mortgage account number and the maximum tax relief which applies to your loan (based on your personal status, e.g. first-time buyer, marital status).
* Your lending institution will calculate your TRS, based on your annual estimated mortgage interest and your maximum tax relief.

TAX YEAR 2009		
Relief Available	Single	Married/Widowed
First Mortgage – Ceiling	€10,000	€20,000
First Mortgage – Tax Credit	€ 2,000	€ 4,000
Other – Ceiling	€ 3,000	€ 6,000
Other – Tax Credit	€ 600	€ 1,200

Local Authority Housing

* Local authorities provide housing for people who cannot afford to get a mortgage from a lending institution.
* There is generally a long waiting list of people who are trying to get local authority housing – demand exceeds supply.
* In order to be eligible an individual must show:
  * That they are in need of housing.
  * That they cannot provide the means to get a house themselves.
  * That they are unable to get a mortgage from a lending institution.
  * That their income falls below a certain threshold.
  * How many dependents they have (if any).
  * If they have any special requirements.

Rental Subsidy Scheme

* Under this scheme, voluntary housing bodies provide housing for renting, particularly to meet the needs of low-income families.
* The houses are let to approved applicants for local authority housing.
* Seventy-five per cent of tenancies in each project are reserved for households with incomes of €15,237 or less in the previous tax year.
* Rents are related to ability to pay, taking account of household earnings and circumstances.
* Tenants of the houses are centrally involved in the management of their estates.

Voluntary housing bodies are non-profit-making organisations. They include: Respond, the Salvation Army and the Iveagh Trust.

Local Authority Loans for House Purchase

* Individuals must have been refused a loan by both a bank and a building society.
* Individuals must meet an income eligibility test: the single gross income must not exceed €40,000 and the two-income limit (2.5 times the gross of the principal earner + 1 times the second income) does not exceed €100,000.

Local Authority Housing Schemes

Tenant Purchase Scheme

* Individuals who have been tenants of a local authority house for at least one year may apply to purchase the house either outright or by way of shared ownership.
* The house of the price will be its market value.
* A discount of three per cent of the value of the house for each year of tenancy of a local authority house (up to a maximum of ten years) is given.

Shared Ownership Scheme

* This is aimed at people who cannot afford to buy their entire home in one go.
* It enables an individual to buy a proportion of a house to begin with, increasing that proportion in steps until they own the whole house.
* Ownership is shared between the individual and the local authority.
* Individuals make payments on a mortgage for the part of the house owned and pay rent to the local authority for the other part at a rate of 4.3 per cent.
* At the start, an individual must buy at least 40 per cent of the price of the house.

Mortgage Allowance Scheme

* An allowance of up to €11,450 is payable over a five-year period to tenants or tenant purchasers of local authority houses in Ireland.

* The allowance is paid directly to the lending agency and repayments are reduced accordingly for the first five years of the mortgage.
* A mortgage of at least €38,092.14 is necessary.
* The allowance paid in any year cannot exceed the amount of the mortgage repayments.

Affordable Housing Scheme

* This aims to help lower-income households to buy their own homes.
* The scheme enables lower-income buyers the chance to buy newly constructed homes and apartments in areas where property prices have created an affordability gap for lower-income house buyers.
* The properties are then offered for sale to eligible purchasers at prices significantly less than their actual market value.
* An individual's income must satisfy an income test: €40,000 gross for a single person and €100,000 gross for a couple.
* The maximum house purchase loan available is €185,000.
* A variable interest rate applies.

Factors Influencing Housing Choices

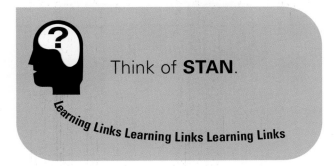

Think of **STAN**.

Learning Links Learning Links Learning Links

Socio-Economic Factors

* The different ages of people in a family will affect their house choice and needs, e.g. a young couple will have different needs from those of a family with small children.
* Whether any family member has any special needs, e.g. wheelchair access.
* The amount of money that is available.

* The location of the house in terms of its proximity to schools, shops, transport, etc.
* The size of the family – the bigger the family, the larger the house that is needed.

Trends in Housing Developments

* Rural areas have seen the development of more housing estates.
* In general, more housing estates have been built with a range of house styles, e.g. detached houses, semi-detached houses and apartments.
* Smaller housing estates with more exclusive houses and bigger gardens
* Urban areas have seen an increase in apartment living.
* The notion of 'commuter-ville' where people buy larger houses in more suburban areas and commute to work.
* The renewal and redevelopment of inner-city areas and houses.

Fig 46.1: Contemporary apartment block.

* More open green spaces in development sites and the provision of amenities, e.g. crèches, shops and other retail units.
* Availability of sites has meant that more people are building their own stand-alone homes.

Availability of Housing

* The amount of money a person earns and the size of mortgage they can obtain affects their house choice.
* There has been a slowdown in the property market in recent times.
* This has resulted in the softening of the housing market, with house prices slowly coming down.
* Local authority housing demand still exceeds supply and there is a long waiting list.

National Housing Policy

* This policy is under the remit of the Department of the Environment, Heritage and Local Government.
* This policy is largely carried out by local authorities.
* The main aim of the policy is to provide decent housing for all.
* The following areas are covered by the policy:
  * Local authority housing schemes.
  * Improvement grants.
  * Homeless shelters.
  * Travellers' accommodation.
  * Rented accommodation legislation which applies to both social and private accommodation.

Part Sample Exam Questions

Questions

1. What are the factors to consider when choosing a mortgage? (12)

2. Discuss three types of mortgages available. (15)

Answers

1. What are the factors to consider when choosing a mortgage? (12)

   4 points x 3 marks each = 12.

- Always consider the APR – should it be variable or fixed? Some institutions offer incentives for first-time buyers.
- Find out if the loan can be paid off early. Find out if there is a fee for clearing the mortgage early.
- Find out if it is possible to take a break from the repayments.
- Find out if the mortgage can be moved from one property to another.

2. Discuss three types of mortgages available (15)

3 types x 5 marks each = 15.

Repayment/Annuity Mortgage	Endowment Mortgage	Pension Mortgage
<ul><li>Most popular mortgage.</li><li>Both capital and interest are payable each month over the duration of the loan.</li><li>This ensures that at the end of the loan the whole mortgage is paid off (redeemed).</li><li>A mortgage protection policy (life assurance) is a compulsory requirement for this type of mortgage.</li></ul>	<ul><li>Less popular option.</li><li>The borrower borrows a fixed sum of money from a lending institution.</li><li>The borrower pays the lending institution interest each month.</li><li>The borrower also pays a sum of money each month to an insurance company for the duration of the loan. These payments are called a premium.</li><li>When the mortgage is completed, the borrower must cash in/surrender the endowment policy with the insurance company.</li><li>The sum of money received at that time may or may not cover the loan outstanding at the lending institution.</li><li>It is because of this element of risk that it is a less popular option.</li></ul>	<ul><li>Most popular with people who are self-employed.</li><li>It is similar to an endowment mortgage.</li><li>Two repayments are made – one to pay off the interest and the other into a pension fund.</li><li>At the end of the loan time, enough money should have matured to pay off the outstanding amount as well as providing a lump sum for retirement.</li></ul>

47 Household Technology

There are many labour- and time-saving devices within the home. Such appliances include washing machines, dishwashers, vacuum cleaners, etc.

Technological Developments	
Food preparation	Food processors, blenders.
Cooking food	Microwave ovens, double ovens, halogen rings.
Cleaning	Vacuum cleaners, dishwashers.
Laundry	Washing machines, tumble dryers.
Entertainment	DVDs, Wii, X-Box.
Communication	Internet, mobile phones.
Security	Sensor lights, security gates, alarms.

Contribution of Technology in the Home

✳ **Labour-saving:** Reduces workload.

✳ **Time-saving:** Less time needed to carry out household tasks.

✳ **Hygienic:** More hygienic procedures, i.e. dishwashers clean dishes more hygienically than hand washing.

✳ **Long-lasting:** Appliances have become more durable.

✳ **Automation:** Timers on cookers and heating provide a valuable contribution in terms of efficiency.

✳ **Communication:** Technology now offers better opportunity in the area of communication, e.g. computers and mobile phones.

✳ **Security:** Alarm systems provide security and peace for mind for individuals in their homes.

✳ **Entertainment:** Advances in entertainment systems, such as PlayStation, Wii and DVD players, can provide hours of recreational activity.

Selecting Household Appliances

There are many factors to consider when selecting household appliances.

✳ **Cost:** When considering cost it is important to take into account not only the cost of the machine but also other costs, such as installation costs and running costs.

✳ **Brand name:** Quality is often indicated by a good reliable brand name. It is important in the selection of location, i.e. where the machine is bought. Small, family-run businesses often offer key information which might not be given in the larger chain stores. However, these small, family-run shops often cannot afford to offer the huge discounts given by larger stores.

✳ **Colour:** The colour of the appliance should reflect the colour scheme of the room it will be in (if it is to be in a fixed position). In some situations, appliances will contrast with the colour scheme, which gives variation.

✳ **Size:** It is important to measure the space available for the appliance; height, length and depth must be taken accurately.

✳ **Ease of cleaning:** The appliance should be easy to clean, e.g. some ovens have a self-clean finish which enables easy cleaning. A minimum number of crevices is an advantage as crevices are dirt-gathering areas where grime can build up and prove difficult to dislodge.

* **Energy Efficiency:** All electrical appliances must have an energy efficiency label on them, which displays the energy efficiency of the appliance. The appliance is rated on a scale from A to G.
    * A indicates that the appliance is very energy efficient.
    * G indicates that the appliance is very energy inefficient.

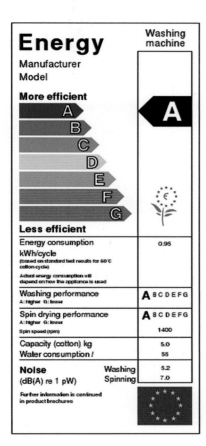

Fig 47.1: Energy efficiency label.

* The energy efficiency label also gives other key pieces of information:
    * The manufacturer's name and product details.
    * Estimate of the amount of electricity that the appliance will use in an average cycle.
    * The noise factor of the machine. The lower the number in this category, the less noise is given off by the machine.
* **Guarantee:** A guarantee is a written contract between the manufacturer and the consumer which indicates that if a fault arises with the product within a certain period of time, the manufacturer will replace or repair the product. It offers extra protection for the consumer.
* **Modern Features:** Many appliances have extra features which add additional time-saving and labour-saving options.
* **Safety:** Always check for safety symbols on appliances before purchasing.

Appliances

There are four main types of appliance: small appliance with a motor, small appliance with a heating element, a refrigeration appliance and a microwave appliance.

Type of Appliance	Example
Small appliance with a motor	• Liquidiser, food processor, carving knife.
Small appliance with a heating element	• Electric kettle, sandwich toaster, toaster, iron.
A refrigeration appliance	• Refrigerator
A microwave appliance	• Microwave

Small Appliance with a Motor: Food Processor

Design and Construction

* **Base unit:** This contains the motor surrounded in plastic casing.
* **Jug/Bowl:** This is made of toughened plastic. The average capacity is two litres. The bowl is composed of the following parts:
  * A locking lid.
  * A feed tube.
  * A feed pusher which also can be used for measuring.

* The bowl rests on a spindle.
* The attachments sit on a shaft, which rests on the spindle.
* The attachments listed in the table below often come with food processors.

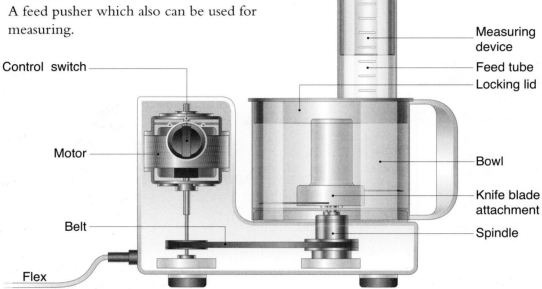

Fig 47.2: Diagram of a food processor.

Accessories	Function
Chopping disc	• Used for chopping vegetables, fruits, parsley, breadcrumbs.
Whisk	• Used to whisk egg whites, cream, mayonnaise.
Grating disc	• Used to grate carrots, cabbage, fruit, vegetables.
Juice extractor	• Used to make juice from fresh fruit, e.g. pineapple juice, orange juice, apple juice.
Dough hook	• Used to make pastry, bread and cakes.

Working Principle

* The food processor is plugged in and switched on.
* Electrical energy causes the motor to rotate the spindle, which in turn rotates the blades. The blades rotate at a fast speed, blending, chopping, puréeing, grinding or mixing the food.

Guidelines for Use

* Always follow the manufacturer's instruction booklet.
* Ensure that all attachments are in the correct position.
* A food processor is used to blend, chop, purée or grind food.
* A food processor should only ever be three-quarters full. Otherwise, the contents will spill.
* Do not turn on the appliance for long periods of time. Allow for intervals to scrape food down from the sides.
* Always ensure that the food going down the feed tube is in small pieces to prevent it becoming lodged.
* For safety, never use the appliance when hands or plugs are wet.

Care of a Food Processor

* Allow the food processor intervals to stop, which gives the motor time to cool down and prevents overheating.
* Always remove the plug from socket before cleaning.
* Use hot, soapy water. The base should never be placed in water. To clean it, a damp cloth should be used to remove any spills from the base.
* Care is needed when washing the attachments to prevent accidents.
* A food processor should be stored with the lid off to enable air to circulate.
* Food processors are double insulated.

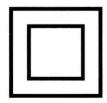

Fig 47.3: Double insulation symbol.

> **Double insulation** is used for small electrical appliances. They have an outer casing of plastic that cannot become live. Double-insulated appliances do not require an earth wire.

Small Appliance with a Heating Element: Kettle

Design and Construction

- Lid
- Heat-resistant handle
- Water level indicator
- Indicator light
- On/off switch
- Concealed heating element
- Lead

Fig 47.4: Diagram of a kettle.

* Electric kettles come in a wide variety of colours, sizes and shapes.
* Kettles are made from a variety of materials, e.g. chrome aluminium, toughened plastic, copper and stainless steel.
* Most kettles have fitted lids. These lids can be removed when the kettle is being filled.
* Handles on kettles are made of heat-resistant plastic or wood as these are poor conductors of heat and therefore prevent the handles heating up, which is a safety feature.
* Most kettles have a maximum and a minimum water level.

* The electrical element is fitted inside near the base of the kettle.
* Automatic kettles have a thermostat which causes the kettle to switch off when the water reaches boiling point (100°C).
* Cordless kettles are very popular today; there is a separate base unit and the kettle automatically turns off when it is removed from the base.
* The capacity of a kettle is measured in litres. There are different sizes, but the most common range from 1.1 litres to 3.4 litres.

Working Principle

* When the kettle is switched on, electricity flows into the element. This causes the element to heat up.
* This heating process causes the water to heat by convection currents (heat is transferred through a liquid; when this occurs the cooler liquid will move towards the heating element to replace the heated water that rises towards the top).
* When all the water reaches boiling point, an automatic switch (thermostat) will turn off the kettle.
* All kettles contain a safety switch which turns the kettle off if it has been turned on with no water in it. The element should always be covered with water when it is turned on.

Guidelines for Use

* Always follow the manufacturer's instruction booklet.
* Always ensure that the element is completely covered with water.
* Do not overfill a kettle. Be aware of the maximum water level.
* Kettles should only be used to heat water.
* Damaged flexes should always be replaced.
* It is important that the correct size fuse be fitted to the plug.

Care of a Kettle

* Never immerse the entire kettle in water.
* Ensure that the kettle is disconnected before cleaning.
* When cleaning, wipe with a damp cloth.
* Avoid using harsh abrasives when cleaning the exterior.
* Always unplug the kettle from the socket when not in use.

Refrigeration Appliance: Refrigerator

Refrigerators enable food to be stored at a temperature of below 5°C, which delays the growth of micro-organisms. The refrigerator is measured in litres, the standard refrigerator is 150 litres.

Types of Refrigerator

There are three main types of refrigerator: standard, larder and fridge-freezer.

Type of Fridge	Explanation
Standard refrigerator	• This type of refrigerator has a variety of moulded shelves. • There is a separate ice box, which generally has a star rating of * or **.
Larder refrigerator	• This type of refrigerator contains no freezer compartment. • A separate freezer is needed for storing frozen food.

Types of Fridge	Explanation
Fridge-freezer	<ul><li>A fridge-freezer has two separate cabinets: a refrigerator and a freezer.</li><li>There is generally a separate door for each compartment.</li><li>This type of refrigerator can be purchased in a variety of forms, e.g. one-third refrigerator, two-thirds freezer (or vice versa), or half refrigerator and half freezer.</li><li>Like the larder and standard refrigerator, there are a variety of moulded shelves.</li></ul>

Design and Construction

✳ The outer casing of the refrigerator is made of enamelled steel. Modern refrigerators can be purchased in a variety of colours. Integrated refrigerators can have a wooden door to match the kitchen units.

✳ The inner casing of the refrigerator consists generally of polystyrene. Between this inner casing and the outer casing a layer of insulating material can be found.

✳ Within the fridge cabinet there are a number of shelves. These are generally clear or frosted.

✳ The door of the fridge contains a magnetic fastening which ensures the refrigerator stays closed and maintains the correct temperature.

✳ When the door of the refrigerator is opened, a light automatically switches on.

✳ The inside of the door also has a number of storage compartments for drinks, eggs, butter, etc.

✳ Vegetable drawers are generally located at the base of the fridge.

✳ A thermostat controls and regulates the temperature of the refrigerator.

Modern Features

✳ **Zoned refrigeration:** This enables certain parts of the refrigerator to have different temperatures.

✳ **Automatic defrost:** This ensures that the ice doesn't build up.

✳ **Ice-makers:** Ice is made using this facility.

✳ **Drinks dispenser:** Enables drinks to be cooled and accessed easily.

✳ **Tall bottle shelves:** This enables tall bottles to be placed upright in the refrigerator.

✳ **American-style fridge:** This is a large refrigerator which is generally one and a half times the size of a standard refrigerator. This fridge contains most of the above modern features.

Fig 47.5: American-style fridge with ice maker.

Working Principle of a Compressor Refrigerator

* Refrigeration is a cooling process.
* In a compressor refrigerator, a compressor is found at the base of the fridge.
* The compressor contains a refrigerant. A refrigerant is a substance that converts easily from a liquid to a gas and vice versa. Examples of refrigerants are freon 12 and liquid ammonia.
* When the motor is on, it activates the compressor, which forces the gaseous refrigerant into the condenser.
* The condenser causes the refrigerant to cool, thus changing it into a liquid.

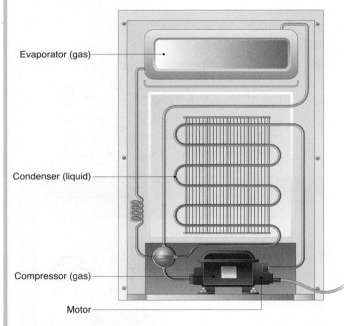

Evaporator (gas)

Condenser (liquid)

Compressor (gas)

Motor

Fig 47.6: Cross-section of a compressor refrigerator.

* The refrigerant then moves into the evaporator where it is converted back into a gas.
* Evaporation of the liquid refrigerant occurs when heat is taken from the refrigerator cabinet.
* This in turn cools the refrigerator.
* The refrigerant returns to the compressor, where the cycle begins again.

Guidelines for Use

* Always follow the manufacturer's instruction booklet.

* Avoid opening the door of the refrigerator unnecessarily.
* Ensure that the fridge is not over full to enable air to circulate.
* Store raw meat on lower shelves to avoid cross-contamination.
* Ensure that food has cooled thoroughly before placing it in the fridge.
* Monitor the fridge temperature, to ensure it is below 5°C.
* All food should be covered to prevent it drying out and to prevent the transfer of flavours.

Care and Cleaning of a Refrigerator

* The refrigerator should be cleaned on a regular basis.
* This can be done using bicarbonate of soda to avoid strong-smelling detergents.
* Wipe up spills immediately using a damp cloth and hot, soapy water.
* It is important not to place the fridge near a heat source, e.g. cooker, as this will reduce the efficiency of the fridge.
* The freezer should be defrosted regularly to prevent a build-up of ice. Most modern fridges have a defrost button.
* The back of the appliance should be dusted regularly.

Star Rating

The star rating indicates the temperature in the ice-box of a refrigerator.

Star	Number of stars	Temperature	Length of time food can be stored
*	1 star	-6°C	Up to one week
**	2 stars	-12°C	Up to one month
***	3 stars	-18°C	Up to three months
****	4 stars	-18°C to -25°C	Up to twelve months Can freeze fresh food.

Microwave Oven

The microwave oven is a common feature in most houses today. It does not replace the conventional oven.

Types of Microwave Oven Available

There are three types of microwave oven available: standard, microwave with grill, and combination.

* **Standard microwave:** This microwave is used for cooking, defrosting and reheating.
* **Microwave with grill:** This microwave includes a heating element embedded in the top wall of the microwave. This microwave allows for cooking, defrosting, reheating and browning (which is not possible in the standard microwave).
* **Combination microwave:** This microwave contains a conventional oven, grill and microwave. This enables browning of food.

Construction of a Microwave Oven

* **Door:** A microwave consists of a glass door with perforated metal. This metal prevents the escape of microwaves. When the door is open, the microwave does not operate. This is a safety feature.
* **Oven:** The oven cabinet is lined with metal and has a vent at the back which enables the steam produced during cooking to escape.
* **Controls:** The controls on a microwave are visible on the front of the oven. These controls can be either digital or manual.
* **Transformer:** A transformer is used to increase domestic voltage to a higher frequency.
* **Magnetron:** The magnetron converts electrical energy into microwave energy.
* **Wave guide:** This guides microwaves into the oven cabinet.
* **Wave stirrer:** This rotates, enabling the distribution of microwaves.
* **Turntable:** Food is placed on the turntable, which rotates to ensure even cooking of the food.

Fig 47.7: Distribution of microwaves.

Working Principle of a Microwave Oven

* Food in microwaves is cooked using electro-magnetic energy.
* In the microwave, the magnetron converts electrical energy to microwave energy.
* A transformer increases domestic voltage (230V) to a much higher frequency.
* This microwave energy enters the oven cabinet via the wave guide.
* The wave stirrer distributes the microwaves evenly throughout the oven.
* These waves **reflect** off the metal-lined cabinet.
* The waves are then **transmitted** through the container.
* The waves are then **absorbed** into the food. These microwaves penetrate food to a depth of 3cm to 5cm.

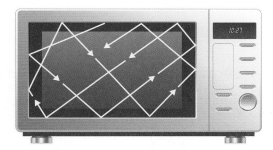

(1) Reflection

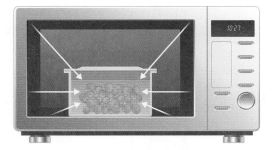

(2) Transmission

(3) Absorption

- Once inside the food, these microwaves cause the food molecules to vibrate rapidly, causing friction, which in turn creates heat and thereby cooks the food.
- Therefore the rest of the food is cooked by a method of conduction (the transfer of heat through solid).
- Any water in the food moves to the surface of the food. This, including the absence of an external heating element, prevents the browning of food.

The Distribution of Electromagnetic Energy

Electromagnetic energy is distributed in three ways: reflection, transmission and absorption.

- **Reflection:** The metal casing of the oven cabinet reflects the microwaves.
- **Transmission:** Microwaves can pass through certain materials, such as glass, paper, microwaveable plastic, china and ceramics. These materials become hot.
- **Absorption:** Microwaves are absorbed by particles of sugar, fat or water.

Modern Design Features

- **Temperature probes:** The probe eliminates the need to calculate cooking times for food. It is inserted into the food during cooking.
- **Auto-weight defrost:** This feature calculates defrosting times based on the weight and type of food.
- **Jet-power button:** By pressing this button, full power is turned on immediately. This reheats food quickly.
- **Keep warm setting:** A 90-watt setting keeps the food warm.

- **Automatic programming:** This allows the individual to pre-programme cooking times and power levels for the types of food cooked most often.

Guidelines for Use

- Follow the manufacturer's instructions.
- Never place metal or metal-trimmed containers in a microwave.
- Always cover food with microwaveable cling film or kitchen paper.
- Turn large pieces of food regularly to ensure even cooking.
- Stir to ensure even cooking.
- Allow for standing time. When foods are removed from a microwave, they continue to cook, so they need to be left to stand, otherwise food may be uncooked.
- Pierce food that has a skin, e.g. potatoes, as this prevents them from bursting.
- Arrange food in a circle to enable even cooking.

Care of a Microwave Oven

- When cleaning a microwave, always ensure that it is completely disconnected.
- Clean the door seal to make sure that no food has become lodged; this would cause inefficient running of the microwave oven.
- Wipe up spills immediately.
- Use hot, soapy water when cleaning out the microwave. Microwave cleaners may also be used.
- Avoid moving the microwave unnecessarily, as this could cause damage to the magnetron.
- If any fault occurs with the microwave, ensure that it is repaired by a qualified person.

Advantages of Microwave Ovens	Disadvantages of Microwave Ovens
• Very quick and efficient to use. • Suitable for the elderly, disabled and children to use as it is safe. • Food can be defrosted in a microwave.	• Standard microwaves do not brown food. • Microwave cooking is not suitable when large quantities of food are being prepared. • Tough cuts of meat will not be tenderised by microwave cooking.

Advantages of Microwave Ovens	Disadvantages of Microwave Ovens
• Food can be cooked and served in the same dish, saving on washing up. • A wide variety of food can be cooked in a microwave. • Due to the fast method of cooking, there is less loss of colour, flavour and nutrients. • Less steam and heat are produced than in a conventional oven.	• Food poisoning may occur if food is not cooked properly, i.e. when standing time has not been allocated. • Food cooked in a microwave has a tendency to cool more quickly than food cooked in a conventional oven.

Containers

Suitable Containers for Use in Microwave Oven	Unsuitable Containers for Use in Microwave Oven
• Microwaveable cling film. • Paper. • Ovenproof dishes. • Heat-resistant plastic. • China. • Ceramic. • Glass.	• Metal containers or containers with metal trimming. • Polystyrene and melamine. • Glazed or painted pottery dishes. • Thick dishes.

Fig 47.8: Containers suitable for microwave cooking.

Fig 47.9: Containers unsuitable for microwave cooking.

Part of Leaving Certificate Question
Higher Level (2005)

Question

1. The microwave cooker has become an integral part of the kitchen in recent years. Set out details of a study you have carried out on a microwave cooker. Refer to: **(i)** Working principle. **(ii)** Modern design features. **(iii)** Guidelines for using the appliance. (30)

Answer

1. **(i)** Working Principle

4 points x 3 marks each = 12.

- Food in microwaves is cooked using electromagnetic energy.
- A transformer increases domestic voltage (230V) to a much higher frequency.
- In the microwave, the magnetron converts electrical energy to microwave energy.
- This microwave energy enters the oven cabinet via the wave guide.
- The wave stirrer distributes the microwaves evenly throughout the food.
- These microwaves penetrate food to a depth of 3cm to 5cm.
- Once inside the food, these microwaves cause the food molecules to vibrate rapidly, causing friction, which in turn creates heat and thereby cooks the food. Therefore the rest of the food is cooked by a method of conduction (transfer of heat through solid).
- Any water in the food moves to the surface of the food. This, including the absence of an external heating element, prevents the browning of food.

(ii) Modern Design Features

3 features x 3 marks each = 9.

- **Temperature probes:** The probe eliminates the need to calculate cooking times for food. It is inserted into the food during cooking.
- **Jet-power button:** By pressing this button, full power is turned on immediately. This reheats food quickly.
- **Automatic programming:** This allows the individual to pre-programme cooking times and power levels for types of food cooked most often.

(iii) Guidelines for Using the Appliance

3 guidelines x 3 marks each = 9.

- Follow the manufacturer's instructions.
- Never place metal or metal-trimmed containers in microwave.
- Always cover food with microwavable cling film or kitchen paper.
- Turn large pieces of food regularly to ensure even cooking.
- Stir liquid food during cooking time to ensure even cooking.
- Allow for standing time. When foods are removed from a microwave, they continue to cook, so they need to be left to stand otherwise food may be uncooked.
- Pierce food that has a skin, e.g. potatoes, as this prevent them from bursting.
- Arrange food in a circle to enable even cooking.

Textiles **48**

Textiles are widely used throughout the home. They are used in clothing, upholstery, duvets, curtains, cushions, blinds.

The Functions of Clothing

* **Protection:** Against weather – sun, wind, rain and cold.
* **Modesty:** Society expects that people are clothed. Different cultures have different clothes.
* **Safety:** Certain items of clothing offer an element of safety. Overalls protect under-garments from dirt. Firefighters have fire-retardant jackets, boots and trousers.
* **Hygiene:** When preparing food a key element, together with safety, is good hygiene. Clothes such as aprons, hair nets, chef's trousers, chef jacket's are therefore worn by people preparing food for sale.
* **Personal identification:** Different clothes are suitable for various professions. Work clothes that are appropriate for office work will vary from the clothes people such as nurses wear when on duty.
* **Self-expression:** People express their personality and interests through their clothes, e.g. punk clothes, evening dresses.

The Functions of Household Textiles

* **To provide warmth:** This is the case with duvets, curtains.
* **To provide protection:** When removing food from the oven, gloves are used. Curtains protect against the sun, which can have a fading effect.
* **To provide privacy:** Curtains and blinds provide privacy.
* **To absorb sound:** Carpets absorb sound, unlike wooden floors, which reflect sound. Other household textiles that absorb sound include curtains and rugs.
* **To absorb moisture:** Dish cloths, towels and tea towels need to absorb moisture in order to be effective.
* **To provide insulation:** Curtains, blinds and rugs offer insulation within the home.

Choosing Household Textiles

There are eight factors to consider when choosing household textiles.

- **Cost:** The amount of money available determines the quality of textile one can choose.
- **Personal choice:** A person's likes and dislikes determine the variety of textile that is chosen.
- **Colour, texture and pattern:** Aesthetic appeal is influenced by colour, texture, pattern, durability, drape and weight of the fabric.
- **Fashion trends:** Various trends influence individuals when choosing textiles. In the early 1970s, velvet was a very popular fabric choice for curtains.
- **Durability:** For household textiles that are used regularly, choosing a hardwearing material is important.
- **Ease of cleaning:** Always consider the care and cleaning of fabrics, e.g. can it be machine washed? If a household fabric must be dry cleaned, this will add to maintenance costs.
- **Safety:** Fabrics should be flame-retardant, especially upholstery.
- **Properties:** The property of the fabric will affect its suitability for purpose. Property refers to the quality or characteristic of the fabric.

Care of Textiles and Scientific Principles

When cleaning textiles, the following six points must be considered:
- Detergent
- Water.
- Temperature.
- Agitation.
- Use of conditioner.
- Water removal.

Detergent

- Always consider the most suitable detergent for the fabric.
- **Ingredients in detergents:** surfactants, conditioner, bleach, enzymes and fluorescents.
  - **Surfactants:** Reduce surface tension and allow water to wet fabric completely.
  - **Conditioner:** Softens the fabric.
  - **Bleach:** Oxygen bleach aids the removal of stains.
  - **Enzymes:** Protease is the enzyme that acts on protein stains (e.g. egg).
  - **Fluorescents:** Whitening agents which cause fabrics to appear whiter than white.

Fig 48.1: A selection of different types of detergent.

Water

- The type of water will affect the efficiency of the wash. Hard water does not produce lather. Fabric may not be cleaned properly and minerals build up in fabrics, which makes them difficult to clean.
- Some fabrics cannot be washed and must be dry cleaned. Always read the care label.

Temperature

- Correct temperature for the fabric is essential. Some temperatures can damage the fabric.
- Cotton can withstand high temperatures, whereas wool requires a low temperature.

Agitation

- This is the movement necessary to remove stains.
- The required amount of agitation will depend on the fabric. Too much agitation could damage the fabric.
- Delicate fabrics, such as silk and wool, require gentle agitation, whereas cotton can withstand more aggressive agitation.

Use of conditioner

✳ Conditioners are used to aid ironing, add a pleasant smell to fabric, soften the fabric and avoid static.

Water removal

✳ Water can be removed from fabrics by drip drying, wringing by hand or tumble drying.

Care Labelling

A care label is permanently attached to a textile product or fabric. It indicates the procedure that should be followed in cleaning the product.

Washing	Drying	Ironing	Dry cleaning	Bleach
Wash at 95°C	Tumble dry	Hot iron	Fabric can be dry cleaned in all solvents	Can be treated with chlorine bleach
Wash at 60°C	Normal setting	Warm iron	Dry cleanable in perchloroethylene, white spirit solvent 113 and solvent 11	Do not bleach
Wash at 40°C	Do not tumble dry	Cool iron	Dry cleanable in white spirit and solvent 113	
Wash at 40°C medium action	Drip dry	Do not iron	Do not dry clean	
Wash at 30°C minimum action	Line dry			
Hand wash	Dry flat			
Do not wash				

Fig 48.2: Care labelling symbols.

Fibre Properties and Care

Natural Fibres		Man-Made Fibres	
Cotton	**Wool**	**Nylon**	**Viscose**
Property • Strong • Absorbent • Dyes easily • Scorches • Creases easily **Care** • Machine wash • Bleach can be used • Hot iron • Hot machine wash (95°C)	**Property** • Scorches easily • Weak when wet • Pills • Soft • Absorbent **Care** • Wash at low temperatures of 40° C • Do not bleach • Warm iron • Dry flat	**Property** • Melts • Crease-resistant • Lightweight **Care** • Moderate washing temperatures of 50°C • Can be wrung out • Do not bleach	**Property** • Weak when wet • Creases • Likely to shrink at high temperatures • Absorbent **Care** • Medium wash (50°C). • Cannot be wrung out • Cool iron

Fabric Finishes

A fabric finish is a finish applied to a fabric to give it extra characteristics.

* **Crease-resistant:** Prevents creasing and shrinking.
* **Mercerising:** Makes fibres stronger and more absorbent.
* **Stain-resistant:** Makes fabric easier to clean.
* **Anti-pilling:** Applied to wool and synthetics to avoid bobbles developing.
* **Anti-static:** Makes fabrics less clingy.
* **Shrink-resistant:** Prevents shrinking of wool.

Safety Considerations When Selecting Household Textiles

All fabrics burn, therefore safety considerations must be taken into account when selecting household textiles. Fabrics have a tendency to burn quickly, therefore the fabrics chosen should be:

* Low-risk fabric.
* Fabrics that have been treated with a flame-retardant finish.

Low-Risk and High-Risk Fabrics

Low-Risk Fabrics	High-Risk Fabrics
• **Wool**: Smoulders and can sometimes be quenched. • **Polyester**: Slow to ignite and shrinks away from the flame.	• **Cotton**: Burns quickly. • **Acrylic**: Burns quickly and melts.

Flame-Retardant Finishes

✳ Flame-retardant finishes reduce the flammability of fabrics.

✳ There are two main types of flame-retardant finish: coated fabrics and inherent flame-retardant finishes.

✳ Two examples of flame-retardant finishes are Proban and Pyrovatex.

Coated Fabrics	Inherent Flame-Retardant Finishes
• Cheap.	• Expensive.
• Comfortable to wear.	• Not comfortable to wear.
• Flame-retardant finish is not permanent.	• Fibres are treated prior to being woven.

Example of Flame-Retardant Finish: Proban

✳ Protects fabrics by adding a layer of phosphorus and nitrogen to the fabric.

✳ Insoluble polymers form.

✳ On lighting, this finish forms charring on fabric which does not melt or smoulder and will eventually extinguish.

✳ Self-extinguishing when removed from the flame and lowers the risk of the fabric catching fire.

✳ Care needed when cleaning.

✳ Makes fabric more expensive.

Fire Safety (Domestic Furniture) Order 1988 (amended in 1995)

✳ The purpose of this order is to reduce the incidents of household fires.

✳ The order covers all upholstered items, sofas, armchairs, cushions and pillows.

✳ Fabrics must undergo rigorous testing, such as cigarette and match tests.

✳ A display or swing label must be attached to all items.

✳ The filling used must be combustion-modified high resilient (CMHR) foam.

Safety Labels

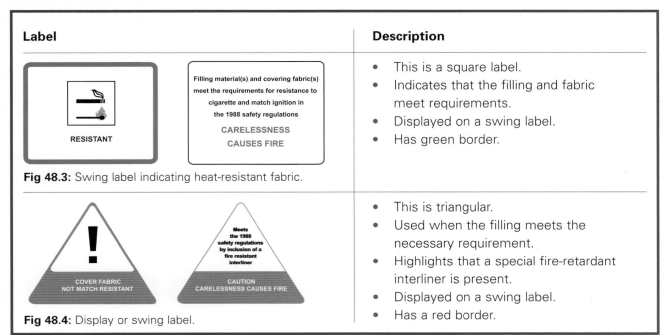

Label	Description
Filling material(s) and covering fabric(s) meet the requirements for resistance to cigarette and match ignition in the 1988 safety regulations CARELESSNESS CAUSES FIRE RESISTANT **Fig 48.3:** Swing label indicating heat-resistant fabric.	• This is a square label. • Indicates that the filling and fabric meet requirements. • Displayed on a swing label. • Has green border.
COVER FABRIC NOT MATCH RESISTANT Meets the 1988 safety regulations by inclusion of a fire resistant interliner CAUTION CARELESSNESS CAUSES FIRE **Fig 48.4:** Display or swing label.	• This is triangular. • Used when the filling meets the necessary requirement. • Highlights that a special fire-retardant interliner is present. • Displayed on a swing label. • Has a red border.

Label	Description

CARELESSNESS CAUSES FIRE
Batch/I.D. No.................
To comply with S.I. No: 336 1988 Industrial Research and Standards (Fire Safety) (Domestic Furniture) Order 1988:
this item does not require a schedule 3 interliner, I. S.419
all foams, fillings and composites have been tested to ensure compliance with the relevant ignitability test
covers and fillings are cigarette resistant
covers are match resistant
Further details are available from your retailer
 	
Fig 48.5: Permanent label.
	• Must be stitched to fabric.
	• This label indicates:
	  – Name and address of manufacturer.
	  – Date of manufacture.
	  – Description of filling.
	  – A warning: Carelessness causes fire.
	• A long or short label can be used:
	  – A long label provides all information.
	  – A short label ensures conformity with regulation.

Part Sample Question

Questions

1. Textiles are used extensively in the home for clothing and household purposes.

   (a) Outline four functions of household textiles. (12)

   (b) Write an informative note on the Fire Safety (Domestic Furniture) Order 1988 (12)

Sample Answer

1. **(a)** Outline four functions of household textiles. (12)

   4 points x 3 marks each = 12.

   • **To provide warmth**: This is the case with duvets, curtains.
   • **To provide protection**: When removing food from the oven, gloves are used. Curtains protect against the sun, which can have a fading effect.
   • **To provide privacy**: Curtains and blinds provide privacy.
   • **To absorb sound**: Carpets absorb sounds, unlike wooden floors, which reflect sound. Other household textiles that absorb sound include curtains and rugs.

1. **(b)** Write an informative note on the Fire Safety (Domestic Furniture) Order 1988. (12)

   4 points x 3 marks each = 12.

Fire Safety (Domestic Furniture) Order 1988

• This order was amended in 1995. The purpose of this order is to reduce the incidence of household fires.
• The order covers all upholstered items, sofas, armchairs, cushions and pillows.
• Fabrics must undergo rigorous testing, such as cigarette and match tests.
• A display or swing label must be attached to all items. The filling used must be combustion-modified high resilient (CMHR) foam.

Consumer Studies

49

Who is a Consumer?

Everyone who buys or uses goods or services is a consumer. Each consumer has consumer rights and responsibilities.

Consumer Choices

The main factors that influence consumer choice include: income, personal choice, personal values, marketing, sales techniques and packaging.

Income

* The amount of discretionary income that is available to individuals will affect consumer choices.
* When discretionary income is limited, this will affect choice as there is less money available for wants.
* Due to the high availability of credit, more people are placing greater dependence on borrowing.

Personal choice

* Factors such as whether something is categorised as a want or a need.
* An individual's personal likes and dislikes influence their choice of goods.

Personal values

* Consumers who seek information in order to make wise decisions will categorise what they deem to be a need or a want.

* Some people will make decisions based on whether the product has been created without harming others, i.e. ensuring the clothes that they buy have been produced in fair working conditions. (fairtrade)

Marketing/advertisements

* Extensive research shows that marketing and advertisement increase the sales of a product.
* Marketing aims to increase sales by encouraging consumers to purchase products.
* Advertisements are displayed extensively in prominent places, newspapers, magazines, TV, radio.

Sales techniques

* Shops and supermarkets offer a wide range of incentives to entice consumers to make purchases in their stores, including 'buy one product get second half price', 'two for the price of one'.
* Loyalty cards aim at ensuring consumers return to the same shops.

Packaging

* People buy what they perceive to be attractively presented. This is an area that is growing in popularity, causing many manufacturers to ensure their product is attractively labelled.

The Purchasing Process

Classification of Retail Outlets

The main types of retail outlet: independent shops, supermarkets, voluntary supermarkets, department stores, multiple chain stores and discount stores.

Retail Outlet	Description
Independent shops	• These tend to be family businesses, e.g. O'Brien Vegetables. • They are more popular in rural areas. • They are inclined to specialise in the products that they sell. • Their prices tend to be higher than those in supermarkets/chains. as independent shops tend to have higher overheads.
Supermarkets	• They allow customers the opportunity to move through the shop and choose their own products (self-service). • They sell own-brand produce together with branded goods. • They tend to be cheaper as they bulk buy their produce and can offer goods at a reduced price. • They sell a variety of grocery products and general goods. • Examples include Tesco, Lidl and Superquinn.
Voluntary supermarkets 	• These supermarkets are a combination of independent shops and supermarkets. • They are growing in popularity and availability. • Examples include Centra, Spar and Londis.
Hypermarkets	• These are larger than supermarkets, often twenty times the size, and contain a wide selection of shops. • They are popular in Europe. • They tend to be single storey with free car parking.
Department stores 	• These shops sell a wide variety of products under one roof. • The products sold include cosmetics, clothes and household products. • Examples include Arnotts and Brown Thomas.

Retail Outlet	Description
Multiple chain shops	• These incorporate a number of shops in different locations (chain) with very similar layout that sell exactly the same products and are managed by one company. • Prices are generally good as these stores are competing with other similar chains. • Examples include Penney's and A-Wear.
Discount stores	• Such shops offer goods at a greater discount as they have a higher turnover. • Discount shops have a selection of goods that can be purchased from catalogues. • Goods can be bought and taken away that day. • The goods are easily returned if any problem should arise. • An example is Argos.

Other Retail Outlets

Other retail outlets include:

* Auctions.
* Party selling, e.g. make-up parties.
* Television buying.
* Catalogue buying.
* Internet shopping (internet-only sites, such as eBay, or through websites of traditional shops).
* Vending machines.
* Street markets.

Retail Psychology

Companies have carried out a wide variety of surveys and researched consumer behaviour and what affects their buying techniques. As a result, shops tactically make arrangements unknown to the general consumer to encourage them to buy. This is known as research psychology. Below is a list of techniques used by shops.

Music:

Shops choose background music to reflect consumer moods. In large supermarkets soft music is played to entice the consumer to take time strolling around the shop, which will encourage them to buy more goods. This, together with a well-heated shop that has good lighting and ventilation, makes the consumer feel comfortable.

Smell:

The bakery in supermarkets is often located at the entrance of the shop so customers get wafting smells of freshly baked bread as they enter.

Product placement:

Essential goods, such as bread and milk, are often located at the back of a supermarket to ensure that the consumer is forced to pass by other products as they pick up essentials.

Product positioning:

Luxury items are often placed at eye level, with cheaper, own-brand produce placed lower down on shelves. Food products are positioned according to associations, such as tea and coffee beside biscuits and sweets.

Product association:

Foods are positioned according to association, i.e. tea and coffee beside biscuits and sweets.

Impulse goods:

Sweets and magazines are often placed near cash registers so that a customer may buy impulsively while they are queuing.

Special offers:

Special offers are often placed at the end of aisles.

Samples and tasting demonstrations:

Samples of food may be given out in supermarkets.

Loyalty schemes:

Loyalty schemes, such as clubcard points, enable customers to get money off purchases or coupons after spending a certain amount of money. This technique encourages a customer to shop in the same supermarket.

Product rotation:

Often shops rotate their shelving arrangements. This confuses consumers and they are forced to search for goods. Shops do this in the hope that consumers will buy more.

Shopping Patterns

The main factors that influence shopping patterns are: income, household size, tradition, advertisements, time and values.

Income

* The amount of money available will affect an individual's choices.
* For families on low incomes there is the option of purchasing own-brand produce or buying goods in discount shops. This is a specific shopping pattern.

Household size

* When a household is large, forward planning and preparation must be carried out to provide for the needs of the entire family.

* Single-person households are less regimented in forward planning as they are free to make decisions that can be altered without interrupting the lives of others.

Tradition

* The shops people choose to shop in can reflect where their parents shopped, e.g. the family butcher.
* This shopping pattern is influenced by the shopping patterns of others.
* The traditional method of payment was cash; today, however, developments in technology have replaced this method with credit cards and laser cards.

Advertisements

* Effective advertisements can alter the traditional shopping patterns. This occurs when there is an increase in sales of new products.

Time

* Time is a key factor for most families as both parents often work, therefore time for shopping is restricted.
* Shops are now accommodating this type of family by offering online shopping, home delivery services, late opening hours, 24-hour opening and Sunday opening.

Values

* People's values affect their shopping patterns. Such values include:
  * Considering the environment by ensuring they buy products that do not have excess packaging.
  * Animal welfare, i.e. buying products that have not been tested on animals.

Consumer Research

This is a process of collecting and collating information in relation to the needs of the consumer. This information is collected by desk research and field research.

Desk research

✳ This is carried out relatively quickly.
✳ It involves collecting information from concrete sources, such as the Central Statistics Office, the internet or trade agencies.
✳ A drawback of this research is that the information can be quite general and lacking detail.

Field research

✳ This form of research includes observation, questionnaires, surveys and interviews.
✳ This is expensive to carry out.
✳ It is much more detailed than desk research and offers the company a clearer insight into consumer behaviour in the marketplace.

Positive Factors of Consumer Research

✳ Manufacturers can categorise consumer profiles in accordance with income, age and gender.
✳ Competitors can be identified and their strengths and weaknesses analysed.
✳ The risk of launching a new product is minimised.
✳ A deeper understanding of consumer behaviour is gained; this information is vital in the creation of new products.
✳ Market size is identified and examined.

Consumer Rights

Consumers have a number of rights which protect them by law. These rights include:
✳ The right to value for money.
✳ The right to redress.
✳ The right to honest and trustworthy information.
✳ The right to choose.
✳ The right to safety.

Veronica Revises Her Consumer Studies

Learning Links Learning Links Learning Links

The Right to Value for Money

✳ Consumers are entitled to get value for money: all products must be of reasonable standard.
✳ This right is protected by the Sale of Goods and Supply of Services Act, 1980.

The Right to Redress

✳ Should a consumer find fault with a purchase, they have the right to complain and have their complaint dealt with.
✳ Should the fault be legitimate the consumer is entitled to a **refund**, **replacement** or **repair** of the product (the 3Rs).

The Right to Honest and Trustworthy Information

✳ Companies are required to provide the consumer with honest information when selling products.
✳ This information enables the consumer to make accurate decisions by comparing price, nutritional information, etc.
✳ This right is protected by the Consumer Information Act, 1978.

The Right to Choose

✳ Consumers are entitled to choose products from the range available.
✳ This entitlement encourages competition between companies.
✳ Such competition brings with it an increase in the quality of goods on the market, which, in turn, gives the consumer influence over the range of products available.

The Right to Safety

✳ Consumers have the right to buy products which are guaranteed to be safe and will not endanger their health in any form.

✳ This right is protected and monitored by legislation, quality marks and safety symbols.

✳ Some products must undergo rigorous testing to ensure that they are up to standard. For example, an upholstery item passes a series of tests before it is approved for use.

Consumer Responsibilities

With consumer rights come responsibilities. These include:

Be **AWARE**!

A　Acquainted with the law
W　Well informed
A　Avoid waste
R　Reader of labels
E　Examiner of products

Learning Links Learning Links Learning Links

Being Acquainted with the Law:

Knowledge of the legislation and their rights provides consumers with protection.

Being Well Informed:

All consumers should know where to get accurate information and should use this information to make wise decisions.

Avoiding Waste:

Each consumer is responsible for the environment, therefore it is their responsibility to ensure that: products with excess packaging are avoided; energy-saving products are chosen; and broken products are safely discarded.

Reading Labels:

If consumers fail to adhere to the manufacturer's instructions, they are not entitled to redress should a problem arise. Instructions on care labels should always be followed. Safety symbols and hazard symbols should be recognised and adhered to.

Examining of Products:

Before purchasing, the product should be thoroughly examined. When a fault does occur it is the responsibility of the consumer to report it to protect themselves.

Consumer Information

Consumer information is acquired from a variety of sources.

Source of information	Information provided
• **Salespeople**	• Offer in-depth information into products available in their shop.
	• However, they can be biased and encourage the consumer to buy the product that offers them the highest commission.

Source of information	Information provided
• **Magazines and newspapers**	• Offer a comparison of products. • Thorough evaluation of products. • Examples include: *Consumer Choice* magazine and *Which?*.
• **TV and radio**	• Thorough evaluation of products.
• **Leaflets**	• Information is given about specific products or services. • Leaflets are also used by statutory and voluntary bodies to provide people with information regarding their campaigns.
• **Other consumers**	• This is an excellent source of information, as other consumers share their own experiences.
• **Exhibitions and showrooms**	• Information is provided on the wide range of products on display. • Exhibitions tend to occur only on specific occasions so information may not be easily available.

Quality Marks

Quality Mark	Symbol
Guaranteed Irish This is found on Irish goods of high quality.	 *promoting irish excellence*
Irish Standards Mark This is found on goods of high quality.	
National Standards Authority of Ireland	NSAI
Kitemark (British Standards Institute mark) This is awarded to goods of a high standard.	

Safety Symbols

Represents:	Symbol
Communauté Européenne (CE) This is found on toys and electrical items.	C E
Double insulated This is found on electrical appliances, e.g. hairdryers.	▢
Irish mark of electrical conformity This is found on electrical goods.	

Hazard Symbols

Meaning	Symbol
Toxic	
Corrosive	
Harmful/Irritant	
Highly flammable	

Consumers' Responsibility Towards the Environment

Environmental misconduct leads to:

✳ Exhaustion of non-renewable fuels, such as coal, turf, gas and oil.

✳ Depletion of the ozone layer which acts as a protective barrier against the sun's harmful UV rays.

✳ Extensive reduction of tropical forest, which brings extinction of certain species.

✳ Global warming (climate change) leads to melting of the polar ice caps and results in water levels rising and to flooding.

✳ Pollution is increasing with huge increases in water, air, soil and litter pollution.

✳ Waste disposal is an ever-growing problem for all governments.

Sustainability

Sustainability is a buzz word associated with environmental problems. It involves respecting future generations and their needs while, at the same time, showing a proactive approach to recycling. Ireland as a nation must work towards reusing, reducing and recycling waste. Ireland, like most nations, is using up more than it needs. Its ecological footprint is at least one and a half times what it should be.

> **Ecological footprint** = The impact humans have on the planet regarding the land and water needed to meet the needs of the population.

Waste Management

In 1996, the government introduced a Waste Management Act. This act sets about reducing waste and conforming to EU regulations on the disposal of waste. In Ireland, there is a hierarchy of waste management. In this hierarchy, prevention is the most favoured method in the elimination of waste.

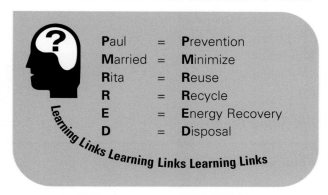

Paul	=	**P**revention
Married	=	**M**inimize
Rita	=	**R**euse
R	=	**R**ecycle
E	=	**E**nergy Recovery
D	=	**D**isposal

Learning Links Learning Links Learning Links

Methods of Waste Management

•	Prevention	Avoid needless packaging. Always consider whether the product is a necessity.
•	Minimise	Maintain and repair where possible, and share goods.
•	Reuse	Always consider reusing goods, e.g. reusing glass jars for jam-making.
•	Recycle	Always recycle as it reduces waste. For example: bottle banks are positioned throughout Ireland.
•	Energy recovery	Energy can be recovered. For example, the burning of manure can be used to heat a home. This is used in developing countries.
•	Disposal	This involves landfill, which should be a last resort in waste management. In Ireland, 91 per cent of waste goes to landfill.

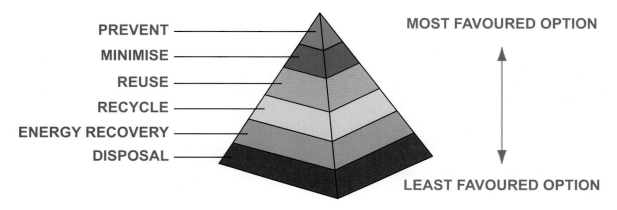

Fig 49.1: Waste management hierarchy pyramid.

Reduce, Reuse, Recycle

We must all reduce, reuse and recycle.

Reduce:

* Wasteful packaging by purchasing products which have little or no excess wrapping.
* Car use; instead opt for more environmentally friendly forms of transport, such as public transport.
* Products which are not environmentally friendly.

Reuse:

* Shopping bags.
* Clothes.
* Newspapers.
* Furniture.

Recycle:

* Paper, cardboard, plastic and metal.
* By using compost bins.
* By ensuring that the products bought can be recycled.
* By checking that the products bought were made from recyclable materials.

Recycling Symbols

Represents	Symbol	Definition
The Green Dot		• This symbol indicates that the packaging suppliers have made a financial contribution to the cost of recycling the product. • In Ireland, this symbol is found on goods from all companies that are members of Repak. • This symbol is a Europe-wide symbol.
The recycling symbol		• This symbol indicates that the goods and packaging can be recycled or are made from recyclable materials.
Eco-Label symbol		• This indicates that the production of the product causes little damage to the environment.
PET label		• PET = polyethylene terephthalate. • This indicates that certain plastics can be recycled.

Pollution

There are different forms of pollution, but all cause huge damage to the environment. Pollution includes air, noise and water pollution.

Pollution	Causes	Consequences	How to avoid
Air pollution	• CFCs (chlorofluorocarbons) from aerosols. • Carbon monoxide emissions from cars, lorries. • Excess use of sprays. • Burning of non-renewable fuels.	• Reduction of the ozone layer. • Global warming. • Acid rain. • Increase in respiratory problems and allergies.	• Purchasing appliances that are energy efficient. • Avoiding products that contain CFCs. • Using smokeless fuels. • Using renewable fuels.
Noise pollution	• Traffic. • House and car alarms. • Construction sites. • Lawn mowers. • Barking dogs. • Loud music from nightclubs.	• Sleep deprivation. • Tension and stress. • Headaches.	• Turn down music systems and TVs. • A well-insulated home will prevent noise escaping. • Houses should not be located near nightclubs.
Water pollution	• Sewage (farm waste and industrial waste). • Over use of cleaning agents and chemicals. • Pesticides and fertilisers. • Oil spillages.	• Makes water unsafe to drink. • Rivers die along with the animal and plant life living in and around them. • Fishing industry is affected.	• Reduction in fertilisers and pesticides used. • An efficient sewage system, which is monitored regularly. • Phosphate-free detergents should be used. • If laws are not adhered to strictly penalties should be implemented.

Energy

The non-renewable fuels that are a source of energy are fast running out and measures are now been taken to implement the use of renewable energy. Non-renewable fuels include coal, oil, turf/peat and gas. These fuels can be used to generate electricity. It is believed that non-renewable resources will run out in the next few decades. Forms of renewable energy include: wind, solar, biomass, geothermal and hydropower.

Fig 49.2: Wind turbine farm.

Wind

✻ This is a popular form of energy in Ireland, particularly in coastal areas where strong winds can be harnessed to provide an alternative to non-renewable fuels.

✻ Wind turbines are used to produce energy for houses. This is particularly popular in Mayo.

Solar

✻ In Ireland, solar panels are often built into the roofs of houses to provide solar energy.

✻ Solar energy is also used to power small public devices, e.g. parking meters and motorway SOS telephones.

Fig 49.3: Solar panels in a house.

Biomass

✻ This involves using plants to produce energy.

✻ Growing wood for this form of energy is sustainable. When the wood is growing, it absorbs carbon dioxide from the air. When the wood is burned, the amount of carbon dioxide released is equal to the carbon dioxide it absorbed during its growth.

Geothermal

This form of energy is produced by harnessing the heat from inside the earth.

Hydropower

This form of energy is produced by harnessing the power of fast-flowing rivers.

Lowering Energy Consumption

✻ Turn off appliances completely when not in use.
✻ Choose energy-efficient appliances.
✻ Shower instead of taking a bath, as this uses less water.
✻ Use thermostats to monitor temperature.
✻ Ensure houses are well insulated.
✻ Choose cars that have low fuel emissions (introduced in July 2008).
✻ Turn off lights when not needed.
✻ Choose microwaves when heating food, as they use less energy than conventional ovens.
✻ Use compact fluorescent light bulbs.
✻ Ensure that the hot water cylinder has a lagging jacket.

Consumer Protection

Consumers are protected by:
✻ Consumer legislation.
✻ Voluntary bodies.
✻ Statutory bodies.

Consumer Legislation

Sale of Goods and Supply of Services Act, 1980

✻ This act covers the following four items:
  ● Goods.
  ● Services.
  ● Guarantees.
  ● Illegal signs.
✻ This is the main law that protects the consumer when they buy goods as a legal contract becomes established between the consumer and the seller.
✻ The act states that:
  ● Goods must be of **merchantable quality**. This incorporates the idea that goods should be durable and perform their function.
  ● **Fit for purpose**, i.e. carry out the function that they were built for without fault.
  ● **As described**: A product should resemble its description, e.g. if a garment states that

it is 100 per cent linen, it should be 100 per cent linen.

- **Correspond to the sample**: Any samples issued by a shop should be direct replicas of the goods available to the consumer to buy.
- Service suppliers must be qualified to carry out the job using the necessary skills and tools required. All safety precautions must be implemented by the service supplier to ensure the consumer is safe.

Faulty Products

If a problem arises with a product after it has been bought, the consumer is entitled to redress. This warrants the consumer to a repair, refund or replacement of the faulty product. All complaints must be made within a reasonable time.

Guarantee

The Sale of Goods and Supply of Services Act also offers the consumer extra protection in relation to guarantees.

- ✱ A guarantee is a contract between the consumer and the manufacturer.
- ✱ Most guarantees have a time limit, e.g. one year from the date of purchase.
- ✱ A guarantee specifies that the consumer is entitled to have the product repaired or replaced should a problem arise.
- ✱ A guarantee does not affect the consumer's rights and not every manufacturer is legally required to issue a guarantee.
- ✱ A guarantee must:
  - Be clearly legible.
  - Give the name of the product.
  - Give the name and address of the company issuing the guarantee.
  - Clearly indicate the time-span of the guarantee.
  - Explain the procedure to be followed should a problem arise.
  - State what the manufacturer proposes should a fault arise.
  - Indicate if the consumer is expected to pay any further charges.

Illegal Signs

It is illegal for shops to display the following signs:
- No cash refunds.
- Goods will not be exchanged.
- Credit notes only given.

Consumer Information Act, 1978

This is another piece of legislation that offers the consumer protection against false or misleading claims about goods or services.

Claims Made About Goods	Claims Made About Services
• Genuine leather.	• 24-hour service.
• 100 per cent wool.	• One hour photo.
• Waterproof.	• Open 365 days.

- ✱ The law states that the consumer may not be presented with a false price for goods or services in relation to price, previous price and recommended retail price.
- ✱ All advertisements in relation to the product must not in any way mislead the consumer.
- ✱ This act is protected by the Office of the Director of Consumer Affairs.

The Electronic Commerce Act, 2000

- ✱ This act protects the consumer when they shop online.
- ✱ It was established as part of the European Union.
- ✱ This act stipulates that all e-bookings and agreements have the same legal standing as that of written documents.

Consumer Protection Agencies

Both statutory and voluntary agencies exist in Ireland to help protect the rights of consumers.

Statutory Agencies	Voluntary Agencies
• The Office of the Director of Consumer Affairs. • The National Standards Authority of Ireland. • European Consumer Centres. • Ombudsman. • The Office of the Financial Regulator. • Comhairle.	• Consumer Association of Ireland. • Advertising Standards of Ireland.

Statutory Bodies

Office of the Director of Consumer Affairs

national **consumer** agency
gníomhaireacht náisiúnta **tomhaltóirí**

putting **consumers** first

Established under the Consumer Information Act, 1978, it has a responsibility to inform consumers about their rights and to encourage consistent codes of advertising. The director's office runs a telephone helpline.

✱ Its main functions are to:
  • **Inform** the public of their consumer rights, e.g. through the publication of information leaflets.
  • **Prosecute** offences relating to false advertising.
  • **Monitor** consumer charges by credit institutions and promote good codes of practices.
  • **Monitor** the safety standards of products on the Irish market.
  • **Investigate** complaints of false or misleading statements made in advertising. The office has the power to ban advertisements and to prosecute offenders.
  • **Advise** the government on consumer issues and publish an annual report.

The Ombudsman

✱ The Ombudsman is appointed by the government.
✱ He/she acts on behalf of the individual and investigates officials within government departments and state bodies, e.g. the Department of Social, Community and Family Affairs, local authorities, health boards, An Post, etc.
✱ Consumers must first try to resolve the problem themselves.
✱ If that does not work, the consumer must make a complaint within twelve months of the problem arising.

The National Standards Authority of Ireland (NSAI)

✱ This is involved in establishing standards in Ireland.
✱ It keeps Irish industry fully informed of developments in standards and related legislation.
✱ It also helps to ensure that Irish products meet EU and international standards.

Comhairle

✱ Operates Citizens Information Centres.
✱ The centres provide free confidential and impartial information.

Citizens
Information

- ✳ Information is provided on topics such as social welfare, health services, redundancy, income tax, housing, family law and consumer affairs.
- ✳ Comhairle also offers the public advice and advocacy on social services.

European Consumer Centres

These centres became established by the European commissioners under the direction of the Director of Consumer Affairs.

- ✳ The aims of the centre are to provide the consumer with easily accessible information.
- ✳ These centres offer on-the-spot information in the form of leaflets.
- ✳ The centre in Ireland is located in Dublin.

Financial Regulator

The Office of the Financial Regulator controls all the financial services in Ireland.

- ✳ It ensures that financial regulation is adhered to and monitored, thus protecting the consumer.

Voluntary Bodies

Consumer Association of Ireland (CAI)

The Consumer Association of Ireland was set up in 1996 to protect and educate consumers. The CAI is an independent, non-profit-making and non-governmental organisation. It provides a number of services to the public:

- ✳ Publishes consumer magazine *Consumer Choice*.
- ✳ Seeks to improve consumer legislation.
- ✳ Provides the consumer with information through the media.

Advertisement Standards Authority of Ireland (ASAI)

This is an independent voluntary body established by the advertising industry in Ireland.

- ✳ Its aim is to ensure that all advertisements are legal, decent, honest and truthful.
- ✳ This organisation investigates any complaints made by consumers in relation to advertisements.

Small Claims Procedure

The Small Claims Court was set up to deal speedily and inexpensively with consumer disagreements.

- ✳ Claims up to the value of €1,270 may be determined by the Registrar or Court and therefore solicitors are not required. This reduces costs significantly.
- ✳ Claims can be made for faulty goods or bad workmanship, minor damage to property or the non-return of rent deposits.

✱ Claims may not be made for personal injuries, goods bought on hire purchase, debts or breach of leasing agreements.

✱ The fee for the court is €9, which is not refundable.

Operation:

1. The claimant (person making the claim) fills in an application form and lodges it with the fee, with the District Court Registrar.

2. The complaint is recorded and a duplicate is sent to the respondent (individual against whom the claim is made).

3. If the respondent does not contest the claim within fifteen days, the claim is settled in the claimant's favour by the Registrar.

4. If the complaint is disputed by the respondent, the Registrar will attempt to settle the dispute. If this is not possible, the case will be resolved by a court hearing.

Exam Questions
Higher Level (2005)

Question

Studies show that impulse buying accounts for 65 per cent of purchases in supermarkets.

(*Consumer Choice*, May 2001)

1. Describe four in-store techniques that supermarkets use to encourage consumer spending. (20)

2. Name three research methods used to gather information on the consumer. Explain how consumer research benefits:
   (a) The retailer.
   (b) The consumer. (19)

3. Name and outline the role of any one voluntary agency concerned with consumer protection. (11)

Sample Answers

1. Describe four in-store techniques that supermarkets use to encourage consumer spending. (20)

   4 points x 5 marks each = 20.

   • **Music**: Shops choose background music to reflect consumer moods. In large supermarkets soft music is played to entice the consumer to take time strolling around the shop, which will encourage them to buy more goods. This, together with a well-heated shop that has good lighting and ventilation, makes the consumer feel comfortable.

   • **Smell**: The bakery in supermarkets is often located at the entrance of the shop, so customers get wafting smells of freshly baked bread as they enter.

   • **Product placement**: Essential goods, such as bread and milk, are often located at the back of a supermarket to ensure that the consumer is forced to pass by other products as they pick up essentials.

   • **Product positioning**: Luxury items are often placed at eye level with cheaper, own-brand produce placed lower down. Food products are positioned according to associations, such as tea and coffee beside biscuits and sweets.

2. Name three research methods used to gather information on the consumer. Explain how consumer research benefits:

(a) The retailer.

(b) The consumer. (19)

3 research methods x 3 marks each = 9.

2 benefits x 5 marks each = 10.

Research methods:
- Questionnaires.
- Surveys.
- Interviews.

Benefits to Retailer	Benefits for Consumer
• Manufacturers can categorise consumer profiles in accordance with income, age and gender. • Competitors can be identified and their strengths and weaknesses analysed. • The risk of launching a new product is minimised. • A deeper understanding of consumer behaviour is gained. This information is vital in the creation of new products.	• The consumer's needs and wants are identified. • Goods are produced for the needs and wants of the consumer. • Helps to improve the quality of the product. • Enables consumers to give feedback regarding advertising, merchandising strategies and pricing.

3. Name and outline the role of any one voluntary agency concerned with consumer protection. (11)

1 name x 3 marks = 3.

2 points x 4 marks each = 8.

Consumer Association of Ireland (CAI)

The Consumer Association of Ireland was set up in 1996 to protect and educate consumers. The CAI is an independent, non-profit-making and non-governmental organisation. It provides a number of services to the public:

- Publishes consumer magazines *Consumer Choice*.
- Seeks to improve consumer legislation.
- Provides the consumer with information through the media.

THE FAMILY IN SOCIETY

50 Introducing Sociological Concepts

51 The Family

52 Marriage

53 The Family as a Caring Unit

54 Family Law

Section

4 5 6

50

Introducing Sociological Concepts

Sociological Terms

Sociology is the study of society and all it involves, such as family, relationships and behaviour patterns.

Culture

This means the values, norms and material goods characteristic of a given group.

* The culture in any given society is transferred from generation to generation.

Fig 50.1: Girls playing in a camogie match.

Kinship

A relationship which links individuals through blood ties.

Mores

These are the norms, values and customs that society recognises as important, e.g. being truthful.

Norms

These are the rules of conduct that are considered normal.

* A norm either stipulates a given type of behaviour or forbids it.
* Norms are usually enforced by members of society by correcting young children or by showing disapproval.

Role

This is an expected pattern of behaviour.

* Different roles carry with them different expectations of behaviour.
* An individual may occupy many different roles, e.g. a mother, a daughter, a sister, a worker, a wife.

Socialisation

The social processes through which children develop an awareness of norms and values and achieve a distinct sense of self.

* There are two methods of socialisation: primary socialisation and secondary socialisation.
  * **Primary socialisation:** This is a process through which learning takes place in the family.
  * **Secondary socialisation:** This is a process through which learning takes place in school and at work.

Social Change

This refers to the changes that happen in society, e.g. wars and technological changes.

Social Institutions

An organised social arrangement in society, e.g. the institution of marriage.

Social Mobility

Movement of individuals or groups between different socio-economic groupings.

* Vertical mobility refers to movement up or down the groupings.
* Social mobility is greatly affected by education and income.

Society

A group of people who share a similar way of life.

* Large society = Irish society.
* Small society = a school.

Socio-Economic Group

People in society can be grouped according to their wealth or income.

* There are three main groupings: lower socio-economic, middle socio-economic and high socio-economic.

Status

The social honour or prestige which a particular group is awarded by other members of a society.

* Status can either be ascribed or achieved.
* Ascribed status, e.g. a prince born into a royal family.
* Achieved status, e.g becoming a doctor (through education).

Values

Ideals held by individuals or groups about what is desirable, proper, good or bad.

* Values are a clear indication of what is right (acceptable) and what is wrong (unacceptable).

51

The Family

> **Definitions of the family:**
> - The family is a group of people related to each other through blood, marriage or adoption.
> - The Irish Constitution, Article 41, defines a family as 'a natural primary and fundamental unit group of society'.

The Universality of the Family

The family as a social institution is evident in every society.

* Culture affects the variations of families that exist.
* There is no single exclusive family structure.
* To be part of a family unit continues to be a universal structure found all over the world.

Different Types of Family Structure

Fig 51.1: A nuclear family.

Nuclear Family

It consists of mother, father and children.

* Usually small families.
* Family is mobile, it can move from place to place for work demands.
* Decisions are made democratically.
* Egalitarian: Shared equal roles, e.g. men share the responsibility of child minding.
* Self-sufficient: Can provide for themselves.
* If extended family live a good distance away, it can be isolating.
* This type of family structure ends with the death of a partner or divorce.

Extended Family

It consists of grandparents, parents, children, uncles, aunts and cousins, living with or in close proximity to each other.

* There are two types of extended family structures: Classic extended and modified extended:
  - **Classic extended:** This is where a number of nuclear families live in close proximity to each other or in the same house.
  - **Modified extended:** Where a number of nuclear families don't live in close proximity but maintain regular contact.
* Usually large families.
* Family is immobile; it is tied to an area and won't move to another area, often involved in farming and agriculture.
* Decisions are made by the head of the house, usually the father, who is authoritarian.
* Segregated: Roles are gender specific, i.e. defined roles for men and women.

Fig 51.2: An extended family.

* Good support network because everybody is around.
* This type of family is long lasting, as each generation usually settles down in the same area.

Lone-Parent Family

It consists of either a mother or father and children. It is usually headed by the mother.

* Can occur due to unplanned pregnancy, separation, divorce or death of a spouse.

Fig 51.3: Lone-parent family.

* Lone-parent families can have more financial difficulties, experience more stress, isolation and an increased workload.
* State benefits become very important for this family structure.

Blended/Reconstituted Family

* Consists of step-mother, step-father, step-brothers and/or step-sisters.
* Occurs due to the 'blending' of two families.
* This is becoming a more common type of family structure due to divorce and separation.
* Families must re-orientate themselves. The youngest child may now have younger siblings to compete with for affection.
* Decision-making is democratic, although initially there may be conflict and discipline issues which need to be teased out.

Social, Economic and Technological Changes Affecting the Family Structure

Social Changes	Economic Changes	Technological Changes
• There has been an increase in the number of people separating and seeking divorce. • This has led to an increase in different types of family structures, e.g. blended.	• There is an increase in the cost of living, which affects family life. Due to this, many parents both have to work to cover household costs. • Improved pay has also resulted in higher standards of living.	• The development of time-saving and labour-saving appliances has meant that housework is done quickly and easily, e.g. vacuum cleaners, dishwashers and washing machines.

Social Changes	Economic Changes	Technological Changes
• Families are having fewer children today. This is due to parents wishing to pursue their own careers, the high cost of childcare and people planning their family by using contraception. • Women are often becoming the main breadwinners while men stay at home. Men are very much involved in child rearing. • Education is seen as essential with more people continuing education and lifelong learning. • Ireland is a multicultural society with different cultures becoming integrated. • An increase in the number of co-habiting couples and gay/lesbian couples. • There is an increase in leisure time for parents because of a reduction in working hours, which can result in an increase in quality time with children.	• Economic opportunities mean people don't stay in one job for their entire working life. Individuals seek different employment opportunities. • Both parents often work outside the home in order to provide for their family. • There has been a reduction in unemployment in recent years, although recently unemployment figures have begun to rise. • Lone-parent families can avail of state benefits. • Women are economically independent as they too work outside the home and have their own source of income. This allows women to become self-sufficient and not dependent on their husbands for money.	• Technological advancements in agriculture has meant that farming systems are less labour-intensive, e.g. milking cows by hand has been replaced by using machines. • Communications technology means it's easier for family members to communicate no matter where they are in the world, e.g. e-mail, Skype, texting. • Technology in entertainment means family members can enjoy a wide variety of pastimes, e.g. TV, DVDs, computer games (Wii, PlayStation), music systems. • Security technology has given families peace of mind by making them feel safe in their homes (e.g. alarm systems).

Historical Development of the Family in Ireland

Pre–Industrialisation (1900–1960)

✳ The **extended family** was the most common form of family.

✳ Families were **large**.

✳ **Children** were vitally important to help out on the land and were seen as an **economic asset**.

✳ Most **marriages** were **arranged**.

✳ **Segregated conjugal roles**: Women did the housework, men worked outside.

✳ **Infant mortality** rates were high.

✳ Decisions were **authoritarian** and made by the father as the head of the household.

✳ **Religion** played a very prominent part in family life.

✳ The period from 1950 to 1960 saw **electricity** being supplied to rural Ireland, reducing some of the workload with cookers, fridges, etc.

✳ Towards the end of this era child mortality rates had decreased.

Fig 51.4: Large family in early twentieth-century Ireland.

Fig 51.5: Father feeding a baby.

Post-Industrialisation (1960–1990)

* A move away from the large extended family to the **nuclear family**.
* Family became **smaller** in size.
* **Children** were **not** seen as an **economic asset**.
* People married younger.
* **Marriages** were generally **not arranged**.
* The husband was still the main breadwinner, but after the 1970s more **women worked outside the home**.
* Wages increased, **improving the standard of living**.
* Fewer children left school at primary level, as **education** was seen as **important**.

Contemporary Family (1990–Present Day)

* Different types of family structure have emerged: **nuclear, extended, lone-parent, blended**.

* Families are having fewer children. The average family size is 1.4 children.
* Many families are **dual earners**, with both partners working outside the home.
* There has been a change in roles. It is now common for women to work outside the home and for men to stay at home.
* Wage increases means that families enjoy a **high quality of life**.
* **Cohabitation has increased** (i.e. men and women living together without being married).
* The state is involved in the functions of the family: intellectual, nurturing, economic.

Family Functions

Think of the word **PRINCE**!

Learning Links Learning Links Learning Links

Family Function	Explanation
Protective	• The family protects its vulnerable members, the elderly, children, and members with disabilities or illnesses.
Reproductive	• Reproduction is vital to continue the human race. • Sexual behaviour is controlled where partners only have one sexual partner. • Uncontrolled sexual behaviour can result in conflict, unwanted pregnancies and the transmission of sexually transmitted diseases.

Family Function	Explanation
Intellectual **Fig 51.6:** Father helping child with homework.	• The family is seen as the primary educator of a child. • Values and beliefs are passed on from parents to children. • Children thrive on praise and encouragement during the early years. • When children go to school, it is important that parents take an active role by being supportive and taking an interest.
Nurturing	• Families provide a nurturing home by meeting the needs of food, clothing and shelter. • How the child is reared and the environment in which the child is brought up will have a huge bearing on their development. • The family provides a setting in which children can observe and imitate acceptable forms of social behaviour.
Caring	• Families provide for the emotional well-being of their children. • By caring, acts of kindness and love, children feel safe and happy. • Children who are brought up in a caring atmosphere should be able to form healthy relationships themselves later in life.
Economic	• Parents provide financially for their children until the children are able to do so themselves. • Money is needed in families for toys, books, clothes, activities. • Money is available through state benefits for parents who are unemployed or have a disability.

How the State Intervenes in These Functions

Protective:

The state intervenes in this function if children are not being properly looked after.

✱ Children may be placed in foster care on a temporary or permanent basis.

Reproductive:

The state does not intervene in this function, although couples who find it difficult to conceive can get tests and treatment in hospitals.

Intellectual:

The state provides schooling from five to 18 years of age.

✱ Children with learning difficulties are provided with state assistance in the allocation of Special

Needs Assistants (SNAs) and psychological assessments to identify learning difficulties.

Nurturing:

The nurturing functions, which enable children to learn to socialise, are helped by the state provision of pre-schools, primary and secondary schools.

Caring:

Parenting skills improvement courses and classes are provided by the state in community resource centres.

Economic:

State benefits, such as unemployment, disability, back to school clothing allowance, medical cards, etc.

Part Exam Questions
Higher Level (2006)

Questions

1. Identify and describe three types of family structure in today's society. (18)

2. Discuss the effects of:
   (i) social change; and
   (ii) economic changes on modern family structures. (24)

Answers

1. Identify and describe three types of family structure in today's society. (18)

3 structures x 6 marks each = 18.

Nuclear Family
- Consists of mother, father and children.
- Usually small families.
- Family is mobile: Will move from place to place for work.
- Decisions are made democratically.
- Egalitarian: Shared equal roles, e.g. men share the responsibility of childminding.
- If extended family live a good distance away, can be isolating.

Extended Family
- Consists of grandparents, parents, children, uncles, aunts and cousins, living with or in close proximity to each other.
- Usually large families.
- Family is immobile: Tied to an area and won't move to another area, usually involved in farming and agriculture so tied to the land.
- Decisions are made by the head of the house, usually the father, authoritarian.
- Segregated: Roles are gender specific, i.e. defined roles for men and women.
- Good support network because everybody is around.
- This family is long lasting as each generation usually settles down in the same area.

Lone-Parent Family
- Consists of either a mother or father and children.
- Can occur due to unplanned pregnancy, separation, divorce or death of a spouse.
- Lone-parent families can have more financial difficulties, experience more stress, isolation and an increased workload.
- State benefits become very important for this family structure.

2. Discuss the effects of:
   (i) social change; and
   (ii) economic changes on modern family structures. (24)

6 points x 2 marks each = 12 marks for social change.
6 points x 2 marks each = 12 marks for economic change.

Social Changes and Modern Family Structures
- An increase in the number of people separating and seeking divorce.

- This has led to an increase in different types of family structure, e.g. blended.
- Families are having fewer children today. This is due to parents wishing to pursue their own careers, the high cost of childcare and people planning their family by using contraception.
- Women are very often becoming the main breadwinners while the men stay at home.
- Education is seen as essential with more and more people continuing education and life-long learning.
- Ireland is an multicultural society with different cultures becoming integrated.

Economic Changes and Modern Family Structures

- There is an increase in the cost of living which affects family life. Due to this many parents both now have to work to cover household costs.
- Improved pay has also resulted in higher standards of living.
- Economic opportunities mean people don't stay in the same job for their entire working life.
- Both parents often work outside the home in order to provide for their family.
- There has been a reduction in unemployment is recent years, although recently unemployment figures have begun to rise.
- Lone-parent families can avail of state benefits.
- Women are economically independent as they too work outside the home and have their own source of income. This allows women to become self-sufficient and not dependent on their husbands for money.

Marriage

52

> **Marriage** has many definitions. In Ireland marriage can be defined as 'a legally binding union between a man and a woman with the exclusion of all others'. In some countries, same-sex marriages are accepted, however this is prohibited by Irish law.

Mono	=	One
Di	=	Two
Tri	=	Three
Poly	=	Many

Cultural Variations of Marriage

* Choice of partners.
* Arranged marriages.
* Minimum age.
* Location.

Number of Partners

* Monogamy.
* Polygamy.
* Polyandry.
* Polygyny.

Fig 52.1: Jennifer Lopez with her first, second and third husbands.

Monogamy

This form of marriage occurs when one person has one spouse.

* Monogamy is the most common type of marriage in western society. Monogamy is the only type of marriage recognised by Irish law.
* Serial monogamy occurs when one person marries and divorces several times.
* Bigamy is when a person enters into a second marriage while still legally married to another person.

Polygamy

This is a form of marriage that involves more than one partner.

* This is generally not seen as acceptable in most western societies.
* There are two forms of polygamy: polygyny and polyandry.

Polygyny	**Polyandry**

• This is a marriage which involves one man and two or more women.
• Polygynous marital relations are commonly practised in certain African nations and in the Islamic community.
• In a polygynous marriage, the dominant figure is the man, who generally controls all financial aspects of the family together with decision-making. This is known as patriarchal (man dominates).
	• Polyandry is a marriage which involves one woman and more than one man. This type of marriage is popular in certain Tibetan tribes and among the Inuit Eskimos.
	• Polyandry is essential to prevent the subdivision of land, therefore this type of marriage can sometimes be seen in agricultural societies.
	• There are two forms of polyandry:
	  – **Fraternal**: when the husbands are brothers.
	  – **Non-fraternal**: when the husbands are not related.

Fig 52.2: Polygynous marriage.

Fig 52.3: Polyandrous marriage.

Arranged Marriages

In arranged marriages, parents will decide on their child's spouse. These arrangements are based on suitability and background.

✴ This type of marriage is traditionally popular in certain cultures, such as Japanese and Sikh.

✴ In some situations, the marriage can be arranged from a very young age.

Minimum Age for Marriage

The minimum age for marriage in Ireland is eighteen years of age, however some other societies have no minimum age for marriage.

Location

On marriage the couple can chose to live in a variety of different locations:

✴ **Matrilocal living**: In the locality of the wife's origin.

✴ **Patrilocal living**: In the locality of the husband's origin.

✴ **Neolocal living**: In a new location for both husband and wife.

Marriage and the Law

The legal requirements for marriage in Ireland include:

✴ Both partners must be over the age of eighteen.

✴ Partners must be of the opposite sex. (Same-sex marriages are not permitted in Ireland; however, they are permitted in other countries, such as England, Denmark and certain states in the USA.)

✴ Both partners must be free to marry, i.e. not married already.

* Partners must not be too closely related. Example, a father may not marry his daughter.
* The wedding must take place in a recognised place of worship/registry office. Today, people intending marriage can also apply for temporary registration of a hotel, beach, garden, etc.
* There must be two witnesses present at the ceremony in order for it to be valid. In contemporary Catholic weddings, the witnesses are generally the best man and maid of honour.
* Three months' notice must be given to the registrar of the district in which the marriage will take place.
* All marriages must be registered after the ceremony.

The Rights and Responsibilities of a Married Couple

* Each partner in a marriage is entitled to the other's company. This is achieved by both partners living together (cohabitation).
* Each spouse is expected to be faithful to the other.
* Married couples have the right to sexual relations.
* Each spouse has the right to provide financial support for a dependant partner and children.
* Both spouses too have joint/equal guardianship of children and therefore must provide for their basic needs together with moral and social education of all children of the relationship.

Marriage Preparation

Marriage preparation occurs in three distinct areas:
* Home.
* School.
* Marriage preparation courses.

Home

* Children first learn about marriage at home, where they see first-hand from their parents how a marriage exists. If parents are supportive of each other and make decisions together, children too will follow this pattern. If, however, a child witnesses parents constantly arguing, this will follow through in their relationships.
* Parents are role models for their child's future relationships.

School

* In school, students learn about marriage in various subjects: Home Economics, Religion, SPHE (Social, Personal and Health Education) and RSE (Relationship and Sexuality Education).
* In Home Economics, students examine a variety of aspects relating to marriage, including law and marriage, roles and responsibilities of marriage partners.
* In Religion, students examine the Catholic Church's belief on marriage and the ceremony of marriage.
* In RSE and SPHE students further examine the basis of a successful marriage.

Pre-Marriage Courses

* Pre-marriage courses are a positive option for people preparing for marriage, as they enable the couple to take a practical and honest look at what married life consists of.
* These courses are provided by two organisations: ACCORD and the Marriage and Relationship Counselling Service.
* ACCORD is a Catholic organisation, however non-Catholics are permitted to attend.

* They examine marriage under the following headings: commitment, communication, conflict resolution, children and the Church.

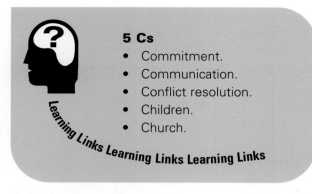

5 Cs
- Commitment.
- Communication.
- Conflict resolution.
- Children.
- Church.

Learning Links Learning Links Learning Links

✱ Each couple examines their vision of marriage. Guidance at these courses is given by priests, doctors and marriage councillors.

Marital Breakdown

Marital breakdown is becoming a regular occurrence in western societies. This is due to the following reasons:

✱ **Age:** Research indicates that a high percentage of couples who marry in their teens separate or divorce. This is often because one or both partners have not reached emotional maturity.

✱ **Background:** In cases where individuals come from different social, cultural or religious backgrounds, marital breakdown is prevalent.

✱ **Women working:** In the past when a woman married, she left her job in order to work in the home. Today, women can attend third-level education and continue working after marriage. Therefore, their attitude towards marriage has changed.

✱ **Infidelity:** Marital relations are based on trust. If trust is lost because a member has been unfaithful, it often results in marital breakdown.

✱ **Social problems:** Problems such as alcoholism, drug abuse, gambling and child abuse are all factors that can contribute to marital breakdown.

✱ **Legal aspect:** In the past, divorce was not permitted and levels of marital separation were low. Since the introduction of divorce in 1996, however, the number of divorce cases is rapidly increasing as divorce is now seen as acceptable in Irish society.

Choices Available when Marriages Break Down

Marriage Counselling

Marriage counselling is provided by ACCORD and the Marriage and Relationship Counselling Service.

✱ Couples sometimes seek counselling to prevent marriage break-up from occurring.

✱ During counselling sessions, both spouses must attend.

✱ A neutral counsellor attends the sessions to offer guidance and support.

Legal Nullity

Legal nullity indicates that a marriage never existed in the eyes of the law.

There are six main reasons why legal nullity would be granted:

✱ One of the partners was **drunk or on drugs** during the marriage ceremony and therefore was not of the correct mind.

✱ One partner was **already married** and had not received a divorce.

✱ The marriage was **not consummated** due to impotence or homosexuality.

✱ Normal marital relations could not be achieved due to one partner's **psychiatric problems**.

✱ A **legal requirement** for marriage was overlooked, e.g. there were no witnesses present at the ceremony.

✱ **Lack of consent** by either partner. One partner was forced into the marriage; this is also known as a shotgun wedding.

Church Annulment

✱ If one wishes to remarry in a church, a Church annulment must be sought.

✱ This dissolves the marriage from ever having existed in the eyes of the Church.

✱ A church annulment is therefore similar to legal nullity, except it has no legal standing.

* The grounds for seeking a Church annulment are similar to those for legal nullity.
* The procedure for gaining a Church annulment is very long and tedious.

> **Church annulment** = Marriage never existed in the eyes of the Catholic Church.
> **Legal nullity** = Marriage never existed in the eyes of the law.

Family Mediation

* When **couples have decided to separate**, they sometimes seek the help of the family mediation service.
* This is a free service which is funded by the Department of Social and Family Affairs.
* A mediator is present who offers support and guidance but has an unbiased approach.
* Mediation services deals with **issues such as children, property and financial division**.
* It enables couples who are willing to communicate and co-operate to make the transition as easy as possible under difficult circumstances.

Separation

Couples seeking separation can do so by either of the following:
* Deed of separation or legal separation.
* Judicial separation.

Deed of Separation or Legal Separation:

* Written legal contract between a couple which clearly indicates the terms of their separation.
* A solicitor will generally draw up the terms of the separation.

* If a couple can agree on terms, they can save on expenses by avoiding court proceedings, which can be quite expensive.

Judicial Separation:

* This type of separation involves the judgment of the court to form a conclusion on the legal rights of separation. Judicial separation is governed by the Judicial Separation Act, 1989.

* A judicial separation is offered when:
  * Normal marital relations have not occurred for at least one year before the application for separation was submitted.
  * Adultery was committed.
  * A couple have not lived together for one year by mutual consent of both parties and where a couple have been living apart for three years when this is not by consent of both parties.
  * A spouse has been deserted for more than one year.

Divorce

* Divorce was first introduced in Ireland in 1996.
* It is governed by the Family Law (Divorce) Act, 1996.
* A divorce is granted when:
  * The couple have lived apart for four of the previous five years.
  * There is no possible chance of reconciliation.
  * Provisions have been made for dependent spouses and children.
* This can also involve areas of child custody and access, property maintenance.

Part Sample Exam Questions

1. List four requirements that are necessary to get married in Ireland. (12)

2. Discuss how people can prepare for marriage. (9)

1. List four requirements that are necessary to get married in Ireland. (12)

   4 points x 3 marks each = 12.

   • Partners must be of the opposite sex. (Same-sex marriages are not permitted in Ireland; however, they are permitted in other countries, such as England, Denmark and certain states in the USA).
   • Both partners must be free to marry, i.e. not married already.
   • Partners must not be too closely related, example, a father may not marry his daughter.
   • The wedding must take place in a recognised place of worship/registry office. Today, people can also apply for temporary registration of a hotel, beach, garden etc.

2. Discuss how people can prepare for marriage. (9)

   3 points x 3 marks each = 9.

Home

Children first learn about marriage at home, where they see first-hand from their parents how a marriage exists. If parents are supportive of each other and make decisions together, children too will follow this pattern. If, however, a child witnesses parents constantly arguing this will follow through in their relationships.

School

In school, students learn about marriage in various subjects. In Home Economics, students examine a variety of aspects relating to marriage, some of which include law and marriage, roles and responsibilities of marriage partners. Marriage is also covered in Religion, SPHE (Social, Personal and Health Education) and RSE (Relationship and Sexuality Education).

Pre-marriage courses

Pre-marriage courses offered by ACCORD and the Marriage and Relationship Counselling Service are a positive option for people preparing for marriage, as they enable a couple to take a practical and honest look at what married life consists of.

The Family as a Caring Unit

53

Family Dynamics

> A **role** is an expected pattern of behaviour.

Family Roles

✱ People occupy roles and every family member has one or more roles to fill.

✱ For example, a teenager could have the roles of son/daughter, brother/sister, friend, pupil.

Role Conflict

✱ This happens when a conflict occurs between the many roles people play. People have expectations that come with their role and if these expectations clash, a role conflict can occur.

✱ This conflict can become a major source of stress.

✱ An example of this might be the expectations parents have of their child compared to the expectations that the child has for itself.

Child's Role	Teenager's Role	Parent's Role	Older Person's Role
• To behave in an acceptable manner. • To show respect to their parents. • To be happy and secure. • To be self-confident. • To know the difference between right and wrong. • To follow rules.	• Teenagers question things in life and challenge their parents' authority. • To fit in with friends – peer pressure. • To do well in school. • To take on extra responsibilities, e.g. part-time job.	• To provide for the physical, emotional and social needs of a child. • To offer guidance and support. • To be a role model to their children. • To discipline children. • To praise, encourage and support their children. • To financially provide for their children.	• To live their life to the best of their ability. • They may play an active role in childminding. • They can be a valuable source of wisdom and guidance to all family members.

Gender Issues in Family Roles

> - The word 'gender' refers to whether a person is male or female.
> - A role is an expected pattern of behaviour.
> - Therefore gender role = an expected pattern of behaviour for males and females

Gender roles have changed over the years and are no longer as stereotyped as they once were, e.g. men cook and clean, women work outside the home.

✱ It can be a slow process to change some stereotypes.

✱ Children imitate their parents and pick up on these gender roles from a young age.

✱ Children's toys are very often gender-orientated, e.g. trucks for boys, dolls for girls.

✱ The duties that children often do around the house are also generally gender-orientated, e.g. girls stay inside and help cook and clean while boys get taken outside to help with fixing the car.

✱ Ideally, there would be no gender roles.

Social and Economic Factors Affecting the Changing Roles in Families

Social Factors	Economic Factors
- The decline of the extended family is very evident. There has been a move away from the extended to the nuclear family.	- More women are now in higher-earning jobs and therefore choose to stay in work while men stay at home.
- Smaller families and shorter working weeks allow parents to spend more time with children.	- There is a better quality of life and standard of living because of better wages. This has resulted in families being able to afford trips aboard or new cars.
- More mothers are working outside the home, which may mean that the husband now stays at home.	- Children have become more financially dependent on their families until later in life, as many young people now continue their education well into their twenties.
- Grandparents and older people live longer, so grandparents take a more active role in childminding duties.	- The state intervenes in a number of the functions of the family, e.g. state benefits.
- Equal and shared roles in families results in both spouses doing household tasks.	- There are a number of welfare entitlements, such as clothing, back to school and fuel allowances and free travel. These entitlements are of great benefit to single-parent families and the elderly.
- The importance of educational achievement has resulted in a highly skilled workforce of men and women. Many women now have highly paid careers.	
- Both parents take an active interest in child rearing. This means both parents contribute to the running of the house and family life, and spending quality time together is seen as very important.	

Rights of the Child within the Family

✻ Every child will enjoy these rights regardless of race, colour, sex, language, religion, political, national or social origin, property, birth or other status.

✻ A child must develop physically, mentally, morally, spiritually and socially in conditions of freedom and dignity.

✻ A child shall enjoy the benefits of social security – the child shall have the right to adequate nutrition, housing, recreation and medical services.

✻ A child who is physically, mentally or socially handicapped will be given the special treatment, education and care required by his or her particular condition.

✻ A child needs love and understanding.

✻ A child is entitled to receive education.

✻ A child in all circumstances is among the first to receive protection and relief.

✻ A child will be protected against all forms of neglect, cruelty and exploitation.

✻ A child will be protected from practices that may foster racial, religious and any other form of discrimination.

Child–Parent Relationship

- A child's relationship with their parents can have a huge impact on them in later life – either positively or negatively.
- A parent's relationship with their children changes over time. Toddlers depend on their parents for physical needs (food, clothing) and mental needs (books, learning toys).
- Many parents are now much more involved in doing activities with their children, resulting in a strong bond forming within the family.
- Discipline is a feature of child-parent relationships. This is a requirement of families where children learn acceptable behaviour.
- Praise, support and encouragement help to provide a stable and happy home life for children. This promotes self-esteem in the child/children.

Teenager–Adult Relationship

- Adolescence is a time of change.
- The relationship between teenager and parent can change.
- The teenage years are a time of questioning and pushing boundaries set by parents.
- This period can be a time of conflict and requires much understanding of each others' role.
- Parents need to recognise and appreciate that their teenage son/daughter is becoming an adult.
- Teenagers also need to appreciate the fact that sometimes 'parents know best'!

Dealing with Conflict

Think of **CHILL** out!

Learning Links Learning Links Learning Links

✻ **Compromise:** A compromise can be reached through good communication on both sides.

✻ **Honesty and openness:** Trust is the basis for all good relationships; it is important that both parties feel safe to talk about any issues.

✻ **Interest** in seeing both sides of the argument. It is important that all people involved understand each other's viewpoint.

✻ **Listening:** Both parties must listen carefully to each other in order to resolve conflict.

Nobody can be heard if two people are talking at the same time.

* **Leave well alone** if necessary. Sometimes, it is best to leave well alone to prevent rash decisions being made.

Importance of Good Communication

* It's a two-way process, enabling all parties to be heard.
* Minor problems can be solved before they develop into bigger ones.
* Communication prevents misunderstandings.
* Everybody should be respected and heard.
* Mutual understanding is necessary.
* A relationship can break down if communication lines are not open.

Generation Conflict

This is a conflict that occurs between different generations.

* Parents seeing their children as 'children': even though the 'children' in question might be grown adults, their parents still treat them as children.
* Conflict may also occur between parents and children in relation of future aspirations, e.g. child might not want to go to college and a parent might insist on this.
* Younger people today often have more liberal views on certain topics, e.g. cohabitation, having children outside marriage, etc.
* Teenagers can become frustrated with their grandparents because they may not be as quick or as sharp as they want.
* Conflict can occur between elderly people and their children when there is a difference of opinion over child rearing.

Importance of Independence for Elderly People in the Family

* Older people have a much longer life expectancy today.
* It's important that older people try to have as much independence as possible.
* The old age pension means that older people are financially independent.
* Free travel gives older people more independence.
* Respect from younger generations ensures that older people feel wanted and this is important for their self-esteem.

The Family Caring for Those with Special Needs

A number of agencies help people with special needs and their families. These include statutory agencies such as the National Disability Authority, the HSE and the Department of Education and Science, and voluntary agencies such as Rehab, Aware and the ISPCC.

Special Physical Needs		
Difficulties	• Lack of mobility. • Lack of independence.	• Dependence on others.
Family Response	• Extra care and attention. • Re-adjusting the home, e.g. making it accessible to wheelchairs. • Trying to give some independence back to the individual.	
Voluntary Support	• Irish Wheelchair Association. • Association of the Deaf. • National Council for the Blind.	• Special Olympics Ireland. • Rehab.

Special Physical Needs		
Statutory Aid	• Providing Rehabilitation Units. • National Disability Authority.	• Grants available to re-adjust the home.

Rehab Group – Voluntary Support

Rehab

Investing in People, Changing Perspectives

Rehab is an independent, non–profit–making organisation working for the social and economic inclusion of people with disabilities and others who are marginalised.

✱ There are 200 centres across Ireland and the UK.

✱ Rehab's role goes beyond providing services that enable their clients to make the most of their skills and talents in the workplace and the wider community.

✱ They are also a leading campaigner for reforms to remove the barriers preventing equal oppor–tunities, particularly for people with disabilities.

✱ Rehab has non–governmental organisation status at the United Nations and has participated in development projects that have benefited women in Kenya as well as hundreds of school children in the South African township of Soweto.

National Disability Authority – Statutory Aid

✱ The National Disability Authority (NDA) is a statutory agency that aims to ensure the rights and entitlements of people with disabilities are protected.

✱ The four main departments of the NDS are:
  • Policy and Public Affairs.
  • Research and Standards Development.
  • Corporate Services.
  • Centre of Excellence in Universal Design.

✱ Members of the NDA include parents with disabilities, parents and carers of people with disabilities and people working the disability field.

Special Mental Needs	
Difficulties	• Addiction: breakdown of family relationships, lies, manipulation, debt, etc. • Depression: low self-esteem. • Schizophrenia: social exclusion, paranoia, confusion, misunderstanding, etc. • Down syndrome: lack of independence, poor access to education, etc.
Family Response	• Providing emotional support. • Communication. • Extra care and attention. • Motivation.
Voluntary Support	• Alcoholics Anonymous. • Down Syndrome Ireland. • Schizophrenia Ireland. • Aware. • Narcotics Anonymous.
Statutory Aid	• Health Service Executive (HSE). • Psychiatric hospitals.

Special Emotional Needs	
Difficulties	• Autism: inability to express emotion, irrational behaviour. • Abuse: leads to an inability to form trusting relationships, feelings of anxiety and worry.
Family Response	• Providing emotional support. • Communication. • Extra care and attention. • Joining support groups.
Voluntary Support	• The HOPE Project. • Women's Aid. • Autism Ireland. • Rape Crisis Centre. • ISPCC.
Statutory Aid	• Health Service Executive (HSE). • Department of Education and Science.

Exam Questions
Higher Level 2007

Questions

'Special needs' refers to a diverse range of needs often caused by a medical, physical, mental or developmental condition or disability.

(Scoil.net)

1. Identify and elaborate on the difficulties that the family unit may experience when a member of the family has special needs. (18)

2. Discuss how a family might respond to the needs of a member who has a disability. (18)

3. Outline the role of the Rehab Group. (12)

Sample Answers

1. Identify and elaborate on the difficulties that the family unit may experience when a member of the family has special needs. (18)

   3 points x 6 marks each = 18.

Special Physical Needs	
Difficulties	• Lack of mobility and difficulties accessing public transport systems and facilities • Lack of independence. • Dependent on others.

Special Mental Needs	
Difficulties	• Addiction: Breakdown of family relationships, lies, manipulation, debt etc. • Depression: Low self-esteem. • Schizophrenia: Social exclusion, paranoia, confusion, misunderstanding, etc. • Down syndrome: Lack of independence, poor access to education, etc.

Special Emotional Needs	
Difficulties	• Autism: Inability to express emotion, irrational behaviour. • Abuse: Leads to an inability to form trusting relationships, feelings of anxiety and worry.

2. Discuss how a family might respond to the needs of a member who has a disability. (20)

4 points x 5 marks each = 20.

Family Response	• Extra care and attention is needed. • Stay at home to look after the individual. • Work with organisations and professionals to assist where possible. • Re-adjusting the home, e.g. making it accessible to wheelchairs. • Ramp access to the house. • Kitchen worktops at a lower level. • Rails beside toilet, bath or shower and raised toilet height. • Wider doorways to allow for a wheelchair. • Door handles, sockets, light switches at lower levels. • A flashing light when the doorbell rings for people with hearing difficulties. • Visually impaired people need alarm bells to inform them of their actions, e.g. level indicators on cups. • Trying to give some independence back to the individual. • Being there to provide emotional support and assistance.

3. Outline the role of the Rehab Group. (12)

3 points x 4 marks each = 12.

• This is an independent, non-profit-making organisation working for social and economic inclusion among people with disabilities and others who are marginalised.

• Rehab's role goes beyond providing services that enable their clients to make the most of their skills and talents in the workplace and the wider community.

• They are also a leading campaigner for reforms to remove the barriers preventing equal opportunities, particularly for people with disabilities.

54 Family Law

Irish Legislation

There are a variety of laws in operation which protect the family as a unit. These include:

* The Family Law (Maintenance of Spouse and Children) Act, 1976.
* The Domestic Violence Act, 1996.
* The Family Home Protection Act, 1976.
* The Judicial Separation Act, 1989.
* The Child Care Act 1991, 1997.
* The Family Law (Divorce) Act, 1996 (see p. 311).

The Family Law (Maintenance of Spouse and Children) Act, 1976

This act specifies that any dependant spouse and dependant children must be financially supported by the other spouse.

* A child is classed as dependant when they are under the age of 18 or below the age of 23 if they are still in full-time education or have a disability.
* Maintenance can be sought even when both spouses live in the same house.
* The sum of maintenance can be agreed by the parties involved and if an agreement can't be reached the sum is calculated by the District Court.
* This sum is calculated under a number of headings, such as the number of children and the parents' earnings.
* A parent is also permitted to apply for maintenance of a child even if the parents aren't married.

The Domestic Violence Act, 1996

This act deals with the protection of the spouse and children when under threat of physical, sexual or mental abuse.

* The partner can apply for a safety order, a protection order or a barring order:
  * **A protection order:** This is a temporary safety order that prevents an individual using violence towards a partner/spouse or children. It is generally given while waiting for a barring order or a safety order. The spouse is permitted to live in the home after this order has been issued.
  * **A safety order:** This prevents an individual from using violence towards a partner/spouse or children. This can last for up to five years.
  * **A barring order:** When issued, a barring order indicates that the abuser must leave the family without returning. This can last for up to period of three years.

The Family Home Protection Act, 1976

This act protects the house being sold or mortgaged without the consent of both spouses.

* The act applies regardless of which spouse owns the house.
* One spouse must have written permission from the other in order to sell the house.

The Judicial Separation Act (1989)

This act was amended by the Family Law Act, 1995.

* This type of separation involves the judgment of the court to form a conclusion to the legal rights of separation.
* A judicial separation is offered when:

- Normal marital relations have not occurred for at least one year before the application for separation was submitted.
- Adultery was committed.
- A couple have not lived together for one year by mutual consent of both parties or have been living apart for three years when it is not the consent of both people.
- When a spouse has been deserted for more than one year.

The Child Care Act 1991, 1997

This act protects the child.

✳ Where abuse has occurred, the Gardaí have the authority to remove the child from the home and place him/her in care.

✳ The health services are also granted permission to remove a child from an abusive home for up to eight days. This right is granted by the Emergency Care Order.

Making a Will

Importance of Making a Will

✳ A person's wishes are carried out.

✳ The executor ensures that the person's wishes are complied with.

✳ Parents ensure that their children are cared for by the people they deem most suitable.

✳ If a will is not made, when a person dies, their estate is dealt with according to the Succession Act, 1965.

The Succession Act, 1965

When an individual dies without making a will, this act provides for the spouse and children of that person.

✳ If there are no children, the spouse gets the entire estate.

✳ If there are children, the spouse get two-thirds of the estate and one-third goes to the children.

✳ If there is no spouse, the entire estate goes to the children.

✳ If there is no spouse and no children, the estate goes to the deceased person's parents.

✳ If there are no parents, the estate goes to deceased person's brothers and sisters.

✳ If there are no brothers or sisters, the estate goes to the next surviving blood relative.

Procedure for Making a Will

Ther stages involved in making a will are:

Stages in Making a Will	Procedure
Stage 1	• Employ a solicitor.
Stage 2	• Make a list of assets to be included in the will, e.g. property, money, etc.

Stages in Making a Will	Procedure
Stage 3	• Make a list of all those who will benefit from the will (include all their contact details).
Stage 4	• Appoint two executors who will carry out the person's wishes.
Stage 5	• Assign the list of estate and assets to those who will benefit from the will.
Stage 6	• Make provisions for funeral arrangements (if an individual has specific requirements).
Stage 7	• The will is signed by the individual and a witness to make it legal.
Stage 8	• The will is kept in a safe place, e.g. a bank.

Note: Changes can be made to the will depending on an individual's life situation, e.g. getting remarried, having children.

Part Exam Question

Question

State how the family is protected by the Family Home Protection Act, 1976. (6)

Answer

2 points x 3 marks each = 6.

This act protects the house being sold or mortgaged without the consent of both spouses.

This act applies regardless of which spouse owns the house. One spouse must have written permission from the other in order to sell the house.

Elective

HOME DESIGN AND MANAGEMENT

1 Housing

2 Designing the House Interior

3 The Energy-Efficient Home

4 Systems and Services

1

2

3

1 Housing

Historical Development of Housing Styles in Ireland from the Nineteenth Century to the Present Day

Early Nineteenth Century

Rural Areas

* Single-storey thatched cottages featured throughout the countryside, and often housed farm labourers. These cottages were small in size with two rooms.

Fig 1.1: Thatched cottage.

* They contained an open turf fire.
* The doorway was a half-door.
* The roof was thatched with straw or reeds.
* Wealthier farmers had two-storey houses that were roofed using slates.
* These houses were large in size with about five rooms, including a drawing room or parlour.
* Wealthier landowners had estate houses with many rooms and servants' quarters.

Urban Areas

The style of architecture that featured at this time is known as the Georgian style.

* This style of house can still be seen in the centre of large towns.
* The walls were made of stone and covered with lime plaster.
* Roofs were slated, and timber floors were a prominent feature.
* The doorway was the main focal point. Doric or Ionic columns framed the doorway, while a fanlight made of iron and glass featured over the door.
* Rooms had high ceilings and decorative mouldings, known as cornices.

Fig 1.2: Doric columns.

* Many of these houses had basements.
* Many urban buildings were tenements: large buildings divided into dwelling spaces for a number of families. The urban working classes lived in tenements.

Fig 1.3: Ionic columns.

* Small terraced houses featured in suburban areas where the middle classes lived.
* Shop owners lived over their shops.

Fig 1.4: Fanlight over door.

Late Nineteenth Century

Rural Areas

* Similar housing styles to the early nineteenth century – small thatched cottages, two-storey houses with slate roofs.

Urban Areas

* A move away from the Georgian style and an introduction of other architectural styles: Gothic, Tudor, formal Italianate, Art Nouveau.
* The Gothic style featured high pitched roofs, pointed windows, arches and doorways.

Fig 1.5: Gothic-style house.

* The Tudor style featured bay windows and detailed plaster facades, which consisted of plaster work with timber framing.

Fig 1.6: Tudor-style house.

* Terraced houses still featured. These had small panel windows, pretty doorways and high pitched roofs.

Early Twentieth Century

Rural Areas

* The Government introduced the rural electrification scheme in 1946 after the Second World War.

* Housing grants were introduced and resulted in changes to the thatched cottages.
* Thatched roofs were replaced with tiles and extra rooms were added to the cottages.
* The emergence of single- and two-storey houses with the cottages used as outhouses.

Urban Areas

* There was a move away from the terraced-style house to detached and semi-detached houses.
* These house styles were built on the outskirts of towns and in suburbs.
* Improvements in building materials emerged:
  * Steel window frames replaced timber ones.
  * Concrete blocks replaced brick and stone.
  * Tiled roofs replaced slate roofs.
* A smaller number of terraced houses were being built.
* Local authority housing schemes began to emerge.
* Commercial and industrial buildings had a modern influence, with flat roofs and horizontal windows.

Late Twentieth Century

Rural Areas

* The bungalow-style house became very popular.
* Styles similar to those found in urban areas were built in rural areas.

Urban Areas

* High-rise apartment blocks began to be built, e.g. the tower blocks of Ballymun in Dublin.
* These tower blocks were built as a solution to housing shortages.
* Private housing estates became very popular.
* Houses were smaller in size and were built on smaller pieces of land.
* Double glazing, fibreglass, PVC (polyvinyl chloride) plastic emerged as new building materials.

Twenty-First Century

Rural Areas

* In rural tourist areas, there has been a shift back to thatched cottages.
* Private sites have enabled individuals to build houses to personal architectural specifications and taste.
* Old houses are being restored and modernised.
* New housing developments have been built in many rural areas.

Urban Areas

* An increase in the number of apartment blocks.
* High-density buildings to maximise the number of people living in a small area.
* Social and affordable housing schemes are evident in many housing developments.

Fig 1.7: A contemporary housing development.

* A mixture of townhouses, duplexes and apartments are all found in one complex.
* Landscaped green areas, shops, chemists and other amenities are included in housing estates.
* Many people are choosing not to move home but to extend and convert the attic in their existing house.

Factors Influencing the Choice of House Style

There are three factors that influence the type of house people choose to live in:

* Social and cultural.
* Economic.
* Environmental.

Social/Cultural Factors

Personal preferences:
- An individual's own likes and dislikes will influence the type of house they choose to live in. For example, a person might prefer a detached house to a townhouse.

Location:
- Where the house is located in relation to schools, work, transport systems, shops and amenities will be a deciding factor.

Availability:
- Where one might like to live might be constrained by what is available in that area.

Size of the house:
- The size of the house needed is most commonly determined by the number of people living in it and what stage of the life cycle they are at. For example:
  - The number of children in a house.
  - The ages of the children.
  - A young couple starting out.
  - A retired couple.

Economic Factors

Finance:
- This has the biggest influence on the type of house a person will choose. What a person wants versus what a person can afford has to be considered.

Sites:
- An individual who is considering building their own home must also pay for a site. The price of sites varies depending on their location.

Hidden costs:
- It is important to be aware that costs for engineers, surveyors, solicitors and stamp duty may also have to be paid.

Investment reality:
- Research into the area and any planned developments should be carried out.
- While there is a slowdown in the market at the moment, it is always hoped that the value of the property will increase.

Environmental Factors

Aspect of the house:
- This refers to the direction the house faces. South-facing houses can benefit from solar panels and thus reduce energy costs. North-facing houses may require larger fuel consumption.

Green areas and amenities:
- An individual's choice of housing style may be influenced by its location near green areas, woodland and parks. New housing developments tend to have green open spaces for their residents to enjoy.

Energy efficiency:
- In order to live sustainably it is important that individuals pay particular attention to the energy efficiency of the house, e.g. insulating the attic, double or triple-glazed windows, energy-efficient appliances, heating and water systems, which can all help to create an energy-efficient house.

Social/Cultural Factors	Economic Factors	Environmental Factors
		Building regulations: • All houses for sale or rent have to have a Building Energy Certificate (BER), which evaluates the energy performance of the building. This is applied throughout the EU under the Energy Performance in Buildings Directive.

Individual Housing Requirements

Single People

✱ Single people require less space than a family.

✱ Bedsits, apartments, house-sharing are all options available to single people.

✱ Access to public transport, college, work and places of entertainment may be determining factors for single people deciding where to live.

✱ Many young people enjoy the benefits of urban living, as many amenities are at hand.

Families

✱ A family's needs and requirements will depend upon the size and composition of the family, i.e. how many children there are, if any; the life stages the children are at and any special needs.

✱ As children get older, many like the benefits of having their own room and personal space.

✱ Plenty of storage is needed for families – wardrobe space in bedrooms, lockers, chests of drawers, hot press and kitchen units all solve the storage problem.

✱ Adequate space for the general day-to-day activities of a family is needed – kitchen, living room space.

✱ A garden is often preferable for families so that children and parents can enjoy more space.

✱ Teenagers studying for exams may require a quiet study area.

✱ The location of the house for a family in terms of local amenities, schools and shops may be a determining factor.

Elderly People

Fig 1.8: An elderly woman in an adapted home.

✱ As people get older, they may become less mobile and have difficulty climbing stairs. Single-storey houses may therefore be a better option for elderly people.

✱ Elderly people may be more accident prone, therefore non-slip flooring, handrails beside the toilet in the shower and in the bath are necessary.

✱ Good lighting in the home will help prevent falls.

* A good heating system in the house is necessary to prevent illness.
* Security is of paramount importance for elderly people, especially for those living on their own. An alarm system is a good investment to provide peace of mind.
* Large gardens or big grounds can be difficult for an elderly person to maintain – a small garden or patio area may be a better option.
* It is sensible for elderly people to live near shops, post offices, church and banks for easy access and independence.
* Many elderly people prefer the option of living in their own homes; however, sheltered housing schemes and institutional care may be a better alternative for some individuals.

People with Disabilities

* A person's specific disability will affect their housing requirements, e.g. an individual who uses a wheelchair may require wider doorways.
* Other requirements may include repositioning wall-mounted light switches, lower counter tops for easier accessibility, an adapted bathroom with handrails and a raised toilet seat.
* People who are visually impaired may have alarm bells that sound for level indicators.
* Flashing lights instead of a doorbell to indicate a presence at the door can be useful for people with hearing difficulties.

Homeless People

* The basic physical needs are food, clothing and shelter. Homeless people lack the basic need of shelter.
* Many live on the streets or in hostel accommodation.

* A lack of privacy and security issues are of great concern to people who are homeless.
* Toilet facilities, showering and changing areas are of concern for this group of people.
* Temporary accommodation can be sought through local authorities and organisations such as Focus Ireland, Threshold and the Simon Community.

Sample Exam Question
Higher Level (2004)

Question

1. (a) Describe the changes that occurred in housing styles in the nineteenth century. (15)
   (b) Outline the housing requirements for a retired elderly person with mobility difficulties. (10)

(c) Outline (i) the social; (ii) the cultural; and (iii) the environmental factors that influence the choice of housing styles. (15)

Sample Answer

1. (a) Describe the changes that occurred in housing styles in the nineteenth century. (15)

15 marks = 5 points x 3 marks each.

Early Nineteenth Century
Rural Areas
- Single-storey thatched cottages featured throughout the countryside, and often housed farm labourers. These cottages were small in size with two rooms. They contained an open turf fire. The doorway was a half door. The roof was thatched with straw or reeds.
- Wealthier farmers had two-storey houses, which were roofed with slates. These houses were large in size with about five rooms, including a drawing room or parlour. Wealthier landowners had estate houses with many rooms and servants' quarters.

Urban Areas
- The style of architecture that featured at this time is known as the Georgian style. This style of houses can still be seen in the centre of large Irish towns. The walls were made from stone and covered with lime plaster.
- Roofs were slated, and timber floors were a prominent feature of this house style. The doorway was the main focal point of these houses with Doric or Ionic columns framing the doorway and a fanlight made of iron and glass above the door.

Late Nineteenth Century
Rural Areas
- Similar housing styles to the early nineteenth century, small thatched cottages, two-storey houses with slate roofs.

Urban Areas
- A move away from the Georgian style and an introduction of other architectural styles – Gothic, Tudor, formal Italianate, Art Nouveau. The Gothic style featured high pitched roofs, pointed windows, arches and doorways. The Tudor style featured bay windows, detailed plaster facades that consisted of plaster work with timber framing.
- Terraced houses still featured – these houses had small panel windows, pretty doorways and high pitched roofs.

1. **(b)** Outline the housing requirements for a retired elderly person with mobility difficulties. (10)

5 points x 2 marks each = 10 marks.

- As people get older, they may become less mobile and have difficulty climbing stairs. Single-storey houses may therefore be a better option for elderly people.
- Elderly people may be more accident prone, therefore non-slip flooring, handrails beside the toilet in the shower and in the bath are necessary.
- Good lighting in the home will help prevent falls. A good heating system in the house is necessary to prevent illness.
- Large gardens or big grounds can be difficult for an elderly person to maintain – a small garden or patio area may be better.
- It is sensible for elderly people to live near shops, post offices, church and banks for easy access and independence.

1. **(c)** Outline (i) the social; (ii) the cultural; and (iii) the environmental factors that influence the choice of housing styles. (15)

5 marks x 3 headings = 15 marks.

Evaluation of Housing Provision in Ireland

Distribution of Housing

✱ Owner occupation continues to be the most prevalent housing occupancy status.

✱ Ireland's home ownership figures are presently at 75–82 per cent, which is one of the highest in the EU.

✱ The number of owner-occupied dwellings increased by 10.2 per cent between 2002 and 2006.

✱ Government policy has focused its support to homeowners on low incomes through measures including a range of social and affordable housing initiatives and tax relief on mortgage interest.

✱ Apartment, flat and bedsit occupancy increased by 1.4 per cent between 2002 and 2006.

✱ Nearly one in four Dublin city dwellers live in an apartment, flat or bedsit.

Urban Distribution of Housing	Rural Distribution of Housing
• The combined population of Dublin, Cork, Limerick, Galway and Waterford cities including their suburbs increased by 4.2 per cent between 2002 and 2006 compared with an increase of 8.2 per cent at national level.	• Smaller towns and villages had an overall population increase of one-fifth between 2002 and 2006. • These towns are dispersed throughout Ireland with 59 in Leinster, 40 in Munster, 16 in Connacht and 16 in Ulster.

Quality of Accommodation

✳ Building laws and regulations have resulted in good-quality homes being built.

✳ The Homebond Guarantee Scheme and the Building Regulations Act 1991 are two such examples of regulations that have resulted in better standards for newly built houses.

✳ The Housing Regulations Act 1996 protects people in rented accommodation and stipulates that all rented properties have to be registered with the local authority.

✳ If rented accommodation isn't registered, it can result in penalties of up to €1,270 and €127 for every day thereafter until the property is registered.

✳ Rented properties must:
  ● Be in good structural repair.
  ● Have good ventilation and heating.
  ● Have a safe, reliable gas and electricity supply that in no way presents any danger to health.
  ● Have adequate lighting.
  ● Have at least one toilet and bath/shower for use between two flats.

✳ The Residential Tenancies Act 2004 sets out the minimum standards required for rented accommodation.

✳ This act puts the landlord and tenant relationship on a more professional footing.

✳ This act stipulates that landlords must register with the Private Residential Tenancies Board (PRTB) for a fee of €70.

✳ Average weekly rents paid for furnished or partly furnished private accommodation ranged in the 2006 census from nearly €275 in Dún Laoghaire/Rathdown to less than €115 in Donegal and Leitrim.

Comparative Costs of Buying and Renting

✳ There are substantial differences between renting and buying.

✳ Renting is generally a cheaper option, however rent is often seen as 'dead money' because the accommodation is never owned.

✳ Buying a property is a good investment, however it incurs many costs. Sound financial planning should be undertaken before buying a property.

Differences between Renting and Buying a Property

Renting a House	Buying a House
Initial Costs ● Letting agency fee (this applies if a person goes through a letting agent to find the accommodation).	**Initial Costs** ● A deposit which is usually 10 per cent of the purchase price. A bigger deposit may be needed if a person cannot secure a 90 per cent loan.

Renting a House	**Buying a House**
• A deposit; the norm is to pay the landlord one month's deposit with the first month's rent.	• Lending agency fees, e.g. application fee, survey fee and an indemnity bond, if the mortgage is more than 80 per cent of the value of the house.
Continuous Costs	• Legal fees of 1–2 per cent of the purchase price of the property, fees for land searches and land registry fees.
• Weekly/monthly rent payments.	• Stamp duty on new and second-hand houses/apartments over €317,500 for first-time buyers and over €127,001 for owner occupiers.
• Household bills, such as electricity, heating, telephone and television.	
• Maintenance charges for the upkeep of the grounds in apartment blocks, bin charges, etc.	**Continuous Costs**
	• Mortgage repayments.
	• Mortgage protection policy.
	• House insurance for buildings and contents.
	• Furniture, appliances and home furnishings.
	• Household bills, such as electricity, heating, telephone and television.
	• Maintenance charges for residents' associations to provide for the upkeep of shared green areas, bin charges, etc.

Note: Negative equity occurs when the value of the house drops to a point where the home-owner owes a mortgage that is higher than the value of the house.

Adequacy of Housing Provision

✱ The building boom of the Celtic tiger period has now slowed down.

✱ At the height of the Celtic tiger era, demand for houses far exceeded supply.

✱ Despite the expansion of the housing stock over the past fifteen years, the number of dwellings per 1,000 of the population is the lowest in the EU at 330 compared to the EU average of 437.

✱ In the present economic climate, house prices have reduced and there is now more choice for buyers.

✱ The Permanent TSB/ESRI House Price Index of 30 May 2008 showed that the average national house prices fell by 1.1 per cent in April 2008. This followed similar reductions in March, February and January. In the first four months of 2008, average national prices fell by 3.3 per cent.

✱ It is expected that the level of house completions will gradually reduce to an annual rate of 50,000 between 2006 and 2011.

✱ Increasing numbers of people are on the waiting lists of local authorities throughout the country.

✱ The information compiled in the Housing Needs Assessment of 2005 indicated that 43,684 households were in need of social housing.

✱ The total number of elderly people on the waiting list in the 2005 assessment was 1,727 and there were 480 disabled persons waiting.

✱ The number of dwellings rented privately from a voluntary body stood at 13.4 per cent of total dwellings in 2006.

Social Housing Provision

Social housing is provided for by the local authority, voluntary housing organisations and co-operative housing associations.

Local Authority Housing	Voluntary Housing	Co-operative Housing

• A local authority provides housing for people who cannot afford to get a mortgage from a lending institution.
• There is generally a long waiting list of people trying to get local authority housing – demand exceeds supply.
• In order to be eligible an individual must show:
  – That they are in need of housing.
  – That they can't provide the means to get a house themselves.
  – That they are unable to get a mortgage from a lending institution.
  – That their income falls below a certain threshold.
  – Whether or not they have any dependents and if so how many.
  – Whether or not they have any special requirement, e.g. wheelchair accessibility.
• Local authority housing schemes include:
  – Rental subsidy scheme.
  – Local authority loans for house purchase.
  – Tenant purchase scheme.
  – Shared ownership scheme.
  – Mortgage allowance scheme.
  – Affordable housing scheme. See pp. 258–9.
	• This is provided by non-profit organisations.
	• They are approved by the Department of the Environment, Heritage and Local Government.
	• Accommodation is provided for people who are on a low income, the elderly or disabled.
	• Examples of voluntary housing organisations include Respond, the Salvation Army, the Iveagh Trust.

	• Funding is available under two schemes:
	  – **Capital Assistance Scheme:** Local authorities provide funding towards the capital costs of accommodation to meet the needs of those with special needs such as elderly, disabled or homeless people, or small families.
	  – **Rental Subsidy Scheme**: Under this scheme, voluntary housing bodies provide housing for renting, particularly to meet the needs of low-income families.
		• These are non-profit housing organisations working to relieve housing needs for community benefit.
		• Co-operative housing options include:
		  – **Home-Ownership Building Co-operatives:** These are group schemes of dwellings available for purchase by members who are financially capable of doing so.
		  – **Rental Housing Co-Operatives:** Families and single people share responsibility for the upkeep and care of housing estates/apartment blocks.
		  – **Co-ownership Housing Co-operatives:** There is an ownership stake with a management system for common areas. This involves shared equity/ joint ownership by members.

Provision of Local Amenities and Services

Schools

✳ The building of new schools is sanctioned by the Department of Education and Science.

✳ The number of children in an area will determine if a new school will be built.

Shops

✳ These are provided when there is a demand in an area for such a service.

✳ These are provided as a business opportunity.

Community Centres

✳ These are part-financed by the Department of the Environment, Heritage and Local Government.

✳ Fundraising by members of the community helps towards the remaining building costs.

✳ Community centres are used for many community-based events.

Transport

✳ Transport systems are provided by the Department of the Environment and set out under the National Development Plan (NDP).

✳ Transport 21 is an example of the transport infrastructure planned by the government. From 2006 to 2015, €34 billion will be invested in Ireland's national roads, railways, buses and regional airports.

Fig 1.9: The LUAS.

Play Areas

✳ Green open spaces must be included in all plans for new housing estates.

Street Lighting

✳ Street lighting is provided by the local authority in the area in conjunction with the ESB.

✳ These lights are sensor controlled, i.e. they are light-sensitive and operate when there is insufficient natural light.

Refuse Collection

✳ Refuse is collected either by the local authority in the area or by a private company.

✳ A set fee is paid or payment is calculated on the number of collections per year or the weight of refuse collected.

Sample Exam Questions

Questions

1. Differentiate between voluntary housing and co-operative housing. (10)

2. Give an account of the comparative costs of buying or renting a place to live. (15)

3. Describe the adequacy of housing provision in Ireland today. (15)

1. Differentiate between voluntary housing and co-operative housing. (10)

5 points x 2 marks = 10

Voluntary Housing

- This is provided by non-profit organisations. They are approved by the Department of the Environment, Heritage and Local Government.
- Accommodation is provided for people who are on low incomes, the elderly or disabled. Examples of voluntary housing organisations include Respond, the Salvation Army, the Iveagh Trust.
- Funding is available under two schemes:
- **Capital Assistance Scheme**: Local authorities provide funding towards the capital costs of accommodation to meet the needs of those with special needs, such as elderly, disabled or homeless people, or small families.
- **Rental Subsidy Scheme**: Under this scheme, voluntary housing bodies provide housing to rent, particularly to meet the needs of low-income families.

Co-operative Housing Schemes:

- These are non-profit housing organisations working to relieve housing needs for community benefit.
- Co-operative housing options include:
- **Home-ownership Building Co-operatives**: These are group schemes of dwellings available for purchase by members who are financially capable.
- **Rental Housing Co-operatives**: Families and single people share responsibility for the upkeep and care of housing estates/apartment blocks.

- **Co-ownership Housing Co-operatives**: There is an ownership stake with management system for common areas. This involves shared equity/joint ownership by members where there is shared responsibility for upkeep and care of estates/apartment blocks.

2. Give an account of the comparative costs of buying or renting a place to live. (15)

5 points x 3 marks each = 15

Buying: Initial Costs

- Deposit: This is usually 10 per cent of the purchase price. A bigger deposit may be needed if a person cannot secure a 90 per cent loan.
- Lending agency fees, including application fee, survey fee and an indemnity bond if the mortgage is more than 80 per cent of the value of the house.
- Legal fees of 1–2 per cent of the purchase price of the property, fees for land searches and land registry fees.
- Stamp duty on new and second-hand houses/apartments over €317,500 for first-time buyers and over €127,001 for owner occupiers.

Buying: Continuous Costs

- Mortgage repayments.
- Mortgage protection policy.
- House insurance for buildings and contents.
- Furniture, appliances and home furnishings.
- Household bills, such as electricity, heating, telephone and television.
- Maintenance charges if residents' associations form to provide for the

House Building and Design

The location where an individual decides to build their own home and the type of house style are two very important considerations.

Choice of Location

Site:

Is a rural site or an urban site preferred?

Cost of the Site:

✳ The location of the site will affect its price.
✳ Urban sites are generally more expensive than rural ones. Very few urban sites are available to buy for private residential use.

Site Orientation:

Orientation refers to the aspect of the site, i.e. whether it faces north, south, east or west. Sites should ideally be slightly sloping for good drainage, with easy access to water, sewerage and roads.

Proximity to Services and Amenities:

The site's proximity to work, schools, shops, transport will affect the decision to locating a property there.

Planning Permission:

During the investigatory stages prior to purchasing a site, it is important to make enquiries regarding planning permission. The planning office of the local authority in the area can give details regarding residential and commercial projects for the next five to ten years in their area.

Building Regulations:

Further investigation into the building stipulations and restrictions should be undertaken, as this will have an affect on housing style.

Choice of Housing Style

Budget:

The amount of money that an individual has at their disposal will affect the size and house type that will be built, e.g. 140 square metre (1,500 square foot) house, 280 square metre (3,000 square foot) house, bungalow, two-storey, dormer house.

Personal Preference:

An individual's personal taste regarding the style of house, the interior layout, the exterior of the house will all affect the house style.

Building Regulations:

Planning offices in a local authority will have a list of guidelines and restrictions regarding the building of houses, for example, the size of the windows, the exterior finish. Some restrictions may only apply to certain areas, e.g. height restriction in an area where the majority of houses already built are bungalows.

The Site and its Location:

✳ The location of the site and its orientation will impact on the choice of house style. The design of the house should fit in with the surrounding environment.

Planning Permission

There are two types of planning permission: outline planning permission and full planning permission.

Outline Planning Permission	Full Planning Permission

• This is used to see if the planning authority agrees in principle to a house being built on a particular site.
 	
• An individual is required to produce the plans and particulars that are necessary to enable the planning authority to make a decision in relation to the site, layout or other proposals for development.
 	
• Full planning permission will have to be received before building work starts.
 	
• Outline planning permission has a three-year duration.
	• You apply for planning permission by filling in an application form and submitting it with the required documents to your local authority. The other documents are:
	  – A location map.
	  – Site or layout plan.
	  – Copies of public notices (newspaper and site).
	  – A plan showing the position of a site notice.
	  – The appropriate fee. The current fee for an application to build a house is €65; the fee for a house extension or the conversion of a garage is €34.

SAMPLE NEWSPAPER NOTICE

WATERFORD CITY COUNCIL

I John Smith intend to apply for permission for one house at New Road, Hillview, Waterford.

The planning application may be inspected, or purchased at a fee not exceeding the reasonable cost of making a copy, at the offices of the Planning Authority (Wallace House, Maritana Gate, Canada Street, Waterford), during its public opening hours (9am to 4 pm). A submission or observation in relation to the application may be made in writing to the planning authority on payment of the prescribed fee (€20) within the period of 5 weeks beginning on the date of receipt by the authority of the application.

Fig 1.10: Public notice in newspaper of application for planning permission.

Fig 1.11: Site notice.

Procedure for Planning Permission

* Before making an application, a person must give a public notice of their proposals.
* This must be done by placing a notice in a locally circulating newspaper and putting up a site notice that can be clearly read.
* The application must be received by the local authority within two weeks of the notice appearing in the local newspaper and the erection of the site notice.
* The site notice must remain in place for at least five weeks from the date of receipt of the planning application.
* Anyone can see a copy of the application and on payment of a fee of €20 can make a written submission/observation on it.
* If the local authority decides to give planning permission, a notice of intention to award planning permission is given.
* If no one appeals the decision to An Bord Pleanála within four weeks of the date of this decision, the individual will get a grant of permission from the local authority.

* If the local authority refuses an application, it will give the reasons.
* An individual then has four weeks from the date of the rejection decision to appeal to An Bord Pleanála.
* Bye-law approval: This may be required for some extensions and outer buildings, e.g. sheds. Bye-laws ensure that any buildings are constructed to a high standard and ensure the safety of those who use them.

Note: It is an offence to carry out any work that requires planning permission before planning permission is received and the offence can carry very heavy fines and imprisonment. However, if a genuine mistake has been made, it is possible to apply for planning permission to retain any unauthorised development. This permission may be refused, in which case the unauthorised development may have to be demolished.

Professional Assistance when Designing and Building a Property

Professional Help	Function
Architect	• Provides advice on the site, design, costs and building regulations. • Creates the designs for the housing style. • May make planning applications. • May advise on building contractors.
Book of House Plans	• These are books which contain house plans of various styles. • These books give prospective individuals who are building a house ideas regarding styles, floor plans, house layout, etc. • Websites also offer house plans that can be purchased online. • All of these plans can be modified to suit an individual's needs and tastes. • These house plans are a cheaper alternative to employing an architect.
Engineer	• Will oversee the whole building project. • Provides advice on the structure of the house. • Provides advice on measures to rectify any potential building problems.
Surveyor	• Carries out a survey of the site. • The lending institution receives the survey report from the surveyor. • Identifies any potential problems that may occur and provides proactive advice on how to solve them.

Professional Help	Function
Builder	• Provides a contract that must be signed by both parties detailing starting date, finishing date, price, etc. • Responsible for site preparation, construction and finishing of the house. • Specialists may be employed or subcontracted to work on areas in the house such as plumbing and tiling.
Solicitor	• Provides advice in relation to planning permission, building regulations, title deeds and rights of way. • Provides the legal expertise in relation to house building.

Designing a House

The factors to consider when designing a house include: aesthetics, family requirements, the environment, ergonomics, costs and technological developments.

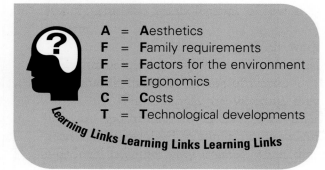

A = **A**esthetics
F = **F**amily requirements
F = **F**actors for the environment
E = **E**rgonomics
C = **C**osts
T = **T**echnological developments

Learning Links Learning Links Learning Links

Aesthetics

* The design of the house should be visually appealing.
* It should complement the surrounding area.
* Consideration should be given to the aspect of the house to ensure windows are positioned to maximise the amount of natural light.
* The exterior finish of the house, e.g. stone-clad, red brick, pebble dash, painted, etc., should also be considered.
* Interior room layouts should be well planned, as should any garden areas.

Family Requirements

* The number of people in the family and their stage in the life cycle should be taken into account.
* The larger the family size, the bigger the house that may be required.
* Consideration should also be given to whether there is a need for nurseries, playrooms, study areas, downstairs bedroom and toilet.
* Specific house designs will have to be incorporated into house plans for individuals with special needs, such as wider doorframes, light switches at appropriate levels, and bedroom and toilet facilities on the ground floor.
* The possibility of future attic conversions, garage space, conservatories or sun lounges should also be taken into account.
* A safe outdoor area for family members to enjoy could also be planned at this stage.

Factors for the Environment

Environmental Factors	Energy Efficiency
• Environmentally friendly materials such as stone and wood should be used.	• Double-glazed windows retain heat in the house.

Environmental Factors	Energy Efficiency
• An investigation into solar panels and other renewable energy options could be carried out. • Strict adherence to guidelines regarding sewage storage should be followed to minimise the risk of water contamination. • Planting trees can help shelter the house from the wind.	• Insulation should be used throughout the house to prevent heat loss and reduce heating costs. • Insulating the roof, cavity walls, windows, etc. can all be done to greatly reduce fuel emissions from the house. • The use of timers and thermostats can help make the house more energy efficient. • Zoned heating systems enable specific areas of the house to be heated, further reducing energy costs. • A lagging jacket on the hot water cylinder will reduce excess heating costs.

Ergonomics

✱ Ergonomics is the study of people in their environment and should be considered when designing the house.

✱ An ergonomically sound house is one that enables movement for all the members of the household.

✱ Ease of access into and around the house ensures that accidents are reduced and people are not colliding with each other. For example, kitchen design uses the idea of the work triangle (an imaginary triangle between the fridge, the sink and the cooker, the three most used objects in the kitchen.

✱ Storage space, counter top heights, table and chair choices should all be considered from an ergonomic point of view.

Costs (Initial and Maintenance)

✱ The amount of money an individual has to spend will influence the design of the house in terms of size and style.

✱ Extra features, such as exterior finishes, solar panels, under-floor heating, etc., will add to the initial costs.

✱ Solicitors' fees, architects' costs, surveyors' fees, etc. must all be taken into account.

✱ The site, labour costs, building materials, painting, decorating, furniture, fittings and landscaping must all form part of the budget as initial outlay.

✱ Further costs will need to be considered and budgeted for, for example mortgage repayments, mortgage protection policy, household bills and garden maintenance.

Technological Developments

✱ Examples of technological advances in house building and design include:
  • Computer-aided design (CAD) for drawing plans and house designs gives a realistic image of what the finished house will look like.
  • Virtual reality tours of room layouts.
  • Security systems.
  • Electronic gates.
  • Sensor lights, solar-powered garden lights.
  • Thermostat controls.
  • Entertainment systems.
  • Zoned heating systems.
  • Easy to clean appliances, e.g. stainless steel work surfaces, reduce maintenance.

✱ Technology is changing all the time and can be used in a wide variety of ways.

Regulation of House Building Standards

Regulation	Function

Buildings Regulations Act, 1991	• This act sets down standards regarding:
	  – Construction. – Insulation.
	  – Structural stability. – Drains and sewage systems.
	  – Heating. – Windows.
	  – Ventilation. – Weather and fire resistance.
	  – Lighting.
	• These regulations ensure the safety and well-being of the occupants of a house.
	• Local authorities must enforce these regulations.

Home Bond Certificate	• This is also known as the National House Building Guarantee Scheme. • It is operated by the National House Building Guarantee Company and the Department of the Environment, Heritage and Local Government. • Under this scheme, builders pay a fee to register each house that they build. • After this, the house will be inspected three times during its construction by a department official. • A Homebond Certificate is issued only when the building complies with the regulations set down in the scheme. • The certificate protects the consumer against any major structural faults to the house for a ten-year period. • If a fault does develop during this time, it will be rectified free of charge by the builder. • Most lending agencies require that new homes for purchase are covered with a Homebond Certificate. • It's important to note that if the builder goes out of business during this time, the deposit for the house is returned to the purchaser.
Floor Area Compliance Certificate (FACC)	• When a house/apartment is provided for sale and is within the specified floor area limit (not less than 38 square metres and not more than 125 square metres), the developer/vendor must obtain a FACC to enable the purchaser to obtain stamp duty exemption. • This certificate also confirms that the house complies with the standards of construction set down by the Minister for the Environment, Heritage and Local Government in the Housing Regulations 2004.

Gaeltacht Area House Grant	• Grants are available in Ireland to build new homes and improve certain existing homes to qualifying applicants in Gaeltacht areas.
	• Grants also apply to certain islands off the coast, e.g. The Aran Islands.
	• The following are the maximum rates available:
	  – Mainland = €5,100.
	  – Designated islands = €15,300.
	• This grant is the responsibility of the Department of Community, Rural and Gaeltacht Affairs.

Designing the House Interior

2

Good design is one that combines both the elements and principles of design.

Elements of Design	Principles of Design
• Colour. • Pattern. • Texture.	• Balance. • Emphasis. • Proportion. • Rhythm.

Elements of Design

Colour

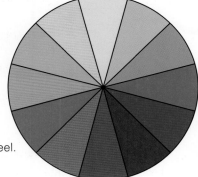

Fig 2.1: Colour wheel.

Primary colours:

✳ Red, yellow and blue.
✳ These are colours that cannot be made by mixing any other colours together.

Secondary colours:

✳ Primary colour + primary colour.
  • Red + Yellow = Orange.
  • Red + Blue = Purple.
  • Yellow + Blue = Green.
✳ Colours that are made when two primary colours are mixed together.

Tertiary colours:

✳ Primary colour + secondary colour.
  • Red + Purple = Mauve.
  • Blue + Green = Turquoise.
✳ Colours that are made when a primary colour and a secondary colour are mixed together.

Classification of Colours

Warm Colours	Cool Colours	Pastel Colours	Neutral Colours
• Red • Pink • Orange	• Green • Blue	• Lemon • Lilac • Baby pink • Duck egg blue	• White • Cream • Beige

Different Types of Colour Scheme

There are four basic types of colour scheme.

Neutral

This colour scheme refers to the use of neutral colours in a room, e.g. white, cream and beige.

Fig 2.2: Neutral colour scheme in a living room.

Contrasting

This colour scheme refers to using colours on the opposite side of the colour wheel, e.g. red and green.

Fig 2.3: Contrasting colour scheme in a kitchen.

Harmonious

This refers to using colours that lie next to each other on the colour wheel, e.g. purple and red.

Fig 2.4: Harmonious colour scheme in a bedroom.

Monochromatic

✳ This colour scheme refers to shades and tints of the one colour, e.g. dark pink, pink, light pink.

Fig 2.5: Monochromatic colour scheme in a living room.

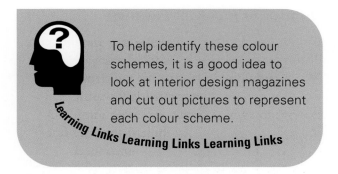
Planning a Colour Scheme for a Home

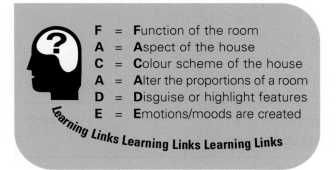
Function of the Room:

Consider what the exact function of the room is. This will have a direct impact on the choice of colours. For example, a bedroom is required for rest and relaxation; too many strong colours could have the opposite effect.

Aspect of the House:

The aspect refers to the direction a house faces. North-facing rooms don't get as much sunlight and therefore warm colours can be used here. South-facing rooms can use cooler colours as they get a lot of sunlight.

Colour Scheme of the House:

It is important to consider the whole house and not to decorate rooms in isolation. Colour schemes should blend with each other to create harmony throughout the whole house.

Alter the Proportions of a Room:

Colour can be used cleverly to visually alter the proportions of a room.

Fig 2.6: Light colour used on a ceiling.

✱ Light colours make a room appear larger. A light colour on a ceiling makes the ceiling appear higher.

Fig 2.7: Dark colour used on a ceiling.

✱ Dark colours make objects seem nearer. A dark colour on a ceiling makes the ceiling appear lower.

Fig 2.8: Warm colour on all walls in the room.

✱ Warm colours make a room feel smaller and cosier.

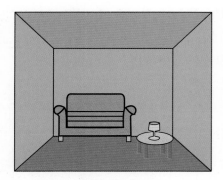

Fig 2.9: Cool colours on one wall to make the wall seem further away.

✱ Cool colours make objects seem further away.

Pattern

✱ Pattern means decorative designs used to create interest in a room.
✱ Patterns can be found on wallpaper, curtains, carpets, cushions, bedspreads, etc.

Disguise or Highlight Features:

Colour can be used in a room to highlight certain features, e.g. alcoves or cornicing.
✱ Colour can also be used to disguise certain features, e.g. radiators.

Emotions/Moods are Created:

Colour has a huge impact on creating mood and therefore on our emotions. Pastel colours like baby pink, dusty blue and lemon can be relaxing and restful.

Type of Pattern	Description/Use
Floral	• This refers to a pattern based on flowers.
Stripes *(photograph)* **Fig 2.10:** Striped curtains.	• Stripes can be vertical, horizontal or diagonal. • Vertical stripes create an illusion of height. • Horizontal stripes create an illusion of width.
Checks *(photograph)* **Fig 2.11:** Checked curtains.	• This refers to coloured squares on a background. • Examples of check patterns include black and white, red and white, pink and white.

Type of Pattern	Description/Use
Small Patterns	• Mini-patterned designs are best suited to small rooms.
Bold Patterns	• Large-patterned designs are best suited to large rooms.
Geometric 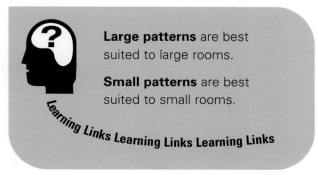 Fig 2.12: Geometric pattern.	• This refers to the use of strong, bold contrasting colours in geometric shapes, such as triangles, squares or circles.

Using Pattern in a Room

The Size of a Room:

The size of the room will influence the size and style of patterns to be used. Too much pattern in a room can make the room appear cluttered.

The Function of a Room:

What is the room going to be used for? Pattern can provide character to a room or define a certain area of the room, e.g. pattern used in a nursery.

The Colour Scheme of a Room:

A harmonious room should be created with a sufficient blend of colour and pattern. Too much of either can have a fussy effect.

The Style of the Room:

Is the desired look going to be contemporary, rustic, antique, etc?

Large patterns are best suited to large rooms.

Small patterns are best suited to small rooms.

Learning Links Learning Links Learning Links

Texture

Texture refers to the feel or touch of an object or surface.

✱ Texture can be soft, smooth, rough, cold, fluffy, etc.

Rough Textures	Smooth Textures
• Examples include rugs, carpets and upholstery fabrics. • These create cosiness and warmth.	• Examples include glass, mirrors, stainless steel. • These create a clean, streamlined effect.

Using Texture in a Room

✱ It is best to use a combination of rough and smooth textures to create a pleasing atmosphere.

✱ A room that uses one type of texture can appear bland.

✱ Kitchen and bathrooms, however, generally have a lot of smooth surfaces for hygiene reasons. Rough texture can be added to these rooms with towels.

✱ A living room is an example of where rough and smooth textures can be used side by side, e.g. a glass mirror, a wooden floor, a rug and curtains.

✱ It is important to note that smooth textures reflect light and sound while rough textures absorb light and sound. For example, notice the difference in noise between walking on a timber floor and walking over a carpeted area.

Fig 2.13: Living room with lots of textures.

Principles of Design

There are four main principles of design:
✱ Balance.
✱ Emphasis.
✱ Proportion.
✱ Rhythm.

Balance

✱ This refers to the relationship between colour, pattern and texture.

✱ No single feature should dominate.

✱ The elements of design should be in harmony with each other.

✱ Three arrangements of balance in a room include:

• **Symmetrical balance:** This occurs when one side of an object is a mirror image of the other, e.g. a vase on each side of the mantelpiece. This is the most popular arrangement.

• **Asymmetrical balance:** This occurs when a lack of balance is used on purpose, e.g. two candlesticks on one side of the mantelpiece and nothing on the other side. This is becoming a very popular arrangement.

• **Radial balance:** This occurs when a design is used on one object only, e.g. a border on a mirror.

Fig 2.14: Asymmetrical balance: Mantelpiece with objects on only one side.

Emphasis

* This refers to drawing particular attention to one item in a room.
* It is often the focal point of a room.
* Emphasis adds interest to a room.

Factors that Influence Interior Design Choices

Aesthetics and Comfort

* It is important that a room looks appealing and is comfortable.
* An individual's personal taste will influence the room's visual appeal.
* Trends in colour, pattern and texture may have a bearing on the style of the room.
* It is important to be aware of changing trends and that some trends may date very quickly. It may be more appropriate to stick to something that won't date very quickly. The addition of accessories to a room, such as cushions, candles, etc., can be used to add these trends at a lesser cost.
* The actual purpose of the room should be considered and the comfort factor taken into account, e.g. an office space in a house requires good lighting and heating, also the office desk and chair should be at the correct

* Examples include the fireplace, a mirror and a piece of art.

Proportion

* This refers to how pieces of furniture relate to one another. For example, breakfast bar stools should be the correct height for the breakfast counter; a coffee table should be the correct height for the couch.
* It also refers to how the furniture relates to the size and scale of the room. For example, furniture that is too big would clutter a small room.

Rhythm

* This refers to the flow and movement in a room.
* It involves linking colour, pattern and texture together.
* An example of this might be the rhythmic use of a colour throughout a room, e.g. picking up the colour teal green in the curtains, cushions and a picture.

height, the chair should be supportive to prevent back strain.

Ergonomics

* This is the term used to describe the study of people in their environment.
* The design of a room should allow for easy movement, efficiency and access, e.g. a kitchen should contain the work triangle. This is an imaginary triangle between the cooker, the fridge and the sink and nothing should interfere with it.

Family Size and Circumstances

* A family's size, stages in the life cycle and the special circumstances of any family member need to be considered when designing a house's interior.

- A large family will require more space for living, storage and ease of movement.
- As children get older, they may want and need their own space and perhaps their own rooms and areas for study.
- Older members of the family may require a downstairs bedroom for easier access than climbing the stairs.
- Consideration should be given to the materials used in the home, e.g. non-slip rugs, stain-resistant work surfaces.
- Any member of a family with special needs will have their own specific requirements, e.g. wheelchair access, the positioning of light switches at a more appropriate level, lower counter tops, specially adapted taps, etc.

Cost

- The amount of money available will have an impact on the interior design of the home.
- A limited budget does not mean a poor interior design.
- Clever and wise shopping can ensure that a room is furnished to a very high standard, e.g. the purchase of accessories such as candles, cushions, photo frames at a low cost can add interest to a room.
- Certain interior design finishes and fittings can be expensive so a thorough investigation of what is needed should be carried out beforehand.

Environmental Awareness

- Consideration should be given to the materials used in the home from an environmental point of view.
- Natural materials, such as wood, cause little impact on the environment.
- Timber and stone are found naturally and should be considered for use where possible.
- Plastic is difficult to break down and carbon dioxide is produced in its manufacture.
- Some paints produce 90 per cent waste as a result of their manufacture whereas organic paints produce 10 per cent waste.

Fig 2.15: A timber house.

Room Plans

When planning a room, consideration should be given to the following.
- **Function of the room:** What is the room going to be used for?
- **Layout of the room:** This refers to the actual size of the room and how best to maximise the space available. The aspect of the room also comes into play here in terms of utilising natural light and choosing colours.
- **Traffic flow in the room:** The potential movement patterns of people in the house need to be considered. There should be easy

access to all areas of the house and careful positioning of furniture can help this.

✳ **Storage:** Adequate storage space ensures maximum living and breathing space. It gets rid of clutter.

✳ **Size of the family:** The number in the family and the stages in the life cycle of family members.

✳ **Heating, lighting and ventilation:** All these features must be given serious attention at initial planning stages, e.g. the number of radiators needed, positioning of sockets and light switches.

✳ **Safety and hygiene:** Consideration needs to be given to asthma sufferers (e.g. pillows and duvets); non-slip flooring; wheelchair access, etc.

Drawing a Floor Plan

✳ A floor plan is a drawing of a house or room showing specific dimensions, doors, lighting, windows, radiators, sockets and furniture.

✳ A draftsperson is the name of the professional who draws floor plans.

✳ CAD (computer-aided design) can be used to draw these floor plans.

✳ Floor plans are drawn to scale and a variety of symbols are used to identify various structures and items of furniture in a house or room.

✳ To draw a floor plan to scale, you need the actual measurements of the room and graph paper to mark out the chosen scale, e.g. if a plan has a scale of 1:20, every metre in the room is represented by one twentieth of a metre (or 5cm) on the plan.

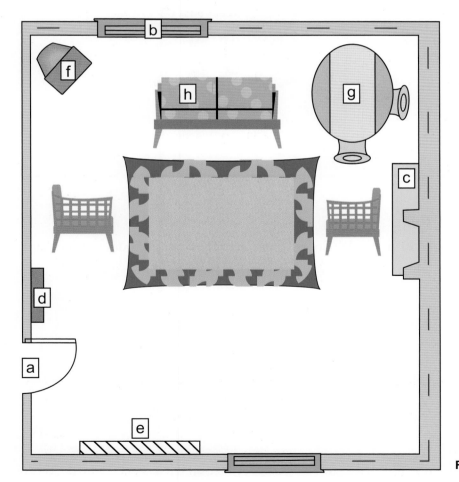

a. Door

b. Window

c. Fireplace

d. Bookshelves

e. Radiator

f. Television

g. Dining table + chairs

h. Couch

Fig 2.16: Floor plan of a living room drawn to scale.

Flooring and Floor Coverings

There are two main types of flooring: solid floors and suspended floors.

Solid Floors	Suspended Floors
• A layer of concrete placed over a hard core. • A damp-proof course and insulation are laid on top. • Another layer of concrete is then laid. • This type of floor is usually used on the ground floor of houses.	• Consists of tongue-and-groove timber floorboards that are laid over joists of wood at right angles to each other with an air space underneath. • The air spaces are well ventilated to prevent dampness and dry rot. • Insulation may be inserted into the air space to absorb sound and conserve heat. • Usually used on upper floors and also on the ground floor of older houses.

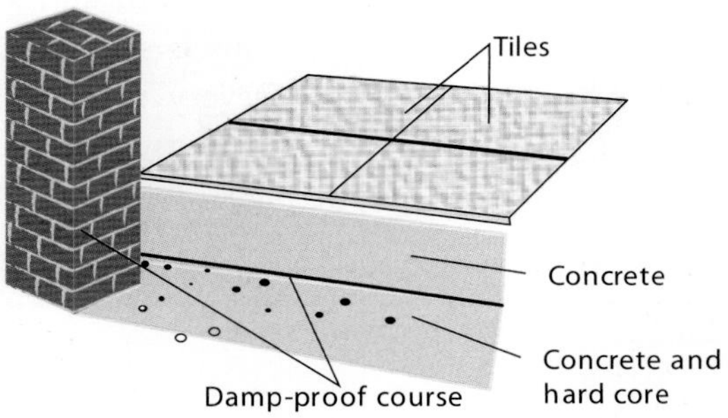

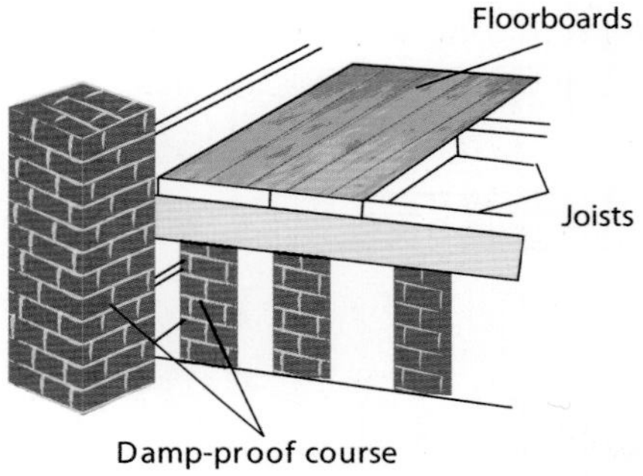

Fig 2.17: A solid floor.

Fig 2.18: A suspended floor.

Classification of Floor Coverings

Floor coverings are placed on top of solid or suspended floors. There are three types of floor covering: hard, semi–hard and soft.

Hard Coverings	Semi-Hard Coverings	Soft Coverings
• Ceramic tiles. • Slate. • Terracotta. • Marble. • Stone.	• Wood. • Vinyl. • Cork.	• Carpet. • Rugs.

Selecting Floor Coverings

Function:

What will the room mainly be used for?

Room decor:

Consideration should be given to the elements and principles of design in creating an aesthetically pleasing room.

Cost:

* The amount of money available to spend will have an effect on the choice of floor covering. For example, a limited budget might not cover the costs of a marble hallway and stairs.
* There is no point in buying cheap floor coverings for a hallway which gets the most traffic in the house, as it may not last and will then need to be replaced again.

Durability:

This refers to how long lasting the floor covering is. The traffic flow in the room and the quality of the floor covering will have a bearing on durability.

Sub-Floor:

Certain floor coverings require specific sub-floors, e.g. a solid base to take the weight of a marble floor.

Hygiene and Safety:

Certain rooms will require specific floor coverings for health and safety reasons, e.g. easy to clean, non-slip floor covering for a bathroom.

Insulation

Soft floor coverings, e.g. carpet, absorb sound and are insulating.

Remember: the term 'properties' refers to the characteristics or qualities of something. It may have desirable and undesirable properties.

Learning Links Learning Links Learning Links

Level of Wear and Tear:

The traffic flow in a room will determine what type of floor covering is needed.

Properties of Floor Coverings

There are many properties of floor coverings.
* Hard.
* Soft.
* Warm.
* Absorbent.
* Durable.
* Comfortable.
* Resilient.
* Noisy.
* Cold.

The cost of floor coverings can also vary greatly.

Hard Floor Coverings:

Type of Floor	**Ceramic Tiles** **Fig 2.19:** Ceramic tiles.	**Terracotta Tiles** **Fig 2.20:** Terracotta tiles.	**Marble** **Fig 2.21:** Marble floor.
Use	• Kitchens. • Utility rooms. • Bathrooms. • Conservatories.	• Hallways. • Living rooms. • Sun rooms.	• Bathrooms. • Living rooms. • Dining rooms. • Hallways.
Properties	• Hard. • Cold. • Durable. • Easy to clean. • Relatively expensive. • Available in a wide variety of colours, shapes, sizes and patterns. • Can chip or crack easily if something heavy is dropped on them.	• Hard and unglazed. • Warmer underfoot. • Durable. • Easy to clean. • Relatively expensive. • Available in warm colours of orange, red, peach and pink. • Can chip and crack easily. • Sealed after laying.	• Can be slippery. • Very expensive. • Suited to luxurious areas of the home. • Sold in thick slabs or in tiles. • Discolours easily as it soaks up liquid. • May be treated to repel liquids.

Wooden Floor Coverings:

* There are many different types of wooden floor covering. Each type has its own characteristic grain, colouring and pattern, which may influence an individual's choice.

* Price ranges, qualities and finishes all affect an individual's choice of wooden floor covering.
* Softwood includes pine and spruce.
* Hardwood includes beech, ash and oak.

Type of Floor	Solid	Semi-Solid	Laminate	Block/Parquet
Construction	• Each floorboard has a tongue-and-groove design which allows the boards to fit tightly together. • Floorboards are placed on a concrete floor or timber batons. • Thicknesses range from 9mm to 22mm.	• Solid wood is glued onto a softwood board.	• Thick softwood base with a thin surface layer fitted on top.	• Individual rectangular blocks of wood are laid in patterns, e.g. basket weave or herringbone pattern. **Fig 2.22:** Block floor.

Type of Floor	Solid	Semi-Solid	Laminate	Block/Parquet
Properties	• Expensive. • Scratches easily. • Noisy. • May warp. • Hard-wearing.	• Relatively inexpensive. • Noisy. • Easy to maintain. • Durable.	• Cheaper alternative. • Scratch-resistant. • Easy to lay. • Hard-wearing.	• Expensive. • Scratches easily. • Noisy. • A lot of work to lay.
Use	• Hall. • Sitting room. • Dining room.	• Bedroom. • Living room.	• Living room. • Bedroom. • Play room.	• Hallway. • Sitting room.

Vinyl Floor Coverings:

✳ Vinyl is short for polyvinyl chloride or PVC.

✳ It is available in a wide range of colours, textures and effects.

✳ It is made from petroleum.

✳ A vinyl sheet is formed as a hot mixture is forced through metal rollers; it can be cut into various lengths or tiles.

✳ One of the main properties of vinyl is that it is badly affected by cigarette burns and plastic castors.

Fig 2.23: Vinyl floor covering used in a kitchen.

Type of Vinyl	Properties	Use
Slip-Resistant	• Available in different finishes. • Available with studded ridges or gritty texture. • Available in plain colours. • Easy to clean. • Durable.	• Commercial kitchens and factories. • Unsuitable for children's bedrooms because it's rough.
Foam-Backed	• Soft. • Warm underfoot. • Absorbs sound. • Not available in tile form. • Easy to clean. • Durable.	• Kitchens. • Bathrooms. • Utility rooms. • Play rooms.
Clear PVC	• This design resembles marble or parquet. • Easy to clean. • Durable.	• Hallways. • Living rooms. • Dining rooms. • Bathrooms.

Carpets:

✱ Carpets are available in a wide variety of colours and patterns.

✱ They vary in price, which is directly linked to the construction of the carpet.

Type	Woven	Tufted	Bonded	Carpet Tiles
Construction	• Pile is woven into a backing. • There are two types: Axminster and Wilton.	• Fibres are glued onto a jute backing. • Jute is backed with foam. • The pile can be cut or uncut.	• Fibres are bonded/glued onto a jute backing in the presence of heat and pressure.	• Rubber or PVC-backed squares of carpet tiles.
Properties	• Expensive. • Soft underfoot. • Durable. • Resilient.	• Variety of colours. • Inexpensive. • Made from synthetic fibres. • Durable.	• Variety of colours. • Inexpensive. • Durable. • Rough texture.	• Easy to lay. • Wide variety of colours and patterns. • Easily replaced. • Durable.
Use	• Hallways. • Living rooms. • Dining rooms.	• Dining rooms. • Bedrooms.	• Bedrooms. • Play rooms.	• Hallways. • Schools.

Woven Carpet

Axminster
- Fibres are woven in a warp and weft manner into a backing.
- A lot of different colours can be introduced by this method.
- This type of carpet is known for its elaborate designs and is often featured in hotel foyers.
- The pile is always cut.

Wilton
- One continuous strand is pulled through a backing in loops.
- This carpet is quite thick and the pile can be cut or looped.
- Wilton carpets contain a limited number of colours due to the method of construction.

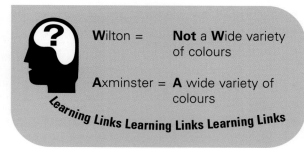

Wilton = **Not** a **W**ide variety of colours

Axminster = **A** wide variety of colours

Learning Links Learning Links Learning Links

Properties of Fibres Used in Carpets:

Natural Fibres	Synthetic Fibres	Blended Fibres
• **Wool** Warm, soft, resilient, insulating, durable, expensive. • **Cotton** Hard-wearing, no resilience, flattens easily.	• **Nylon** Warm, hard-wearing, builds up static tension. • **Acrylic** Similar to wool, warm, durable, tends to pill. • **Polyester** Easy to clean, soft, waterproof, not very hard-wearing.	• **80 per cent wool, 20 per cent nylon** This is the most desirable carpet as it has the best properties of both wool and nylon.

Note: The higher the percentage of wool, the better. Carpets with a high percentage of man-made fibres lose their appearance faster than wool carpets.

Classification of Carpets According to Their Durability:

Durability	Use	Type of Fibre and Why it is Used
Light Domestic	• Bedrooms.	• Blended fibres: Inexpensive.
Medium Domestic	• Bedrooms. • Studies.	• Blended fibres: Inexpensive.
General Domestic	• Living rooms. • Dining areas.	• 80 per cent wool, 20 per cent nylon blend: Expensive. • Need something durable, as a lot of wear and tear in this area.
Heavy Domestic	• Hallways. • Stairs and landings.	• 80 per cent wool, 20 per cent nylon blend: Expensive. • Need something durable, as a lot of traffic flow in this area.

Natural Flooring

* Made from 100 per cent plant fibre.
* Available in many different weaves, neutral shades and weights.
* Very practical and easy to care for.
* Can be specially treated with a stain–resistant finish if using in areas with high levels of wear.
* Not recommended for kitchens and bathrooms, where there is too much moisture in the air.
* The main types of natural flooring available are coir, sisal and jute.

Coir	Sisal	Jute

Fig 2.24: Coir flooring.	**Fig 2.25:** Sisal flooring.	**Fig 2.26:** Jute flooring.
• Made from coconut fibres softened in water. • It is prickly under foot. • It is hard-wearing and inexpensive.	• Made from spiky green plants grown in sub-tropical climates. • It is not as rough as coir. • It is expensive.	• This is traditionally the backing material used for carpets. • It is now used as a floor covering in its own right. • It is not as durable as other floor coverings but it is cheaper.

Wall Finishes

* There are various wall coverings that can be used in the home
* Examples include wallpaper, paint, wall tiles, wood panelling.

Selecting Wall Finishes

Function:

What is the function of the room? The room's intended purpose will impact on the choice of wall covering, e.g. the use of expensive wallpaper in a kitchen with a lot of moisture is not practical.

Room decor:

The aesthetic appeal of the room and the choice of colours for the wall covering will impact on the mood of the room.

Cost:

Different wall coverings are available at different costs. It is important to keep in mind the available budget when choosing a wall covering.

Durability:

Its durability will depend on the traffic flow in the room, the stage in the life cycle of the family members and the number of people living in the house. For example, a wall covering which is washable is important in a house where there is a small child.

Upkeep:

The maintenance of the wall covering should be considered, i.e. cleaning, painting or repapering.

Paint

✳ Paint is relatively inexpensive, easy to apply, easy to maintain, durable and available in a wide variety of colours and finishes.

✳ There are two types of paint: water-based paint and oil-/solvent-based paint.

Water-Based Paints

- **Emulsion paints**: Two types are available:
  - *Matt vinyl:* Inexpensive, washable and hides imperfections, e.g. uneven walls.
  - *Silk vinyl:* Suitable for bedrooms and living rooms. Inexpensive, quick to dry and more washable than matt vinyl.
- **Kitchen and bathroom paint**: Used on walls and ceilings. It has anti-mould/ anti-fungus and anti-condensation properties. Contains vinyl, which is easy to wipe clean.
- **Thixotropic paint**: Non-drip paint. Easy to apply and suitable for ceilings. One coat is generally enough. Colours cannot be mixed, which limits the choice of colours available.
- **Textured paint**: Has a rough finish due to the presence of plastic fibres. Used to hide blemishes on wall surfaces.

Oil-/Solvent-Based Paints

- **Gloss**: Used for kitchen presses, skirting boards, doors and stairs. It is hard wearing and easy to clean. No undercoat is needed with special one-coat formulas. Not suitable for areas that have imperfections as it will highlight them.
- **Satin finish**: All-purpose paints suitable for walls, ceilings, areas of high condensation such as bathrooms and kitchens. It is washable and durable. No undercoat is needed.
- **Polyurethane/strengthened paint**: Contains strong plastic binders, which gives it its durability. Can be difficult to apply as it dries very quickly. Suitable for doors, skirting boards and furniture.

Properties of Emulsion Paints

- Inexpensive.
- Easy to apply.
- Quick drying.
- No strong odour.
- Durable and easy to clean.
- Unlimited range of colours available.
- Minor blemishes can be hidden with matt finishes.

Properties of Oil-/Solvent-Based Paints

- Relatively inexpensive.
- Not as easy to apply as emulsion.
- Slow to dry.
- Strong odour.
- Durable and easy to clean.
- Good range of colours available.
- Minor blemishes may become more obvious if a shiny finish is used.

Other Types of Paint

✳ **Radiator paint:** It is specifically designed for use on radiators and will not discolour over time.

✳ **Flame-retardant paint:** Used for high-risk areas, e.g. kitchens, caravan and boat interiors, as it is a non-flammable paint.

✳ **Floor and step paint:** Hard-wearing, durable.

✳ **Exterior paint:** Used for painting outside as it has a special plastic resin which gives it weatherproof protection. It also has UV-resistant and water-repellent properties.

Paint Effects

✳ These are used to give a room an individual look or feel.

✳ Paint effects are becoming very popular due to magazines and television programmes about home improvements. Many paint effects can be done by amateurs.

✳ Some common paint effects are sponging, rag rolling, stencilling and colour washing.

Sponging	Rag rolling	Stencilling	Colour washing
• Dabbing paint using a sponge onto a base coat to produce a textured effect.	• Rolling a piece of fabric in wet paint to give a flowing finish. 	• A motif or pattern is applied to the wall by painting through a cut-out stencil.	• A soft, cloudy effect is created by mixing acrylic glaze with emulsion paint.

Fig 2.27: Wall with rag rolled finish.

Wallpaper

Type	Design	Use
Lining Paper	• This is applied to improve the wall surface to even it out before painting or wallpapering. • The paper is hung horizontally.	• Underneath wallpaper or before paint is applied.
Printed Paper	• **Machine printed:** Colours, patterns or textures are printed or stamped onto paper of various thicknesses. • **Hand printed:** These papers can be expensive as designs are hand printed onto the paper.	• Living rooms. • Hallways.

Type	Design	Use
Washable/PVC-Coated Paper	• These papers have a surface coating of silicone or resin, which means they can be gently washed or sponged down.	• Kitchen. • Play rooms. • Children's bedrooms.
Vinyl-Coated Paper	• Waterproof and easy to handle. • A printed design is fused onto paper backing. • Some papers are ready pasted.	• Kitchen. • Play rooms. • Children's bedrooms.
Textured Vinyls	• **Blown fibre vinyls:** These have a raised effect as a result of heat being applied. • **Sculptured vinyl:** These usually have a spongy effect.	• Hallways. • Living rooms. • Dining rooms.
Embossed Paper **Fig 2.28:** Embossed paper.	• The design is stamped onto paper. • A thick embossed paper, which is usually painted over, is known as 'relief' paper.	• Hallways. • Living rooms. • Dining rooms.

Properties of Wallpaper

* Available in a selection of designs and colours.
* The thickness of the wallpaper can vary depending on the type of wallpaper.
* Rolls of wallpaper are sold in a standard width.
* Minor marks or blemishes can be easily hidden with embossed wallpaper.
* In rooms with high levels of condensation, e.g. kitchens, vinyl wallpapers are suitable, as they are washable and very durable.

Wall Tiles

* Ceramic tiles are used for kitchens and bathrooms.
* They are ideal for high-moisture areas, as grease and steam can damage wallpaper or paint.
* They are easy to clean and available in a wide variety of colours, shapes, sizes and patterns.

Common Types of Wall Tile:

* **General purpose tiles:** Available in square or rectangular shapes. Available in a range of colours and designs.
* **Tile panels:** These are often used as a focal point: picture panels are aligned to give a full picture. Often used behind a hob.
* **Mosaic panels:** Small, coloured ceramic tiles that are set into concrete or plaster. Often used in bathrooms or kitchens.
* **Shaped tiles:** Many different tile shapes can be purchased, such as diamonds, triangles and crosses.
* **Patterned tiles:** These contain a pattern, such as flowers, fruits, that are raised out of the tile.

Furniture

✳ Furniture can complete a room.
✳ It can make a bland, empty room come to life.
✳ Furniture design is always evolving.

Choosing Furniture

Function:

What is the purpose of the room? The type of furniture that is needed is directly linked to what the room is being used for.

Room Decor:

The style of the room and the colours, patterns and textures in the room will influence the choice of furniture.

Cost:

The amount of money available will have a bearing on the furniture that can be bought, e.g. antique furniture can be very expensive whereas the opening of new furniture stores, such as Ikea, has enabled people to furnish their homes for less money.

Size of the Room:

The size of the room will help determine the choice of furniture for the room. Consideration will have to be given to the size of the furniture in relation to the size of the room.

Personal Taste:

An individual's own personal likes and dislikes will have an impact on the choice of furniture for the room.

Construction and Quality:

The construction of the furniture must be considered. Is it good quality? Are there any quality symbols?

Furniture Styles

Antique

✳ This is furniture that is over 150 years old.
✳ It is hand-crafted and carved.
✳ It is very expensive due to its age, rarity and high-quality craftsmanship.

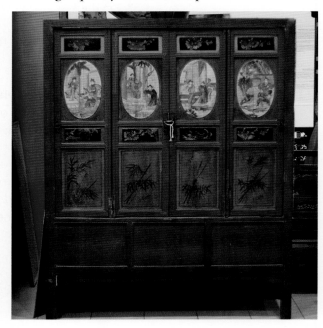

Fig 2.29: Antique furniture.

Traditional

Fig 2.30: Country-style kitchen.

✳ This is furniture that has been made in the past hundred years.
✳ It is made of solid wood.
✳ Typical traditional furniture includes country dressers and cottage-style furniture.

Contemporary

* This style of furniture is often made from artificial materials such as glass, chrome and brass.
* The designs are simple and sleek.
* This type of furniture is now widely available and affordable.

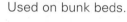

Fig 2.31: Contemporary-style living room.

Bedroom Furniture

* The main pieces of furniture in a bedroom include the bed and storage units, such as wardrobes, lockers and chests of drawers.
* Alternatives to the traditional style bed include futons, waterbeds and sofa beds.

* Beds come in a variety of sizes, including single, double and king size.
* A bed is made up of two main parts: the base and the mattress.

---

* **Spring-edged base**: Expensive but very comfortable.

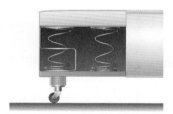

Fig 2.32: Spring-edged base.

* **Box-edged base**: Strong and durable.

Fig 2.33: Box-edged base.

* **Stretched wire/ wooden planks**: Used on bunk beds.

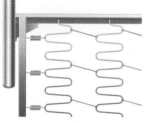

Fig 2.34: Stretched-wire base.

Types of Mattress

* **Spring mattress**: Springs are padded with horsehair, foam or synthetic wadding.
  The springs may be arranged in three different ways: individual springs, continuous coiled springs or pocketed springs.
* **Foam mattress**: Various thicknesses of latex or polyester foam are used.
  These are recommended for asthma suffers.
* **Memory foam**: This provides support by moulding itself to the shape of your body.
* **Orthopaedic mattress**: This relieves pressure to the spine.

Storage

* Storage is very necessary in every house.
* Storage space enables you to remove clutter and tidy things away.
* Furniture used for storage can be free-standing, e.g. chests of drawers, or built-in, e.g. wardrobe units in a bedroom.

* Kitchens are usually fitted with a range of storage options, such as drawers, cupboards and open shelves.
* An individual's personal taste, budget constraints, the style of the room will all influence the choice of storage furniture.

Upholstered Furniture

Fig 2.35: Chaise longue in a bedroom.

* Upholstered furniture is made up of a wooden frame with springs and padding or filling and an outer covering of fabric.
* It can be covered in a variety of fabrics, such as silk, wool, cotton.
* This type of furniture includes couches, armchairs, dining room chairs and music stools.

Soft Furnishings

Choosing Upholstered Furniture

Construction:

How solid is the construction of the furniture? Are the castors secure? Are the springs firm and supportive?

Cost:

How much a person has to spend will influence their choice of upholstered furniture.

Fire Safety Symbols:

Does the item of furniture meet fire safety legislation? Is there a swing and permanent label? Is the filling CMHR (combustion modified highly resilient) foam?

Dining Room Furniture

* Dining room furniture consists primarily of a table and chairs.
* The table should be large enough to seat people comfortably.
* The chairs should be the correct height for the table.
* The chairs should provide good back support.
* The furniture should be sturdy and easy to clean.
* Different materials can be used for dining room furniture, including glass tables with wrought iron legs, plastic chairs, wooden tables and chairs.
* Textiles used on the chairs should be easy to clean.

Curtains	Blinds	Bed Linen	Duvets
Functions of curtains: • To provide privacy. • To insulate the room. • To keep out light. • To provide comfort and atmosphere in a room.	• Blinds are made to measure. • They fit exactly in the window. • In roller blinds, fabric is attached to a wooden pole and can be rolled up and down using a string cord.	Bed linen consists of: • Sheets (fitted, flat or valance). • Pillow cases. • Duvet covers.	• A duvet's warmth rating is measured in togs. • The higher the tog rating, the warmer the duvet. • Tog ratings range from 1.5 tog to 15 tog.

Curtains

Fabrics used:
- Cotton, e.g. chintz.
- Linen.
- Velvet.
- Dralon.
- Wool, e.g. tweed.
- Polyester.

Curtain style:
This will depend on:
- The type of window.
- Budget.
- Sill or floor length.
- Style of heading: track, pelmet or valance.

Properties of curtains:
Curtains should:
- Drape well.
- Be pre–shrunk.
- Be easy to clean.
- Be fade-resistant.
- Be flame-retardant.
- Provide insulation.

Blinds

- A range of different colours and styles are available to choose from.

Three popular types of blind:
- **Roller blinds**: These roll up tightly around a metal or wooden roller.

Fig 2.36: Roller blinds.

- **Austrian blind**: These have deep swags of fabric that roll down like a ruched curtain.

Fig 2.37: Austrian blinds.

- **Wooden Venetian blinds**: These have horizontal wooden slats that lie on top of each other when folded up.

Fig 2.38: Wooden Venetian blinds.

Bed Linen

Properties of bed linen:
- Easy to clean.
- Shrink resistant.
- Absorbent.
- Smooth.

Pillows can contain the following fillings:
- **Feather**: Duck or goose feathers.
- **Synthetic**: Terylene, Dacron.
- **Latex**: Suitable for individuals with allergies.

Duvets

- A duvet should overlap the sides of a bed.
- Duvets of different tog ratings can be used together if necessary.
- Duvets consist of two layers of closely woven fabric sewn together with a filling between the layers.
- The filling may be:
  - **Down:** Obtained from the breast of ducks and geese. These are expensive but are an excellent filling.
  - **Down and feather:** This is a mixture of duck and geese feathers with down.
  - **Cotton:** Cotton is cool and suitable for asthma sufferers.
  - **Synthetic:** Terylene, hollow-fibre and Dacron are cheaper fillings.

Materials Used in the Home

Wood

Type	Properties	Use
Hardwood: From slow-growing trees, such as oak, ash, maple, beech, mahogany and teak.	• Expensive. • Has an attractive grain. • Durable. • Variety of shades and colours are available. • May be varnished. • May warp when affected by water.	• Kitchens. • Floors. • Furniture. • Doors.
Softwood: From fast-growing trees, such as pine, spruce and fir.	• Not as expensive as hardwood. • Not as durable as hardwood. • Damaged by heat and moisture – can warp and swell. • Can get scratched easily.	• Kitchens. • Floors. • Furniture. • Doors.
Man-made: • **Plywood:** Sheets of softwood glued together.	• Strong. • Laminated/veneered with hardwood/plastic. • Inexpensive.	• Flooring. • Furniture.
• **Hardboard:** Made from wood pulp that has been compressed.	• Hard-wearing. • Dark rich colour. • Inexpensive.	• Backing for furniture. • Notice boards. • Flooring under tiles.
• **Medium density fibreboard (MDF):** Made from wood fibres compressed together under heat. **Fig 2.39:** MDF.	• Durable. • No grain or knots. • Inflexible. • Cheap.	• Furniture. • Cabinets. • Storage units.
• **Chipboard:** Made from woodchips that are glued together.	• Not very durable. • May be laminated. • Affected by moisture – may warp. • Inexpensive.	• Flooring. • Furniture. • Worktops.

Metals

Type	Properties	Use
Stainless Steel	<ul><li>Durable.</li><li>Strong.</li><li>Resistant to rust.</li><li>Shiny finish.</li><li>Easy to clean.</li><li>Poor conductor of heat.</li></ul>	<ul><li>Cutlery.</li><li>Kitchen utensils.</li><li>Sinks.</li><li>Appliances.</li><li>Trimming on furniture.</li></ul>
Aluminium	<ul><li>Lightweight.</li><li>Durable.</li><li>Strong.</li><li>Discolours with use.</li><li>Reacts with acidic food.</li><li>Good conductor of heat.</li></ul>	<ul><li>Cooking utensils.</li><li>Saucepans.</li><li>Windows.</li><li>Appliances.</li></ul>
Copper	<ul><li>Tarnishes easily.</li><li>Has to be lined with tin or chromium.</li><li>Expensive.</li><li>Excellent conductor of heat.</li></ul>	<ul><li>Antique lamps.</li><li>Water cylinders.</li><li>Pipes.</li></ul>
Tin	<ul><li>Durable.</li><li>Lightweight.</li><li>Rusts easily.</li><li>Inexpensive.</li><li>May be treated with a non-stick coating.</li></ul>	<ul><li>Baking tins.</li><li>Baking trays.</li></ul>
Cast iron Fig 2.40: Cast iron pot.	<ul><li>Durable.</li><li>Heavy.</li><li>Enamelled or finished with a non-stick coating.</li></ul>	<ul><li>Saucepans.</li><li>Casserole dishes.</li><li>Pot roasting dishes.</li><li>Griddle pans.</li></ul>

Glass

Type	Properties	Use
Soda Lime Glass	<ul><li>Transparent.</li><li>Breaks easily.</li><li>Damaged by extremes in temperature.</li><li>Inexpensive.</li><li>Most common type of glass used in the home.</li></ul>	<ul><li>Drinking glasses.</li><li>Jars.</li><li>Bottles.</li><li>Light bulbs.</li></ul>

Glass contd

Type	Properties	Use
Heat Resistant Glass (Pyrex)	• Hard. • Stain-resistant. • Damaged by extremes of temperature. • May be scratched easily.	• Ovenproof dishes. • Ovenproof plates. • Coffee makers. • Teapots.
Stained Glass	• Transparent or coloured glass. • Available in various designs. • Easily damaged.	• Windows. • Doors.
Crystal Glass	• Transparent or coloured glass. • Available in various cuts and designs. • Can be quite expensive. • Easily damaged.	• Glasses. • Candlesticks. • Vases. • Ornaments.

Plastic

❋ Plastics are made from petroleum, coal, wood, natural gas, water and salt in the presence of heat and pressure.

❋ Plastic is used in a variety of ways around the house. There are two main types of plastic: thermoplastic and thermosetting.

Type of Plastic	**Thermoplastic:** These are soft plastics that can be moulded, melted and remoulded several times.	**Thermosetting:** Hard plastics which, once moulded, cannot be reshaped.
Properties	• Flexible and soft. • Acid- and alkali-resistant. • Damaged by solvents. • Further heating softens them.	• Hard and rigid. • Damaged by acids and alkalis. • Not damaged by solvents. • Can withstand high temperatures. • Overheating causes them to blister and crack.
Examples and Uses	• **Fluorocarbons:** Anti-stick finishes on cooking utensils and other kitchen utensils. • **Polystyrene:** Cake dish covers, blender bowls, food bins and canisters. • **Polyethylene:** Ice cube trays, flexible mixing bowls and utensils. • **ABS (Acrylonitrile–Butadiene Styrene):** Casings for mixers, hoovers, soap dispensers and drainpipes.	• **Melamine:** Mixing bowls and laminated counter tops. • **Bakelite:** Control knobs on cookers and other appliances. • **Phenolics:** Handles on utensils, light switches and telephones.

Fabrics

* There is a wide variety of fabrics that can be used in the home for curtains, cushions, towels, blinds and tablecloths.
* Fabrics add colour, pattern and texture to a room.

Classification of Fibres that Make Up Fabrics

There are two main groups of fibres: natural and synthetic.

Natural:
* Wool.
* Silk.
* Cotton.
* Linen.

Synthetic:
* Nylon.
* Acrylic.
* Polyester.
* Viscose.

Type	Properties	Uses
Wool	<ul><li>Soft.</li><li>Warm.</li><li>Durable.</li><li>Strong.</li><li>Good insulator.</li><li>Comfortable.</li><li>Flame-resistant.</li><li>Can be used in blends, e.g. with acrylic or nylon.</li></ul>	<ul><li>Carpets.</li><li>Rugs.</li><li>Blankets.</li><li>Curtains.</li><li>Upholstery.</li><li>Cushion covers.</li></ul>
Silk	<ul><li>Drapes well.</li><li>Smooth.</li><li>Luxurious.</li><li>Expensive.</li><li>Special care needed when laundering.</li></ul>	<ul><li>Cushion covers.</li><li>Curtains.</li><li>Upholstery.</li></ul>
Polyester	<ul><li>Strong.</li><li>Crease-resistant.</li><li>Can be used in blends, e.g. with cotton.</li><li>Inexpensive.</li><li>Easy to care for.</li></ul>	<ul><li>Cushions.</li><li>Curtains.</li><li>Tablecloths.</li><li>Bed linen.</li><li>Napkins.</li></ul>
Viscose Damask	<ul><li>Easy to care for.</li><li>Durable.</li><li>Inexpensive.</li></ul>	<ul><li>Tablecloths.</li><li>Napkins.</li><li>Cushion covers.</li></ul>

Sample Exam Questions
Higher Level (2007)

Question

1. Discuss the factors to be considered when selecting floor coverings for a family home. (12)

2. Set out details of one hard and one semi-hard flooring you would recommend for the hallway. In each case refer to: (a) type of flooring; and (b) properties. (18)

Sample Answers

1. Discuss the factors to be considered when selecting floor coverings for a family home. (12)

   4 points x 3 marks each = 12.

   a) **Durability:** This refers to how long-lasting the floor covering is. The traffic flow in the room and the quality of the floor covering will have a bearing on this.
   Level of wear and tear: The traffic flow in a room will determine what type of floor covering is needed.

   b) **Room decor:** Consideration should be given to the elements and principles of design in creating an aesthetically pleasing room.

   c) **Cost:** The amount of money available to spend will affect the choice of floor covering. For example, a limited budget might not cover the costs of a marble hallway and stairs. There is no point in buying cheap floor coverings for a hallway, which gets most traffic in the house, as it may not last and will then need to be replaced.

   d) **Sub–floor:** Certain floor coverings require specific sub-floors, e.g. a solid base to take the weight of a marble floor.
   Insulating: Soft floor coverings, e.g. carpet, absorb sound and are insulating.
   Hygiene and safety: Certain rooms will require specific floor coverings for health and safety reasons, e.g. easy to clean, non-slip floor covering for a bathroom.

2. Set out details of one hard and one semi–hard flooring you would recommend for the hallway. In each case refer to: (a) type of flooring; and (b) properties. (18)

   2 types x 3 marks = 6.
   2 properties for each type x 3 marks each = 12. Total = 18.

   Hard Flooring: Terracotta tiles
   Properties:
   - Hard and unglazed.
   - Warm underfoot.
   - Durable.
   - Easy to clean.
   - Relatively expensive.
   - Available in warm colours of orange, red, peach and pink.
   - Can chip and crack easily.

   Semi-Hard Flooring: Solid wooden floors
   Properties:
   - Expensive.
   - Scratch easily.
   - Noisy.
   - May warp.
   - Hard-wearing.

The Energy-Efficient Home

3

Energy in the home is most often supplied by peat, gas, coal or oil. Energy can also be supplied by wind, water, solar and bio-energy. Energy can be divided into two distinct forms.

Non-Renewable Energy	Renewable Energy
• Oil. • Gas. • Peat/turf. • Coal.	• Wind. • Water. • Solar. • Bio-energy.

✱ **Renewable energy** is energy that causes little, if any, damage to the environment and is not a finite resource.

✱ **Non-renewable energy** is energy that is damaging to our environment and will eventually run out (is finite).

Fossil fuels are fuels that are produced from dead plants and animals that became compressed under the earth's crust over a long period of time.

Learning Links Learning Links Learning Links

Non-Renewable Sources of Energy

Electricity

Electricity is often categorised as renewable energy: however, it is mainly produced from burning fossil fuels, such as oil and gas. It can be made from some non-renewable fuels, such as wind and water.

Properties of Electricity

Sources	Sustainability	Advantages	Disadvantages
• Fossil fuels. • Solar. • Wind. • Water.	• It is unlikely that electricity will run out. • However, the sources of	• Reliable. • Efficient when used correctly. • No fumes are produced.	• Power cuts can leave people without lighting. • Electricity dries the air in a room.

Sources	Sustainability	Advantages	Disadvantages
	• non-renewable energy that are used to make the majority of electricity will. • Renewable sources will become the main source of electricity, these include wind, water, solar and bio-energy.		• Can be expensive when appliances that are energy inefficient are constantly being used.

Oil

Oil is a black liquid which is often referred to as crude oil. This oil is used to heat homes.

Properties of Oil

Sources	Sustainability	Advantages	Disadvantages
• Decayed plant and animal remains which became compressed under the earth's outer crust. • Generally obtained from the Middle East.	• Oil is at its most expensive today. • Oil is expected to run out in the next few decades unless new reserves are found.	• Does not dry out the air. • Relatively easy to obtain. • Operates immediately.	• Prices fluctuate and oil is presently expensive. • Needs exposure to air (ventilation). • Can be hazardous if not properly handled. • Needs a storage tank to be stored.

Fig 3.1: An oil rig.

Gas

Gas is a non-renewable source of energy. It can be obtained in two states: bottled, known as butane gas, or natural gas (methane), which is pumped to homes.

Properties of Gas

Sources	Sustainability	Advantages	Disadvantages
• Found in the sea bed. • Formed as a result of decaying plant and animal life becoming compressed.	• In Ireland, gas is pumped from the Corrib fields and off the coast of Kinsale. • Gas is being used up at a particularly fast rate and, although Ireland has an inter-connector pipe off the east coast that connects us to Britain and the rest of Europe, gas supply is predicted to run out in about fifty years.	• Instant. • Clean. • Has a smell added to it which acts as a safety factor.	• Regular servicing of all gas appliances is essential. • Is not sustainable.

Peat/Turf

Peat is a solid fuel. In Ireland, it's the main fuel used to generate electricity. Peat is incomplete coal formation. This form of energy is very popular in rural areas.

Properties of Peat/Turf

Sources	Sustainability	Advantages	Disadvantages
• Bogs: There are two types of bog: raised bogs and blanket bogs. **Raised bogs**: These have a depth of approximately seven metres. **Blanket bogs**: These have a depth of 2–3 metres.	• The large commer-cial bogs that are monitored by Bord na Mona are set to run out in the next thirty years. • Privately owned bogs will last considerably longer.	• Produces a lot of heat. • Useful in power stations. • Produces an aesthetically pleasing fire. • Can be cheap to buy. • Does not dry the air.	• Produces a lot of smoke when burned. • Requires a large storage area. • Fires must be cleaned manually.

Coal

Coal is a solid fuel. Its formation is similar to that of oil, gas and peat.

Sources	Sustainability	Advantages	Disadvantages
• In Ireland, most coal is imported. • Coal that is mined in Ireland comes from two main sources in Tipperary and Kilkenny.	• Coal, like most other fossil fuels, has a limited supply. • Research is being carried out to find a method to change coal into a liquid fuel which may prove to be a cleaner, cheaper, more efficient fuel; however, this has not yet been successful.	• Relatively cheap. • Produces an aesthetically pleasing fire. • Does not dry the air.	• Smoky. • Difficult to clean. • Requires a large storage area. • Produces less heat than other fuels.

Renewable Energy

Fig 3.2: Wind turbines.

Wind

✱ Ireland is an excellent area for wind farms, which produce wind energy.

✱ Large wind turbines are used to harness this energy.

✱ Off the west coast, the winds from the Atlantic are very strong. These winds enable the turbines to rotate at a very fast speed to produce energy.

✱ This method is also used off the east coast in Arklow.

✱ To date, there are 31 wind farms situated in Ireland.

✱ Disadvantages:
  • Noisy.
  • They take from the appearance of the local environment.
  • Expensive to set up.

Water

✱ When water is harnessed to produce energy this is known as hydro-electric energy.

✱ Hydro-electric power stations are located near fast-running water.

✱ These stations harness the energy from the water to produce electricity.

✱ In Ireland, about 7 per cent of energy is produced in this way.

✱ Disadvantage: the start-up cost of building the power stations is very expensive.

Fig 3.3: Hydro-electric power station.

Solar

* The source of solar energy is the sun.
* It is becoming more popular today with an increasing number of Irish families installing solar panels on the roof of their houses.
* This form of energy is very sustainable and once harnessed in the correct way will prove to be very cost effective.

* There are three ways that solar energy can be used within the home:
  * Passive solar design.
  * Active solar technology.
  * Photovoltaic technology.

Fig 3.4: Solar panels.

Passive Solar Design	Active Solar Technology	Photovoltaic Technology
• This means designing the house to gain maximum solar energy. • The design incorporates the fabrics used in the house and the direction the house is facing in order to gain maximum natural light and thereby minimise the amount of artificial light needed.	• Solar energy is converted to heat energy. • Solar collectors absorb the light from the sun. • These solar collectors are positioned on a south-facing roof in order to absorb the most sun.	• This method involves converting solar energy to electrical energy. • This is commonly seen in calculators and parking meters. • In the home, this system uses the sun's energy when it is available during the day and depends on a regular (traditional) electricity supply at all other times. • At present such a system can be expensive to install; however, it is one of the fastest-growing methods of renewable energy.

Bio-Energy

✱ This is energy manufactured from biomass.

✱ Biomass uses plant growth to produce energy. The most popular bio-fuel is wood.

✱ There are two main forms of bio-fuel: solid (wood) and liquid (oil).

✱ Plants such as rapeseed are now grown throughout Ireland and this is then converted into oil which is used to fuel cars.

✱ In developing countries, manure is used. This manure is converted to biogas, which is used to heat homes.

Emissions from Burning Fossil Fuels

When fossil fuels are burned, they release gases into the atmosphere. These gases include:

✱ **Carbon dioxide:** Released into the atmosphere when fossil fuels are burned.

✱ **Sulphur dioxide:** This can lead to acid rain.

✱ **Nitrogen oxide:** These occur when ammonium nitrate is heated. The use of fertilisers is the main cause.

✱ **Smoke/smog:** Smog is a mixture of smoke and fog. Smog was very common in densely populated areas, such as cities or large towns.

✱ **Chlorofluorocarbons (CFCs):** These are produced from aerosols and incorrect disposal of refrigerators. These are gases forty times more destructive to the ozone layer than CO_2.

Problems Associated with Fuel Emissions

✱ Acid rain.
✱ Smog.
✱ Global warming/greenhouse effect.
✱ Respiratory problems.

Acid Rain

Stages in the creation of acid rain:

1. Industry burns a large quantity of fossil fuels in order to provide energy.

2. When this occurs carbon dioxide and sulphur dioxide are produced.

3. These gases are released into the atmosphere.

4. The gases combine with water vapour in the atmosphere.

5. This combination of gases and water vapour changes the pH level to slightly acidic.

6. Rain falls as acid rain.

Fig 3.5: Acid rain.

The Effects of Acid Rain:

✱ Damage to **buildings** and statues reducing their life spans.

✱ Acid rain destroys **flora and fauna**. When acid rain falls on the soil, it changes the pH level, which prevents the growth of trees and other plants. The destruction of such plant life, in turn, leads to the death of the insects and animals that are dependent on them.

✱ **Rivers and lakes** are also affected by acid rain, which can lead to a reduction in fish stocks and bird life in and around them.

✱ When acid rain falls on **farmland**, the growth of crops is hindered. Crop quantity is decreased.

Smog

✱ Smog forms when smoke becomes mixed with fog or mist.

The Effects of Smog:

✱ Respiratory problems, in particular asthma and bronchitis.

✱ A reduction in sunshine level, which in turn, can affect the growth of plant life.

✱ Increase in air pollution.

✱ Decrease in visibility.

Global Warming

* The earth's source of heat is the sun.
* Around the earth's atmosphere there are approximately thirty greenhouse gases which maintain the earth's surface temperature at 15.5°C.
* These gases (including water vapour, methane, ozone and carbon dioxide) have been present in the earth's atmosphere for millions of years.
* These gases act as a barrier, preventing all the sun's heat from escaping back into space.
* Global warming is caused by an increase in these gases, in particular CO_2 and chloro-fluorocarbons.
* When released, these gases trap a high proportion of the sun's heat preventing it from escaping, which causes an increase in global temperature (referred to as global warming).

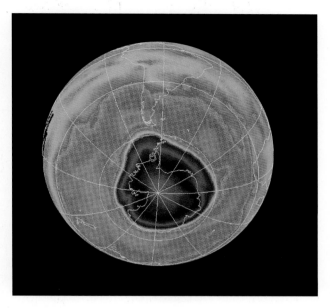

Fig 3.6: Map showing the hole in the ozone layer over Antarctica caused by global warming.

Problems Associated with Global Warming

* **Increase in global temperature**
  * At present the earth's surface temperature is 15.5°C. Scientists believe that by 2020 this temperature will increase by between 1.5°C to 4.5°C.

* **Rising sea levels**
  * Due to an increase in temperature, the polar ice sheets are beginning to melt.
  * This process has already begun. In the past century, sea levels have risen by 15 centimetres.
  * It is predicted that in the next century sea levels will rise by approximately 4.5 metres.

* **Climate change**
  * This problem manifests itself in extreme weather conditions.
  * Rainfall patterns are changing.

* **Effects on farming**
  * Plants grow because of the natural fertiliser CO_2.
  * If the CO_2 level rises, not only will plants grow at a faster rate, but so too will weeds and pests.
  * Controlling these weeds and pests may become a problem, leading to a destruction of crops.

* **Health problems**
  * An increase in global warming to date has shown its effects in humans with an increase in respiratory problems and an increase in allergies.

Energy Inefficiencies in the Home

Inefficiencies in the home	Area	Problem	How to overcome inefficiencies
• Heating	• Open fire. • Boiler. • Central heating.	• Burns fossil fuels. • No thermostat. • No thermostat.	• Only light fire when necessary. • A **thermostat** set at correct temperature can reduce waste and minimise bill. • **Service** boiler regularly. • A **thermostat** controls the temperature and usage time of central heating systems.
• Appliances		• Energy inefficient. • Bad practices. • Leaving appliances on standby.	• Always check the **energy labels** when purchasing electrical products. Choose energy level A or B. (These use least amount of energy.) • When using machines, think energy efficient i.e. **batch bake**, only turn on dishwasher when completely full or **hand wash** dishes instead. • Always ensure all plugs are unplugged; this is not only energy efficient but also a safety precaution.

Inefficiencies in the home	Area	Problem	How to overcome the inefficiencies
• Lighting		• Using high-strength bulb when not needed. • Leaving lights on.	• Use correct wattage bulbs. • Choose CFLs (compact fluorescent light bulbs); these are energy efficient. • Turn off lights when not in use.
• Insulation	• Attic. • Windows, doors and floors. • Hot water cylinder.	• No attic insulation. • Draughts. • No lagging jacket.	• 25–30 per cent of the heat in a house can be lost through the attic. A well-insulated attic will greatly reduce this heat loss. • **Windows**: Use well-lined curtains to reduce heat loss. • **Double-glazed windows**. • Fit draught excluders at letter boxes and at the bottom of doors. • **Floors: Carpet** is a good insulator. • Fitting an 80mm lagging jacket will greatly reduce heating bills.
• Water	• Bath. • Taps.	• Excessive use of hot water for bathing. • Dripping taps.	• Choose a shower instead of a bath. • Fix dripping taps immediately.

How to Reduce Emission Levels

1. Switch to renewable sources of energy: wind, solar or water.
2. Avoid using aerosols containing CFCs.
3. Choose products that are labelled ozone-friendly.
4. Leave the car at home: walk or cycle instead.
5. Wear extra layers of clothing instead of switching on the central heating.
6. When lighting an open fire, choose smokeless fuels.
7. Only light the fire when really necessary.
8. Recycle as much as possible.
9. Choose energy-efficient options, such as compact fluorescent light bulbs.
10. Make sure the hot water cylinder is lagged.

Exam Questions (2007)

Questions

'Sustainable energy refers to a way we can use and generate energy that is more efficient and less harmful to the environment.'

1. Give details of **one** type of renewable energy that you would recommend when building a new house. Refer to:
   • Source.
   • Sustainability.
   • Efficiency/Effectiveness. (18)

2. Describe three different methods of reducing harmful emissions in the environment. (12)

Sample Answers

1. Give details of **one** type of renewable energy that you would recommend when building a new house. Refer to:
   • Source.
   • Sustainability.
   • Efficiency/Effectiveness. (18)

Source = 5 marks.
Sustainability = 5 marks.
Efficiency/effectiveness = 2 points x 4 marks each = 8.

Solar Energy

Source	Sustainability	Effectiveness

• The source of solar energy is the sun.	• It is becoming more popular today with an increasing number of Irish families installing solar panels in the roofs of their houses.
	• This form of energy is very sustainable and once harnessed in the correct way will prove to be very cost effective.
		• There are three ways that solar energy can be used within the home:
		  – Passive solar design.
		  – Active solar technology
		  – Photovoltaic technology.

Passive Solar Design	Active Solar Technology	Photovoltaic Technology
• The design incorporates the fabrics used in the house and the direction the house is facing in order to gain maximum natural light and thereby minimise the amount of artificial light needed. • This form of design is very cost effective, both in construction and in energy saving. This method minimises the amount of artificial light, heating and ventilation used, thereby making the house more energy efficient.	• Solar collectors absorb the light from the sun. • They can provide approximately 60 per cent of a household's hot water needs for a year. This method is becoming increasingly popular in Ireland and although it is expensive to install, in the long run the saving made will be greater.	• In the home, this system uses the sun's energy when it is available during the day and depends on a regular, traditional electricity supply at all other times. • Such a system can be expensive to install; however, it is becoming cost effective and this method of energy is being used in commercial buildings.

2. Describe three different methods of reducing harmful emissions in the environment. (12)

3 methods x 4 marks each = 12

• When lighting an open fire, choose smokeless fuels. Avoid lighting bonfires, as the rubbish burned produces high amounts of CO_2.

• Choose energy-efficient appliances/ equipment. These products will help reduce emissions.

• Choose cleaner fuels, such as natural gas, as opposed to oil or coal, because gas produces less carbon dioxide when burned.

Test Yourself
eTest.ie

4 Systems and Services

Electricity

Electricity Supply

1. Electricity passes via a service cable into the home.
2. This cable unites with the ESB fuse box, which is located outside the house and can only be opened by an ESB official.
3. Electricity then travels into the meter. The meter measures the amount of electricity that each house uses.
4. In some houses, there are two meters. The second metre is used to measure the amount of off-peak electricity used.
5. The electricity flows into the consumer unit located inside the house. From the consumer unit electricity is distributed to all areas of the house.

Household Circuits

✳ From the consumer unit there are a variety of wire circuits. These circuits include:
  ● Socket circuit.
  ● Lighting circuit.
  ● Immersion circuit.
  ● Cooker circuit.
✳ There can be separate socket and lighting circuits for upstairs and downstairs.
✳ The safety element for these circuits is the fuses. As each circuit carries a certain amount of current, the fuse used for this circuit is of the correct size to protect the current.

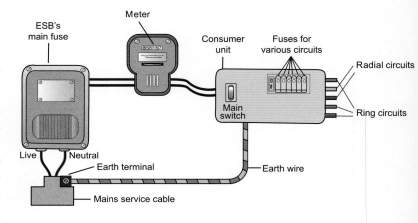

Fig 4.1: Electricity supply.

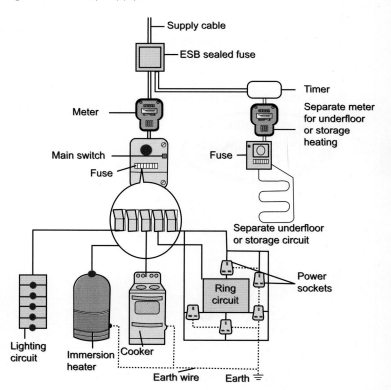

Fig 4.2: A household circuit.

* A radial circuit is used for appliances that require a separate circuit, e.g. immersion or cooker. These appliances tend to be more powerful and therefore need fuses of higher than normal strength.

* A ring circuit is present in most modern houses. This wiring system leaves the consumer unit and travels to a number of sockets before returning to the consumer unit. Each ring circuit is connected to a 35-amp fuse. In a two-storey house, there are often two ring circuits, one upstairs and one downstairs.

Electrical Terms

Term	Explanation
Amperage	• Also known as amp. • This is the measure of the flow of electricity. • In an appliance, the greater amount of electricity used, the greater the amp. $$\text{Amp} = \frac{\text{Wattage}}{\text{Voltage}}$$
Current	• This is the flow of electricity. • Current is measured in amperages.
Kilowatt hour	• A kilowatt is a unit of electricity. • 1 kilowatt hour is the engery used by 1 kilowatt in a single hour.
Voltage	• This is a measure of the force needed to drive the electrical current. • In Ireland, the standard voltage is 230V.
Wattage	• This is the amount of electrical power an appliance uses. • Wattage is measured in watts.

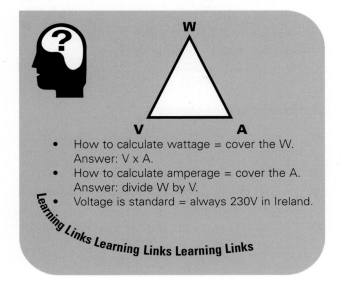

* How to calculate wattage = cover the W. Answer: V x A.
* How to calculate amperage = cover the A. Answer: divide W by V.
* Voltage is standard = always 230V in Ireland.

Learning Links Learning Links Learning Links

Costs

* In Ireland, the ESB supplies the majority of household electricity.

* Every second month, each household is issued a bill which shows how much electricity they have consumed and how much must be paid to the ESB.

* These bills include:
  * **Standard charge:** This charge is constant and is always the same price. It covers the costs of maintaining electricity flow to the house, taking meter readings and issuing bills. This figure is given as a yearly figure and paid according to the time allocated on the bill.

- **Unit charge:** This is the amount of electricity that a house has consumed. The unit charge is measured in units: 1 unit =1000 watts. The unit consumption will vary from house to house, however winter time is when the unit charge tends to be highest.
- **Public service obligation levy:** This levy was introduced to cover the cost of the electricity board buying electricity from generating stations that use renewable energy.
- **VAT:** Every bill issued includes 13.5 per cent VAT.

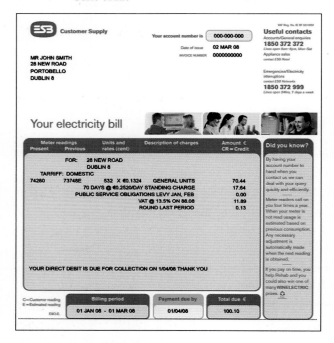

Fig 4.3: An electricity bill.

Safety Devices used in Electricity

Safety devices in electricity include:
* Fuses.
* Miniature circuit breakers (MCB).
* Residual current devices (RCD).
* Earth wires.

Fuses

* Fuses are safety devices in electrical circuits.
* A fuse is a deliberate weak link.

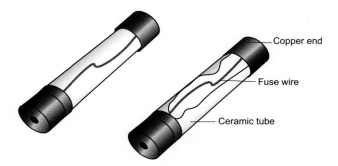

Fig 4.4: Fuses.

* A fuse contains a thin piece of wire that forms part of the circuit.
* If a fault occurs, the fuse wire melts or breaks, stopping the flow of electricity and breaking the circuit.
* This prevents injury and fire.
* There are a variety of fuses available in different sizes.
* Reasons a fuse can break:
  * Incorrect wiring.
  * Overloading of circuit.
  * A fault in an appliance.

Miniature Circuit Breakers

* Miniature circuit breakers are found in most modern homes.
* They work on the same principle as fuses.
* When a fault occurs the MCB switches off.
* When the problem is located and fixed the MCB can be reset by flicking it to the upward position.

Fig 4.5: Miniature circuit breaker.

Residual Current Devices

* This is a safety feature found in modern houses.
* RCDs are found in electric shower circuits.
* RCDs detect a fault when there is an unusual flow of electricity.
* The RCD stops the flow of electricity to the circuit.

Earth Wires

✱ Earth wires in plugs act as an additional safety device.

✱ If a fault occurs in the appliance, the earth wire carries the electrical current to the ground thereby preventing electrocution.

Wiring a Plug

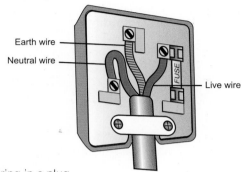

Fig 4.6: Wiring in a plug.

Steps in wiring a plug.

1. Remove the outer casing of the plug by unscrewing the cord grip.
2. Remove the fuse.
3. Loosen the screws attached to each of the three terminal screws: the earth, the live and the neutral.
4. The flex is prepared by stripping back the outer covering by approximately 5 centimetres.
5. Reposition the flex under the cord grip.
6. The insulation around each of the separate wires must be stripped back about 5 millimetres.
7. Insert this wire under the screw, ensuring that each is attached to the correct terminal.
8. Tighten screws and replace fuse.
9. Replace the outer casing and screw into place.

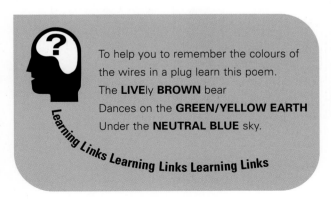

To help you to remember the colours of the wires in a plug learn this poem.
The **LIVE**ly **BROWN** bear
Dances on the **GREEN/YELLOW EARTH**
Under the **NEUTRAL BLUE** sky.

Learning Links Learning Links Learning Links

Electrical Safety

In order to prevent accidents from occurring when using electricity, it is important to know some safety guidelines.

Kitchen Safety

✱ Always ensure that hands are completely dry before handling electrical appliances, plugs or touching sockets.

✱ Always ensure that all appliances are unplugged before cleaning.

✱ Never overload sockets.

✱ Flexes should not be left to trail near a sink or cooker hob.

✱ Never attempt to repair a faulty appliance.

Bathroom Safety

✱ Portable electric heaters should not be operated in a bathroom.

✱ All switches should be operated by a pull cord or by a switch outside the bathroom door.

✱ There should be no sockets in a bathroom, except for a shaver outlet.

Bedroom Safety

✱ Check electric blankets regularly to ensure there are no indications of wear and tear. If a fault occurs it should be checked professionally.

✱ Carefully read the manufacturer's instructions when installing electric blankets.

✱ Always keep electric heaters a reasonable distance from the bed to prevent fire.

✱ Do not heat clothes over an electric heater.

✱ Always unplug all appliances in the bedroom when they are not in use.

Appliance Safety

✱ Always read the manufacturer's instructions and follow with care.

✱ Always check that safety symbols illustrated on new appliances are understood.

✱ Always check that plugs are correctly wired.

* Check appliances to ensure that there is no wear and tear.

Water

Water is an essential service to the home. It is supplied by local authorities, who ensure that the water is safe for human consumption and use.

The Path of Water

* The sun evaporates water from rivers and oceans.
* The evaporated water vapour turns into clouds.
* The water droplets in the clouds fall from the sky as rain, snow, hail or sleet.
* Rainwater seeps into the ground and collects in lakes and reservoirs.
* This water requires treatment before it is fit for human consumption.

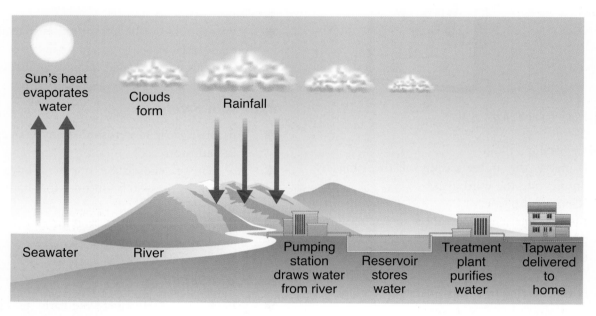

Fig 4.7: The source of water.

Water Treatment

There are seven stages in making water fit for human consumption.

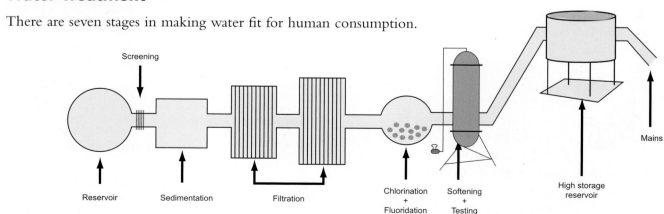

Fig 4.8: Water treatment.

Screening	• Large floating pieces of debris are removed from the water.
Sedimentation	• Chemicals are added to the water. These chemicals cling to the dirt and cause it to sink to the bottom of the tank.
Filtration	• Water passes over a series of filter beds composed of sand, gravel and stones. This removes any excess dirt.
Chlorination	• Chlorine is added to the water. • Chlorine kills germs.
Fluoridation	• Fluoride is added to the water. • Fluoride strengthens teeth.
Softening	• Chloride of lime is added to the water to soften it.
Testing	• The water is tested for purity. • After that, it is stored until it is needed for use.

Water Supply to a House

✱ Water is transferred from the reservoir via a **mains pipe**.

✱ The mains pipe brings the water to the **service pipe** of the house.

✱ Outside each house there is a **stopcock** which enables the water to be turned off.

✱ The service pipe carries water to the **cold water tap** in the kitchen and to the **storage tank** in the attic.

✱ The water in the storage tank supplies water to all other taps, toilets and the hot press tank.

✱ The location of the storage tank (attic) creates sufficient pressure to transport the water. This storage tank should be covered and insulated.

✱ It is important to remember that water should only be drunk from the cold water tap in the kitchen.

Natural Wells

✱ In rural areas water is often obtained from deep wells.

✱ The water from the well is tested for impurities.

✱ An electric pump transfers the water from the well to the house.

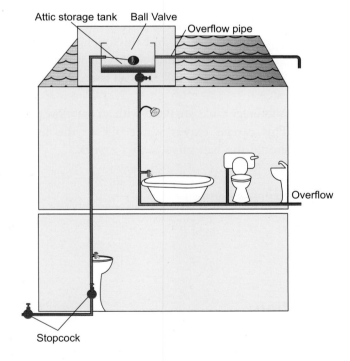

Fig 4.9: A house's cold water supply.

Water Storage

Storage Tank

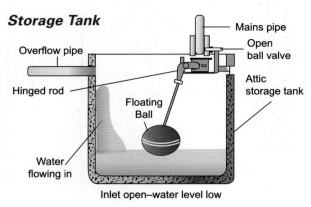

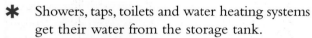

Fig 4.10: Storage tank – level low.

* Showers, taps, toilets and water heating systems get their water from the storage tank.
* An average storage tank holds approximately 230 litres of water.
* A ball valve controls the level of water in the storage tank.
* The ball valve is made up of a plastic ball which is connected to a valve by a hinged rod.
* When the level of water drops in the storage tank, the ball sinks and this opens the valve. This enables the tank to fill with water.
* When the tank is full, the ball rises, closing the valve.
* All storage tanks are fitted with an overflow pipe. This carries excess water out of the house should the ball valve cease to work.

Heating

* Heat in the home is provided by:
  * The sun.
  * People.
  * Electrical appliances.
  * Heating system.
* In the home, the heat requirement varies according to the activities being carried out, the season and the insulation provided.

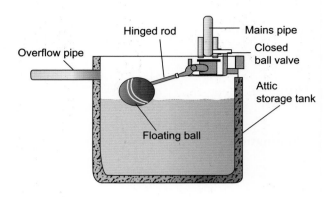

Fig 4.11: Storage tank – level high.

Hard Water

* Hard water is found in areas where there are large amounts of calcium and magnesium salts.
* There are two types of hard water:
  * **Temporary hardness:** This is caused by calcium magnesium bicarbonates. Temporary hardness is removed by boiling.
  * **Permanent hardness:** This is caused by calcium and magnesium sulphates. This water can be softened by adding washing soda, bath salts or commercial water softeners, e.g. Calgon tablets.

Effects:

* Difficult to produce a lather.
* Can lead to dry skin and dull hair.
* A scum forms around baths and sinks.
* 'Furring' of the water pipes can lead to blockages, preventing heating systems working efficiently.
* Furring of kettles and other appliances which contain a heating element – this reduces their effectiveness.

* The ideal temperature varies according to the room.
  * Bedroom: 15°C.
  * Bathroom: 19°C.
  * Sitting room: 21°C.
  * Kitchen: 19°C.

* The temperature can be monitored and controlled by:
  * Thermostats.
  * Thermostat radiator valves.
  * Time clocks.
  * Data term controllers.
  * Zone controls.

Thermostats (Electrical):

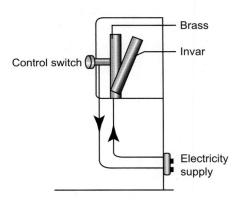

Fig 4.12: Inside a thermostat.

* A thermostat works on the principle of thermal expansion, where solids expand on heating and contract on cooling.
* A thermostat has a bi-metal strip (two metals: brass and invar). When heat is applied to the strip, the brass expands and breaks the electrical circuit.
* This causes the appliance to switch off.
* When the temperature drops, the connection is made and the cycle begins again.

Thermostats (Gas):

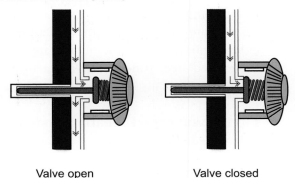

Valve open   Valve closed

Fig 4.13: A gas thermostat.

* Gas thermostats contain an invar rod, which is located inside a brass tube.
* An increase in temperature causes the brass tube to expand which, in turn, pulls the invar rod with it.
* A valve is located at the end of the invar rod and this limits the gas flow.
* As the brass cools, the valve opens, which enables more gas to flow.

Thermostat devices:

A room thermometer:
* This is mounted on the wall of a room and is set to the desired temperature.
* Room thermostats detect the surrounding temperature and respond by turning the heating on when the temperature falls below the desired level, and off when the temperature is reached.

A boiler thermostat:
* This is a thermostat connected to the central heating boiler.
* When the desired temperature is reached, the thermostat switches off the boiler.
* When the water temperature falls, the boiler restarts.

Thermostat radiator valves:
* These are attached to radiators in separate rooms.
* This controls the temperature in the individual room.

Time clocks:
* They automatically switch the heating on or off at times set by the user.

Data term controller:
* This combines all the controls needed for home heating in one unit. The unit decides the temperature outside.
* It can switch off if a lower temperature is required.

Zonal heating:

✳ This system enables certain parts of the house to be heated independently, e.g. the downstairs living area can be heated without heating the upstairs sleeping area.

Choosing a Heating System

Cost:

Always consider the installation, running costs and maintenance costs.

Level of control:

Always consider whether the heating system meets the necessary comfort level and how easily the heating system can be controlled.

Design:

This relates to the appearance of the heating system. Aesthetic appeal is a key factor when choosing household appliances.

House size:

Bigger houses tend to need larger, more elaborate heating systems to provide the required levels of heating.

Age of the house:

Older houses may lack adequate levels of insulation. This in turn will affect the choice of heating system.

Energy efficient:

Energy efficiency awareness is becoming more important today, with more people choosing an environmentally friendly heating system.

Fuel:

The type of fuel needed to operate the heating system must be considered. Factors include storage space, delivery, cost and sustainability.

Safety:

Always ensure that household heating systems are installed and serviced regularly by a professional.

Types of Heating

Full central heating:

Heating the whole house to a controlled temperature.

✳ There are two main types of central heating:
- Wet central heating (radiators).
- Dry central heating (hot air blown through grilles).

Partial central heating:

The main living areas are heated and the rooms upstairs are heated by the overflow heating as the hot air rises.

Background central heating:

A low temperature of about 13°C is achieved in the house just to remove the chill.

Spot or local heating:

Heating provided by an individual heater.

Passive solar heating

The aspect of the room affects heating. South-facing rooms with large windows enable the room to heat up during the day: however, another form of heating will be needed.

Central Heating System

✳ Water is heated in the boiler, fuelled by gas, oil or coal, and a pump circulates it through the pipe work to the radiators.

✳ The water runs from the boiler to the radiators and back again to the boiler.

✳ The water for this system is taken from a separate tank in the attic.

✳ Radiators are the most common method of transferring heat into the room. They are made from pressed steel panels with a corrugated surface.

Stages in the wet central heating system:

1. Water is heated in the boiler.
2. Hot water leaves the top of the boiler.
3. From here, it travels through a narrow pipe in the cylinder called the heat exchanger. This

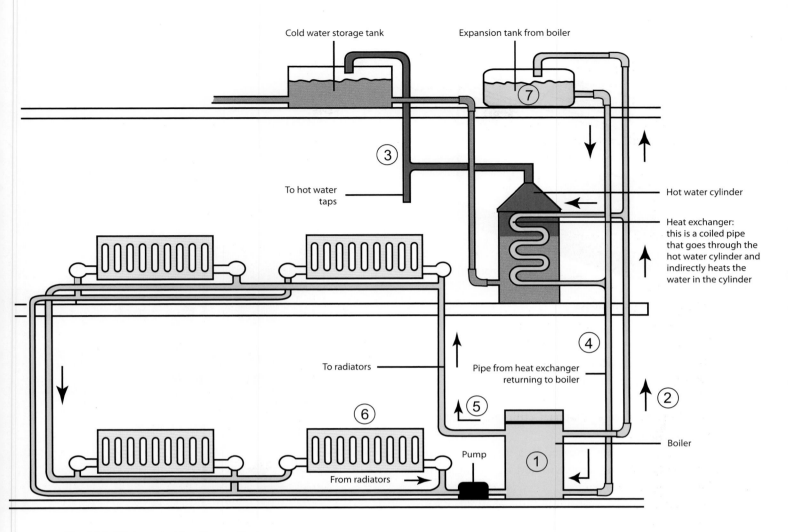

Fig 4.14: Wet central heating system.

indirectly heats the water in the hot water taps.

4. The water that travelled through the heat exchanger returns to the boiler.

5. A separate pipe leaves the top of the boiler and goes to the radiators. Heat is emitted from the water flowing through the radiators.

6. This water returns to the boiler where the cycle starts again.

7. In the attic, a pipe from the expansion tank removes overheated water. This releases pressure in the system.

Scientific principles:

✶ **Convection:** This is the transfer of heat in a cyclical movement (currents) in a gas or a liquid.
  ● In the boiler and the hot waster system the method of heat transfer that is used is convection.

✶ **Radiation:** This is the transfer of heat in direct lines from the heat source.
  ● Around the radiators, the air space is heated by radiation.

✶ **Thermal expansion:** This is the expansion of materials when heat is applied.
  ● It enables hot water to flow in an upward movement to the hot water cylinder.

Dry Central Heating System

✶ Examples of dry central heating systems include:
  ● Electric storage heaters.
  ● Under-floor heating.
  ● Warm air heating.

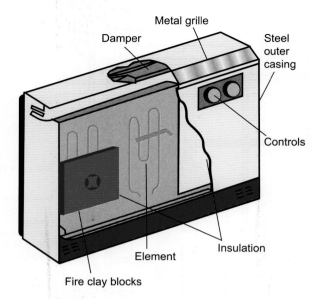

Fig 4.15: An electric storage heater.

Electric Storage Heaters:
* Heating elements are embedded in fire clay blocks.
* An insulating material, fibreglass, surrounds these blocks.
* This is further encased in a steel outer casing.
* The elements are switched on at night using off-peak electricity.
* The materials surrounding the elements heat up.
* The insulating material prevents the heat escaping.
* The radiator gradually emits heat during the day by convection.
* Difficult to control the temperature.
* Separate water system required.

Under-Floor Heating:
* Works on the same principle as storage heating.
* Elements are embedded under the floor.
* The system is wired to off-peak electricity.
* Must be installed during building.
* Only suitable for concrete floors.
* Separate water heating system required.
* Heat is transferred by convection.

Individual Heaters:
* These heaters are fuelled by:
  * Solid fuel.
  * Electricity.
  * Gas.

* Examples include fan heaters and electric heaters.

Insulation

The aim of insulation in the home is to reduce heat loss.

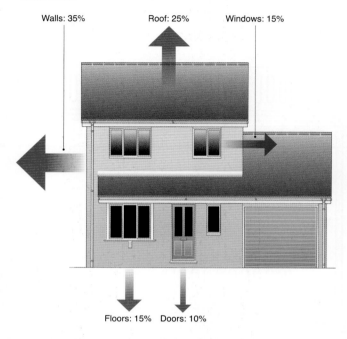

Fig 4.16: Where heat is lost in a house.

Principles of Insulation

* Using insulating materials reduces heat loss in the home. These materials include air, poly-styrene, fibreglass and fabric.
* Insulating materials are poor conductors of heat.
* When these materials are carefully placed in the house, the overall effect is a reduction in costs and more efficient use of energy.

Advantages of Insulation

* Saves energy, so less damaging to the environment as fewer fuels are used.
* Saves on energy bills.
* Good insulation acts as a noise barrier in the home.
* Decreases heat loss in all areas of the home.
* Creates a comfortable temperature in the home.

Methods of Insulation in the Home

* Attic insulation.
* Wall insulation.
* Hot water cylinder.

* Window and door insulation.
* Floor insulation.

Attic Insulation

Approximately 25–30 per cent of heat is lost through the attic when it is not insulated.

Types of attic insulation:

Blanket Insulation	Loose-Fill Insulation	Foam Insulation	Blown-Fibre Insulation
• Traditional form of attic insulation. • Composed of glass fibre or mineral fibre. • This insulation is sold in rolls, which are laid down between the joists in the attic. 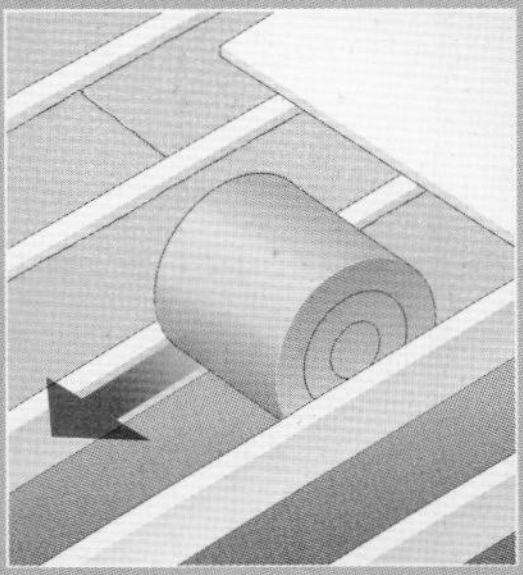	• This form of insulation is composed of loose material, such as cellulose fibre, vermiculite or polystyrene pellets. • These, like blanket insulation, are placed between joists in the attic. 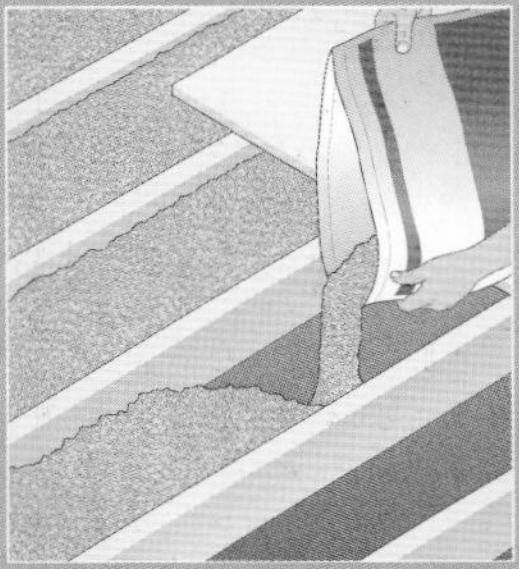	• This is spray foam. • The foam is sprayed between rafters. • When the foam sets, it becomes solid. • This type of insulation is often used in attic conversions.	• Blown-fibre insulation is useful for awkward areas. • Glass fibres, cellulose fibres and mineral fibres are the materials used. • As the name suggests, these materials are blown into the attic. • This type of insulating must be installed by trained contractors.

Fig 4.17: Blanket insulation.

Fig 4.18: Loose-fill insulation.

Wall Insulation

* This type of insulation includes:
  * Cavity walls.
  * Solid wall insulation: internal and external.

Cavity walls:

* This occurs when two concrete walls are constructed side by side 10 m apart.
* The cavity (space between the two walls) is then filled with an insulating material such as polystyrene.

Cavity Wall Insulation:

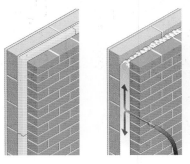

Fig 4.19: Cavity wall insulation.

* Foam polystyrene can be injected into existing cavity walls.
* Polystyrene beads can be blown into the cavity.
* During building, slabs known as batts can be fitted to the outside of the inner cavity wall.
* Air acts as an insulator together with the polystyrene.

Solid wall insulation:

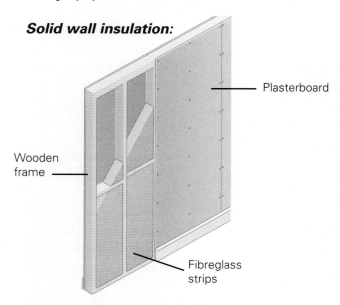

Fig 4.20: Internal solid wall insulation.

Internal:

* Fibreglass strips are fitted to the inside wooden frame of the house and then covered with plasterboard.
* A disadvantage of this type of insulation is that it reduces the size of the room.

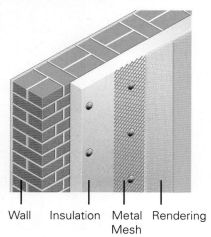

Fig 4.21: External solid wall insulation.

External:

* This involves placing fibreglass between the wooden frames on the wall.
* This is then covered with a metal mesh.
* Waterproofing is carried out by applying a layer of insulating slabs which, in turn, are covered with plaster material.

Hot Water Cylinders

* An unlagged hot water cylinder can cause electrical bills to be high as well as wasting energy.
* Lagging jackets vary in width; the average is 80 millimetres.
* Most copper cylinders today have sprayed-on insulation, which is very efficient.

Windows and Doors

* About 15 per cent heat is lost through windows. This heat loss can be minimised by installing double-glazed windows.
* These windows work on the principle that air is a poor conductor of heat, therefore less heat is lost through double-glazed windows than through a single pane.
* With double-glazed windows, there are two panes of glass with an air space between them. This reduces the rate at which heat escapes.

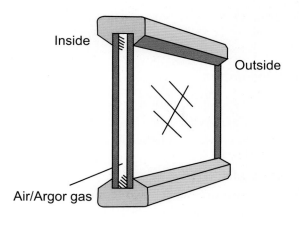

Fig 4.22: Double-glazed windows.

Types of Double Glazing Available:

Double Glazing	Argon-Filled Double Glazing	Low-Emissivity Double Glazing
<ul><li>Two panes of glass separated by a space.</li><li>The space contains air.</li><li>Cheapest form of double glazing.</li><li>Efficient.</li></ul>	<ul><li>Two panes of glass separated by space filled with argon gas.</li><li>More efficient than double glazing.</li></ul>	<ul><li>On the inside pane of double-glazed windows, a coating known as low-e is applied.</li><li>This is the most effective form of double glazing as the least amount of heat escapes and light can pass easily through.</li><li>Most efficient form of double glazing.</li></ul>

✱ Together with double glazing, another practical way of minimising heat loss is to use fully lined curtains.

✱ The opening parts of doors and windows can be insulated in a number of ways. These include:
- A self-adhesive foam.
- A rubber strip.
- A copper, plastic or bronze strip, which tends to be more durable.
- A silicone sealant, which is squeezed into gaps but can be quite expensive.
- A flexi strip, which is suited to sliding doors.

✱ Doors are insulated by placing draught excluders at the bottom of the door and around the letter box.

✱ Types of draught excluder for the bottom of the door include:
- Flap excluders.
- Brush excluders.

Floor insulation

✱ Floors can be insulated by using carpet with a thick underlay.

✱ When a house is constructed, insulation together with damp-proof coursing are put in place to further insulate the floors.

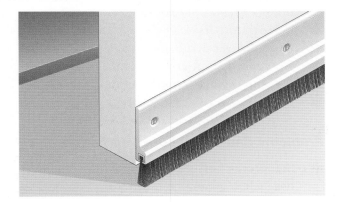

Fig 4.23: A brush excluder.

Ventilation

Ventilation is the process whereby stale air is removed and replaced with fresh air without causing a draught, thus maintaining a comfortable temperature.

Air Composition

Gas	Fresh Air	Stale Air
Nitrogen	79%	79%
Oxygen	21%	17%
Carbon Dioxide	0.04%	4.04%
Water Vapour	Varies	Varies
Temperature	Varies	Varies

Principles of Ventilation

* Ventilation works on the principle that when air is heated it rises and expands.
* This warm air is then replaced by cool air.
* This forms convection currents, enabling stale air to exit a room and replacing stale air with fresh air.
* Vents are placed high up on walls; these offer an exit route for the stale air.
* Fresh air enters a room at a lower level, such as under doors or down chimneys.

Advantages of Good Ventilation

* Provides an oxygen-rich environment for respiration.
* Removes impurities in the air, e.g. dust, odours, carbon dioxide and water vapour.
* Temperature levels in the air are monitored.
* Humidity levels are controlled.
* Air is needed for combustion, e.g. open fires.
* Prevents/reduces condensation.
* Reduces the risk of respiratory problems.

Problems Caused by Poor Ventilation

* Symptoms of poor ventilation include: headaches, poor concentration, drowsiness and fainting.
* A build-up of condensation may lead to structural damage in buildings.
* There may be an increase of illness and infection due to the presence of micro-organisms in the air.
* Respiratory diseases, e.g. bronchitis.

How to spot poor ventilation

* A prolonged build-up of condensation on glass surfaces in kitchens and bathrooms.
* Mould growth on walls and ceilings.
* A musty smell.

Humidity

Humidity is a measure of the amount of moisture in the air. Warm air contains more moisture than cold air. Rooms which have a high humidity level include kitchens and bathrooms.

Why humidity levels increase:

* Cooking.
* Drying clothes.
* Showering/bathing.
* Washing clothes.

Problems associated with high humidity levels:

* Drowsiness.
* Respiratory problems.
* Increased condensation.

Condensation

Condensation occurs when humid air meets cold surfaces, e.g. mirrors in bathrooms. The water vapour changes into water droplets.

Effects of condensation:

* Mould growth on walls and ceiling.
* Damage to wood, which can lead to structural damage.
* Metals rust.
* Because of damp insulation, there is an increase in heat loss from the house.
* Aggravated bronchial problems.

Preventing condensation:

* Ensure that there is adequate ventilation.
* Monitor ventilation in the kitchen and bathrooms and increase ventilation when necessary.
* Check that good insulation is provided, as good insulation raises the house temperature and prevents condensation.
* An efficient heating system will correctly monitor house temperatures.
* Remove moisture at source by having vents and windows open, in particular in the kitchen and bathroom.
* Reduce the amount of cold, glassy surfaces in the house.
* Make use of hydroscopic (water absorbing) materials in soft furnishings and floorings.
* Always vent tumble driers to the exterior of the house.

Methods of Ventilation

Natural
- Doors.
- Windows.
- Open fireplaces.
- Room vents.

Artificial
- Extractor fans.
- Cooker hoods.
- Air conditioning.

Improving Natural Ventilation

✱ Use an **open door** to ventilate a room: however, if used too often this can make a room cold and uncomfortable by causing a draught.

✱ **Windows** have the same effect as doors. When the weather is good, windows should be opened in all rooms to supply ventilation.

✱ Closed **chimney places** can prevent ventilation. Always ensure when closing a chimney to offer sufficient space for ventilation.

✱ There are two types of **room vents**: the hit and miss vent and the trickle vent. These vents enable a constant air change in the room.

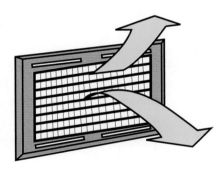

Fig 4.24: A hit and miss vent.

✱ **Airbricks** which are located in the wall of the house enable air change while also preventing dry rot and wet rot. These bricks are often covered with a metal mesh.

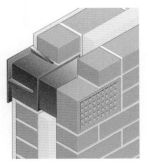

Fig 4.25: Airbricks.

Artificial Methods of Ventilation

Extractor Fans

Construction:

✱ The outer casing is composed of aluminium or plastic.

✱ Underneath the casing are electrically powered rotating blades.

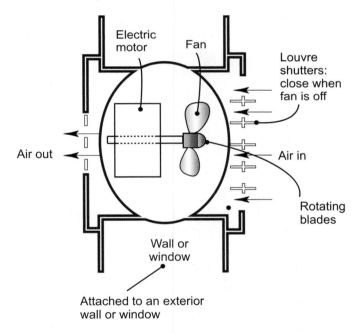

Fig 4.26: An extractor fan.

✱ Extractors are available in a wide variety of colours and sizes.

✱ The extractor fan can be turned on by pressing a switch or pulling a pull cord.

Working principle:

* When the switch is turned on, or the pull cord is pulled to the on position, the shutter opens and the electrical motor starts.
* The motor causes the blades to rotate at a fast speed.
* This causes suction, drawing out the stale air from the room.
* Fresh air enters the room through filtration.

Cooker Hoods

There are two types of cooker hood: ducted and ductless.

Fig 4.27: A ducted cooker hood.

A ducted hood:

* All ducted hoods are fitted to an external wall.
* These hoods tend to remove more stale air and humidity than their ductless counterparts.
* These hoods are composed of a metal canopy, grease filter, a charcoal filter which aids the removal of odours, and a fan.
* The grease filter traps dirt and grease.

A ductless hood:

* These are used above cookers not positioned on an external wall.
* The air is purified and then re-circulated into the room.
* The construction is similar to that of a ducted cooker hood.
* The charcoal filter must be changed regularly in order to remain efficient.

Fig 4.28: A ductless cooker hood.

Working principle of cooker hoods:

* An electric fan rotates at a very high speed.
* This creates suction, which draws the stale air out of the room.
* In the case of the ducted hood, stale air is removed from the house.

Lighting

Function of Lighting:

* Prevents eye strain.
* Enables the performance of various activities.
* Emphasises key features of decor.
* Prevents accidents by providing visibility.
* Creates mood and ambience.

Natural Lighting	Artificial Lighting
<ul><li>Doors.</li><li>Windows.</li><li>Glass bricks.</li></ul>	<ul><li>Tungsten filament bulbs.</li><li>Tungsten halogen bulbs.</li><li>Low-voltage tungsten halogen (quartz lamp).</li><li>Fluorescent lighting.</li><li>Compact fluorescent lights (CFLs).</li></ul>

Natural Lighting

Natural lighting enters the home through doors, windows and glass bricks. The amount of light getting into a room depends on:

✱ **The size of the windows:** The bigger the window, the more light enters.

✱ **Aspect of the room (the direction the room is facing):** South versus north facing. South-facing rooms get more light.

✱ **Colour scheme:** Light colours reflect the light; dark colours absorb the light.

Artificial Lighting

Artificial lighting is either incandescent or fluorescent.

✱ Incandescent lighting occurs when an electric current passes through a filament and causes the filament to heat up and glow.

✱ There is a range of incandescent lighting including tungsten filament, tungsten halogen and low-voltage tungsten halogen bulbs.

Tungsten Filament Bulbs

✱ This type of bulb gets its name from the coiled tungsten filament which, when heated, creates a white glow.

✱ The outside of the bulb is made of clear, pearlised or coloured glass.

✱ The bulb is filled with a mixture of nitrogen and argon gas.

✱ The tungsten wire can have a single or double coil; the greater the coiling, the higher the light output.

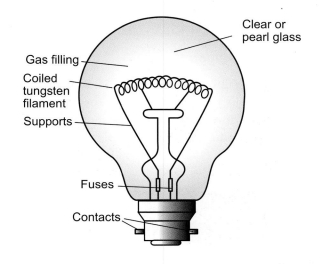

Fig 4.29: A tungsten filament bulb.

✱ When the light is switched on, electricity passes though the tungsten wire, which heats up quickly, producing a white glow.

✱ This is due to the resistance to the flow of electricity.

✱ The tungsten in the filament evaporates with time; this causes blackening of the bulb and weakens the tungsten to the point that it can no longer carry the current and so the bulb 'blows'.

✱ These bulbs last up to approximately 1,000 hours.

✱ They are available in various strengths from 15 watts to 200 watts.

✱ Bayonet or screw-in types are available.

Advantages of Tungsten Filament Bulbs	Disadvantages of Tungsten Filament Bulbs
• The light is instant. • They are relatively inexpensive to buy. • There is a range of power ratings and shapes available. • They are widely available. • They are easy to fit, replace and dispose of. • The light emitted provides a warmish glow. • These bulbs can be dimmed if required.	• They have a short life span, approximately 1,000 hours. • They are not environmentally friendly. • They are hot to handle. • They are unsuitable for use outdoors, as a change in temperature can cause the glass to split. • They are expensive to run.

Tungsten Halogen Bulbs

✳ These bulbs are similar to tungsten filament bulbs, but the evaporation of the tungsten is slowed down by the presence of halogens, such as iodine, in the gas filling.

✳ This extends the bulb life and also prevents the bulb from blackening.

✳ The filament can heat to a higher temperature.

Advantages of Tungsten Halogen Lamps	Disadvantages of Tungsten Halogen Lamps
• They light immediately. • They have a lifespan of up to 3,000 hours. • They can be dimmed. • There is a wide range of bulb types and wattage. • The light they produce is similar to that of daylight.	• They generate a lot of heat, which restricts their uses in the house. • They are costly to run. • They are energy inefficient. • They are not as readily available as tungsten filament bulbs.

Low-Voltage Tungsten Halogen Bulbs (Quartz Lamps)

✳ These bulbs give a sparkling effect.
✳ They are small in size.
✳ They are used to focus the light in a narrow beam.

Fluorescent Lighting

✳ Fluorescent bulbs tend to be long, cylindrical glass tubes.
✳ Fluorescent bulbs are available in standard, compact and 'mini' designs.

Fig 4.30: Low-voltage tungsten halogen bulb (quartz lamp).

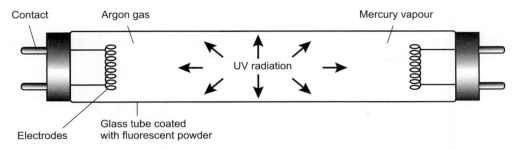

Contact   Argon gas   Mercury vapour

UV radiation

Electrodes

Glass tube coated
with fluorescent powder

Fig 4.31: Standard fluorescent bulb.

* The inside of the glass tube is coated with phosphorus (a fluorescent chemical).
* Electricity passes into the glass tube through small electrodes positioned at each end of the bulb.
* The argon or krypton gas inside the bulb is excited, which results in the production of invisible radiation.

* The mercury present is vaporised into the argon gas.
* These gases in turn interact with the phosphorus coating, causing it to fluoresce or glow.
* The price and wattage of fluorescent bulbs increase with the length of the tube.
* These bulbs are available in various lengths from 30 centimetres to 2.5 metres.

Advantages of Standard Fluorescent Bulbs	Disadvantages of Standard Fluorescent Bulbs
<ul><li>They require less energy, therefore they have low operating costs.</li><li>They are suitable for use next to flammable materials, as they remain cool when in operation.</li><li>They do not 'blow' immediately but instead weaken over time.</li><li>These bulbs can last for up to 8,000 hours.</li></ul>	<ul><li>There tends to be a delay between the light being switched on and the light coming on.</li><li>The light produced may seem clinical in a home setting.</li><li>Care must be taken when disposing of the bulbs as there are chemicals present.</li><li>The bulbs tend to make a noise, like a humming sound.</li></ul>

Compact Fluorescent Lights (CFLs)

* With energy efficiency coming more and more to the fore, compact fluorescent lights (CFLs) are becoming more popular.
* Their compact size is achieved by folding the path of the discharge so that the narrow tube has two or more limbs.
* CFLs function in the same way as standard fluorescent bulbs.
* They are sold in sizes ranging from 7 watts to 23 watts, while providing a light similar to standard light bulbs.
* CFL bulbs are more expensive to buy, for

example a conventional bulb costs €0.89, whereas a CFL bulb costs €15.29, but it uses 80 per cent less electricity than an ordinary bulb and lasts ten times longer. The largest savings can be achieved by using CFLs in places where the light is likely to be left on for long periods, such as a living room, hall or porch.

Fig 4.32: A CFL bulb.

Advantages of CFLs	Disadvantages of of CFLs
• They save money on lighting bills. • They are available in a range of shapes and sizes. • They last ten times as long as a standard bulb. • They can be fitted into ordinary light fittings. • They are suitable for awkward locations where constant bulb replacement is difficult.	• They take a few minutes to reach full brightness. • They are longer and bulkier than standard bulbs. • More light comes from the sides of the bulb than from the end. • They are not suitable for all types of lamp shades. • In cold conditions, less light is produced. • They do not work with dimmer switches.

Principles in Planning a Lighting System

Types of Lighting	• Always consider the type of light needed, i.e. general lighting, task lighting or mood lighting.
Comfort	• Avoid glare. • Glare can lead to eye strain.
Mood	• Dim lighting can create a romantic mood.
Colour and Texture	• Rough textures absorb light; smooth textures reflect light. • Dark colours absorb light; warm colours reflect the light.
Decoration	• Lighting can be used to highlight pictures or features in a room or in a glass cabinet.
Room Function	• Always consider the function of the room and the tasks being carried out, e.g. in a living room, task lighting is needed for reading, but mainly accent lighting is needed.
Safety	• There should always be sufficient light to carry out all tasks. • Always consider a two-way switch for stair lighting. • Make sure not to have shades positioned too closely to light bulbs. • Don't overload sockets. • Avoid using paper shades. • Stick to the recommended wattage. • Use rounded bases for children's rooms.
Create Space	• Clever use of lighting can be used to create an illusion of space in a room.

Properties of Light and their Application

Light travels in a straight line until it meets an obstacle. The light is then reflected, absorbed, diffused, refracted or dispersed.

Reflected light:

When light falls on a shiny or pale-coloured surface it is reflected, e.g. mirrors, white ceiling.

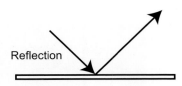

Fig 4.33: Reflected light.

Refracted light:

This occurs when light passes through thick glass. This causes the light to bend, e.g. light shining through a glass block or frosted glass.

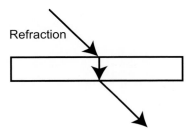

Fig 4.34: Refracted light.

Absorbed light:

Dark colours absorb light. A room painted with a dark colour makes the room appear smaller.

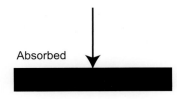

Fig 4.35: Absorbed light.

Diffused light:

When light passes through a translucent substance or shines on a dull surface, it is diffused or scattered in many directions e.g. opaque lampshades and indirect lighting, where the light is scattered in all directions.

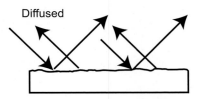

Fig 4.36: Diffused light.

Dispersed light:

When light passes through a prism or crystal, it is broken down into its component colours, e.g. in crystal chandeliers.

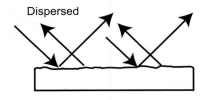

Fig 4.37: Dispersed light.

Outline of Contemporary Lighting Developments

* Developments have occurred in lighting technology.
* These developments have been brought about due to an increased awareness in energy efficiency, changes in aesthetic appeal and technological advances.

Lighting Developments

Outdoor Lighting	Inside Lighting	Technological Developments in Lighting
• Sensor lights. • Solar-powered lights. • Fountain lights. • Pond lights. • Column lights.	• Swivel lights. • Recessed lights. • Touch lights. • Pivot action lamps. • Track lighting.	• Dimmer switches. • Fibre optics. • Sensitive-to-touch lights. • Halogen lights.

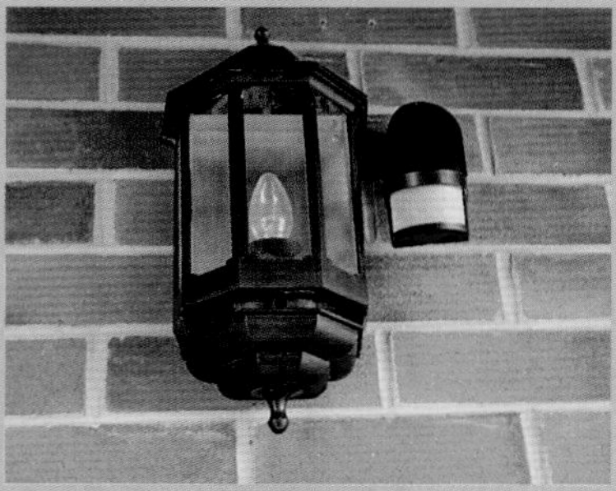

Fig 4.38: Modern outdoor lighting.

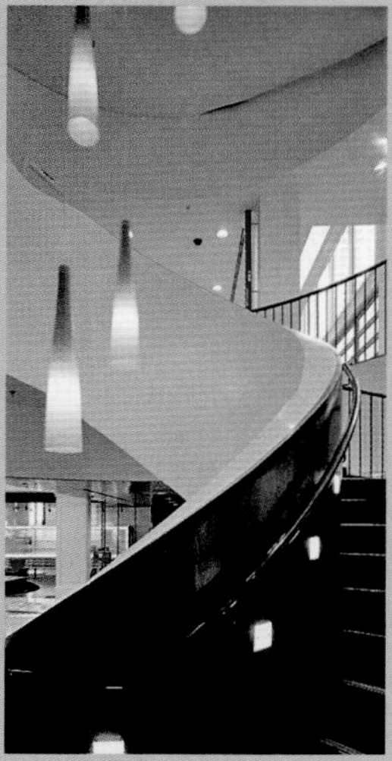

Fig 4.39: Contemporary inside lighting.

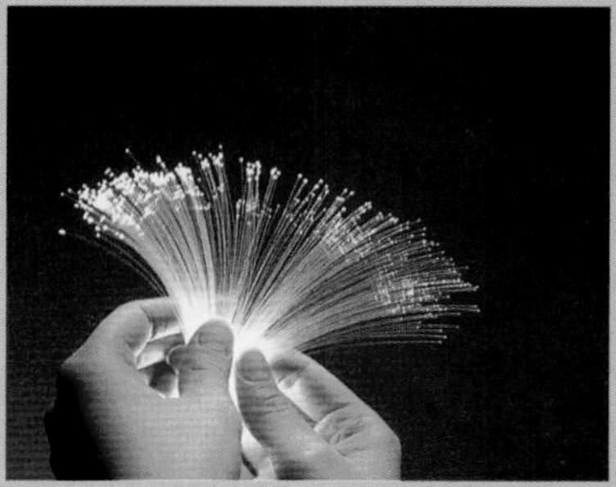

Fig 4.40: Fibre optics.

Exam Questions (2004)

Questions
Elective 1, Question 1b

Excessive ventilation is as undesirable as insufficient ventilation as it can lead to low room temperatures, excessive draughts and high heating bills.

1. State the importance of adequate ventilation in a house. (9)

2. Explain how natural ventilation is provided in a modern house. (9)

3. Suggest a suitable method of artificial ventilation for a kitchen. Explain the underlying principle of the suggested method. (12)

Sample Answers

1. State the importance of adequate ventilation in a house. (9)

   3 points x 3 marks = 9.

Adequate ventilation:

- It provides an oxygen-rich environment for respiration. It removes impurities in the air, e.g. dust, odours, carbon dioxide and water vapour.
- It enables temperature levels in the air to be monitored and controls humidity levels.
- It prevents/reduces condensation. It reduces the risk of respiratory problems.

2. Explain how natural ventilation is provided in a modern house. (9)

   3 points x 3 marks = 9.

Natural ventilation:

Natural ventilation in a modern house is achieved through:

- Doors.
- Windows.
- Open fireplaces.
- Room vents.

- **Doors:** Use an open door to ventilate a room: however, if used too often this can make a room cold and uncomfortable by causing a draught.
- **Windows:** Windows have the same effect as doors. When the weather is good, windows should be opened in all rooms to supply ventilation.

- **Chimney:** Closed fireplaces can prevent ventilation. Always ensure, when closing a chimney, that there is sufficient space for ventilation.
- **Vents:** There are two types of room vent: the hit and miss vent and the trickle vent. These vents enable a constant air change in the room.
- **Airbricks:** Located in the wall of the house, they enable air change while also preventing dry rot and wet rot. These bricks are often covered with a metal mesh.

3. Suggest a suitable method of artificial ventilation for a kitchen. Explain the underlying principle of the suggested method. (12)

   Method = 4 marks.
   Principle: 2 points x 4 marks = 12.
   Method = Extractor Fan.

Working principle:

- When the switch is powered to on, or the pull cord is pulled to the on position, the shutter opens and the electrical motor starts. The motor causes the blades to rotate at a fast speed.
- This causes suction, drawing out the stale air from the room. Fresh air enters the room through infiltration.

Elective

SOCIAL STUDIES

1 Social Change and the Family

2 Education

3 Work

4 Unemployment

5 Leisure

6 Poverty

1 2 3

1

Social Change and the Family

Impact of Social and Economic Change on the Family

The ways in which social and economic change has had an impact on family life include:

* Changes in settlement patterns from rural to urban areas.
* Reduction in working hours and an increase in leisure time.
* Improvements in the provision of education and social welfare

* Changing attitudes to marriage, parenting, and the roles of men and women.
* Improved pay and working conditions.
* Increased participation of women in the work-force.
* Legislation on equal pay and employment opportunities.
* Unemployment.

Change in Settlement Patterns from Rural to Urban Areas

The rural population in Ireland has decreased over recent years whilst the urban population has increased.

Rural Areas	Urban Areas
• The agricultural industry is not as labour intensive today, so fewer people are required to work on the land. • Rural areas have an increased elderly population, and a decline in marriage and birth rates. • Younger people are leaving rural areas to find work in urban areas. • Social life in rural areas has declined as amenities have closed down. • Post offices, banks, etc. may also be at risk of closing down in rural areas.	• Extensive social life as many amenities and entertainment venues are located in urban areas. • An increase in population leads to traffic congestion, and air and noise pollution. • Employment opportunities may become more difficult to obtain due to increased competition. • There is a risk of greater social problems and anti-social behaviour, e.g. drugs, crime and vandalism.

Government schemes and initiatives have focused their attention on correcting the imbalance between rural and urban areas. For example, the Government Redeployment (Decentralisation) Plan and the Rural Resettlement Programme.

Reduction in Working Hours and an Increase in Leisure Time

❋ Irish and EU legislation govern the maximum number of hours an individual can work.

❋ Any extra work is viewed as overtime and payment should be made accordingly.

❋ Legislation also governs issues relating to maternity leave and paternity leave.

❋ On average the weekly working hours are 40 hours a week.

❋ An individual may choose to take a career break from their work or reduce their working hours by opting to job share.

❋ Other individuals may be able to do shift work or work flexitime.

❋ These various options available to individuals enable them to increase their leisure time.

❋ This leisure time can be spent having quality time with children, e.g. playing, trips to the zoo, family picnics and other outings.

❋ This reduction in working hours can relieve stress and tiredness from the intensity of the working week.

❋ Parents can enjoy all the advantages of spending extra time on family activities.

Improvements in the Provision of Education and Social Welfare

Education

❋ Education is available to all ages, from pre-school to primary, secondary, third-level, adult and second-chance education.

❋ Successive governments have invested in school buildings, resources, sports facilities, etc.

❋ The education system caters for a range of different abilities so that every student can reach their full potential, e.g. Leaving Certificate, Leaving Certificate Applied and Leaving Certificate Vocational Programme.

❋ Access to third-level institutions has been made easier, e.g. means-tested grants, elimination of third-level fees, access programmes for students in disadvantaged areas.

❋ Improvements in the area of special needs has meant that every child's needs are catered for, e.g. through Special Needs Assistants.

❋ Parents are seen as valuable stakeholders in the education system and are involved in parents' associations in schools.

❋ Parents have a greater understanding of the importance of education and offer valuable support and encouragement to their children, e.g. helping with homework, going to parent-teacher meetings.

Social Welfare

❋ Social welfare payments have relieved the financial burden for many families who live in poverty.

❋ Families on low incomes can avail of financial assistance, e.g. Family Income Supplement, Supplementary Welfare Allowance.

❋ Government schemes are in operation to assist low-income families at particularly expensive times of the year, e.g. the Back to School Clothing and Footwear Allowance.

❋ Child benefit has helped families cover their day-to-day expenses.

* Social welfare entitlements have relieved the strain for those who are unemployed, retired or disabled.
* Elderly people can enjoy free travel, a reduction in electricity bills, a medical card and the old age pension, etc.

Changing Attitudes

People's attitudes today have changed towards:
* Marriage.
* Parenting.
* Roles of men and women.

Marriage

* People no longer see marriage as a means of securing their future, therefore people are not getting married at a young age.
* In some cases, individuals consciously choose not to get married.
* Young couples today are cohabiting prior to marriage.
* An increasingly secular society has caused a reduction in the influence of the Catholic Church's teaching on marriage.
* Separation and divorce are more common and acceptable in today's society.
* Family structures have changed from the traditional extended and nuclear family to the emerging blended and lone-parent family.

Parenting

* Couples are adopting a more egalitarian approach to parenting.
* Men today show a keen interest in 'hands on' parenting.
* In today's society not only is the woman entitled to take maternity leave but the father is entitled to a number of days' paternity leave.
* If both parents work, childcare is often used as a partial substitute for parenting.

Roles of Men and Women

* Men are no longer the sole breadwinners in the family. This is due to an increase in the number of dual earner families.

* The traditional segregated roles have diminished and men are more involved with house duties and childcare.
* Roles are more egalitarian, with both partners sharing responsibility for household finances.

Improved Pay and Working Conditions

* There has been a reduction in the working week from 60 hours to the standard 39 hours.
* Because of this, people have more time to spend with their family.
* Improvements in pay have led to an increased standard of living.
* People have more disposable income which can be spent on luxury goods/services.
* The minimum hourly wage has increased to €8.66.
* Legislation has given people more statutory rights in relation to work.

Increased Participation of Women in the Workforce

* When both parents work (dual earners) there is an increase in the standard of living for the family.
* It is the norm for women to work and it is very much socially acceptable.
* With an increase in the number of women working, families tend to be smaller.

* Women who work are seen as positive role models for children, in particular daughters.
* Equal opportunities at work provide women with the chance to further their working status.

Legislation on Equal Pay and Employment Opportunities

* Legislation provides people with equal opportunities within the workplace including: women, the disabled and minority groups, etc.

* A problem in relation to current legislation is the idea that women today still get less pay than that of men.
* It is men who generally tend to dominate positions of authority within companies.

Unemployment

* Up until the mid-2000s unemployment levels in Ireland were considerably below the EU average.
* Recent times have seen an increase in unemployment in certain sectors due to a downturn in the economy.
* Unemployment tends to be focused in lower socio-economic areas of society.
* High levels of unemployment tend to be concentrated in the inner city, large social housing areas and remote rural areas.

Unemployment Rates	
Year	Rate (%)
2006	4.4%
2007	4.6%
2008	6.3%
2009 (1st quarter)	8.3%

Source: CSO.

2 Education

Purposes of Education

The main purposes of education include:
* Being a method of socialisation.
* Being an agent of social control.
* Contributing to the child's development.
* Being a preparation for work.

A Method of Socialisation

Socialisation is the social processes through which children develop an awareness of social norms and values and achieve a distinct sense of self.
* **Primary socialisation:** This is a process through which learning takes place in the family.
* **Secondary socialisation:** This is a process through which learning takes place in school and at work.

An Agent of Social Control

* Schools encourage children to conform to the school rules, to comply with codes of behaviour that are in the school. For example, wearing

the school uniform, being on time for class and having respect for those in authority.
* The curriculum teaches responsibility, rules and respect for others through the curriculum, e.g. SPHE (Social, Personal and Health Education) and through what is known as the 'hidden' curriculum, e.g. school rules and respect for authority.
* Sanctions and rewards are used to encourage pupils to conform. An example of a sanction is detention; an example of a reward is prize-giving ceremonies.

Contributing to a Child's Development

Physical Needs	Emotional Needs	Intellectual Needs	Moral Needs
• Encouraging the development of physical skills, e.g. dexterity and hand-eye co-ordination.	• Children develop emotionally to become mature in their feelings towards themselves and others.	• Schooling promotes intellectual development by the wide range of subjects it offers.	• The school's ethos sets out the values and thinking of the school.

Physical Needs	Emotional Needs	Intellectual Needs	Moral Needs
• Physical skills are developed in subjects such as Home Economics, Art and PE (Physical education).	• Emotional skills are developed in subjects such as SPHE and RSE (Relationships and Sexuality Education).	• Continuous assessments, class tests and exams motivate pupils to achieve academically.	• Each student is expected to behave according to the ethos of the school. • Moral development is explored in subjects such as Religion, SPHE, CSPE (Civic, Social and Political Education) and Home Economics.

A Preparation for Work

✱ Schools provide individuals with a wide range of skills for the workforce.

✱ Examples of skills include numeracy, literacy, artistic, musical, woodwork, technical, graphics, cooking, science and computing.

✱ Punctuality at school and respect for authority are all part of the school structure and are valuable in the workplace.

✱ Educational programmes such as the Leaving Certificate, the Leaving Certificate Applied and the Leaving Certificate Vocational Programme are offered in schools to take account of the different needs of pupils and to enable pupils to achieve their full potential.

✱ State examinations differentiate between abilities and are used to determine career choices.

Factors that Influence Educational Achievement

Parents' Attitude to Education

Parents who value education will instil this in their children. A positive approach to education, encouragement and support from home generally result in students who want to learn.

Parents' Level of Education

Children of parents who are well educated tend to do better in school. Educated parents can offer support in terms of subjects, career choices and the exam system because they understand the education system themselves.

Child's Intellectual Ability

Sociologists often debate the theory of nature versus nurture, i.e. that a lot of who we are is inherited but it can also be shaped by the environment in which we are brought up. Intellectual ability can be inherited but also aided by a supportive and encouraging school and home life.

Family Size

The greater the number of children in a family, the greater the financial and emotional strain placed on it. Children from larger families may be more constrained due to financial limitations, e.g. access to third-level college. Also there may not be sufficient time available to help with homework and project work.

The Home Environment

Poor housing conditions can hinder, and good housing conditions can advance, a student's performance in school. For example, poor heating may cause a child to be susceptible to illness and therefore be absent from school regularly. Poor diet can affect school attendance. A warm, comfortable home with space for study can promote a healthy child in mind and body.

The School Environment

Classroom size, pupil-teacher ratio, streaming, mixed ability classes, classroom management and discipline can all affect the student's educational achievement. Bullying and negative peer pressure can have a negative impact on the student's educational achievement.

The Local Environment

Students from areas where there are high levels of crime, anti-social behaviour, vandalism, drug abuse, etc. are often poorly motivated and this impacts on educational achievement. Schools in deprived areas may have more students with discipline problems, attendance issues and who see no real value in education.

Peers

There are two types of peer pressure: positive and negative. The type of friends a person has can lead to one or the other type of pressure. Generally, when a person's friends are interested in school and achieving, this will result in positive peer pressure. Generally, when a person's friends are uninterested in school and achieving, this results in negative peer pressure.

The Provision of Education in Ireland

There are six aspects to the provision of education in Ireland.

* Pre-school.
* Primary.
* Second level.
* Third level.
* Adult and second-chance education.
* Special needs education.

Pre–School Education

Crèches/Nurseries	Playschools	Montessori Schools	Early Start Pre-School Programmes
• Cater for children up to five years of age. • Allow children to play, sleep, eat and change. • Can be community based or privately run. • Run by qualified people. • The ratio of children to carers is generally kept low. • Grants are available from the Department of Health and Children and the Department of Justice, Equality and Law Reform.	• Cater for children between two and five years of age. • Allow children to be involved in pre-school activities where children are learning in a fun and active environment. • Can be community based or privately run.	• Cater for children up to seven years of age. • Allow children to learn in a stimulating environment. • Privately run. • Run by Montessori-trained teachers.	• Cater for children between three and four years of age in disadvantaged areas. • Allow children to get a positive start to education and develop in language, social, cognitive and personal areas. • Run by the Department of Education and Science. • Students are taught by teachers, parents and childcare assistants.

Primary School

* There are four categories of primary school: state-funded primary schools, non-aided private primary schools, Gaelscoils and special needs schools.

* They cater for children between the ages of four and twelve.

* There are approximately 445,000 children in primary schools in Ireland.

* There are 3,600 primary schools.

* There are 107 special schools.

* Primary schools are funded mainly by the Department of Education and Science.

* Primary schools are run by boards of management.

* Special funding is also provided for schools in disadvantaged areas.

* The majority of primary schools are denominational (religion specific).

* The curriculum is divided into the following areas: languages, maths, social, environmental, scientific, arts education (including visual art, music and drama), PE and SPHE.

* The National Council for Curriculum and Assessment (NCCA) is responsible for reviewing and overseeing the curriculum.

* There is no formal state exam at the end of primary school.

* Full-time or part-time remedial teachers provide extra support and help to students who have difficulty with certain aspects of learning.

Second-Level School

* Types of second-level school include:
  • Secondary.

  • Vocational.
  • Community.
  • Comprehensive.
  • Private.

* Second-level education caters for children between the ages of twelve and eighteen.

* Secondary schools are privately owned and generally single-sex schools. They are managed by the trustees; in the majority of these schools either religious or a board of governors.

* Vocational schools are generally co-educational schools and managed by VECs (vocational education committees).
* Community and comprehensive schools are managed by boards of management.

* All schools provide a three-year Junior Cycle programme and a two- or three-year Senior Cycle programme.

Junior Cycle	Transition Year	Senior Cycle

• This is a three-year programme.
• Subjects at Junior Cert level include: Irish, English, Maths, History, Geography, CSPE, a modern language and a choice from Business Studies, Home Economics, Science, Art and Music.
• Subjects are offered at higher and ordinary levels and some subjects are offered at foundation level, e.g. Maths.
• A written examination is offered at the end of three years.
• Some subjects have a practical, project or listening component.
	• This is a student-centred one-year programme.
	• It is not exam-based.
	• It encourages students to take responsibility for learning and teamwork and aims to build confidence.
	• Students learn new skills and explore new subjects.
	• Students complete work experience.
	• Students participate in mini companies.
		• Students undertaking one of the following Leaving Certificate programmes.
		  • Leaving Certificate.
		  • Leaving Certificate Applied.
		  • Leaving Certificate Vocational Programme.

There are a variety of Leaving Certificate programmes available. These include:
• The Leaving Certificate.
• The Leaving Certificate Vocational Programme.
• The Leaving Certificate Applied Programme.

Leaving Certificate Programme

* This is a two-year programme.
* A state exam is held at the end of the programme.
* Students are required to study at least five subjects.
* Some students study up to nine subjects.
* A wide variety of subjects are offered to students.
* Compulsory subjects include Irish, English and Maths.
* Optional subject choices include Home Economics, Business, Biology, Chemistry, Geography, History, French, Art and Music.

* These subjects are examined at higher and ordinary level. Maths and Irish are offered at foundation level.
* A student's best six subjects are used to calculate points, which are used to gain access to third-level education.

Leaving Certificate Vocational (LCVP) Programme

* This is a two-year programme. A state exam is held at the end of the programme.
* The aim of this programme is to introduce people to the world of business and employment.

* Pupils who opt for LCVP study five Leaving Certificate subjects, including two subjects to be chosen from a set of vocational subjects: Home Economics, Business, Accounting, Art, Music, Construction Studies, Agricultural Science and Technical Graphics.
* Students must also study a European language.
* There are three mandatory modules that must be carried out by students:
    * Enterprise education.
    * Preparation for work.
    * Work experience.
* These modules are assessed by a portfolio (60 per cent) and a written exam (40 per cent).
* A pass, merit or distinction may be awarded.
* These results can then be converted to points that are used to gain access to third-level education.
* Many students use the points from this programme instead of those from one of their traditional Leaving Certificate subjects.

Leaving Certificate Applied Programme

* This is a two-year programme.
* A state exam is held at the end of the programme for some subjects.
* Students are continually assessed throughout the two years by way of key assignments and tasks.

* Tasks are assessed based on a written report and an interview.
* Attendance is also monitored and credits are awarded on the basis of key assignments and attendance.
* This programme is aimed at students whose needs are not met by other Leaving Certificate programmes.
* It prepares students for work.
* The programme is taught in four half-year modules.
* Subjects are grouped under the following three headings:
    * General education: English and Communications, Mathematical Applications, Social Education, etc.
    * Vocational education: Vocational Preparation and Guidance, work experience.
    * Vocational preparation: Hotel, Catering and Tourism; Hair and Beauty; Graphic and Construction Studies; Information and Communications Technology; Active Leisure Studies.
* Graduates of the Leaving Certificate Applied who progress to an approved further education award (e.g. PLC) can become eligible for admission to some third-level courses in the institutes of technology and pursue some degree courses in these institutes and in universities.

Learning Links Learning Links

Post-Leaving Certificate (PLC) Courses
These are full-time courses that range from one to two years.
* PLC courses take place in schools, colleges and community education centres around the country.
* Over 90 per cent of PLC courses are delivered by VECs (vocational education committees). At present, over 1,000 courses are on offer in 229 centres.
* Courses include Childcare, Hotel and Catering, Business and Secretarial Skills, Sport and Leisure, Theatre and Stage.
* Post-Leaving Certificate courses adopt an integrated approach, focusing on technical knowledge, core skills and work experience.
* Fifty per cent of the time spent on these courses is devoted to knowledge and skill training related to employment, with a further 25 per cent on relevant work-based experience.
* The qualification received at the end of training is awarded by FETAC (Further Education and Training Awards Council).
* Advanced courses may offer FETAC Level III, which can lead to further studies at third level.

Third-Level Education

The main sectors of third-level education are:
* Universities.
* Institutes of technology (ITs).
* Colleges of education.
* Private colleges.

Universities

* Ireland has four universities:
  * The National University of Ireland, which consists of the following:
    – UCD.
    – UCC.
    – UCG.
    – NUI Maynooth.
  * The University of Dublin (Trinity).

Fig 2.1: Trinity College campus.

  * The University of Limerick (UL).
  * Dublin City University (DCU).
* Universities offer degree programmes at three levels: bachelor, master's and doctorate.
* Examples of courses include: Medicine, Law, Arts, Social Science and Business.
* External examiners are used to check consistency.
* The Higher Education Authority (HEA) monitors the work of the universities on behalf of the Department of Education and Science.

Institutes of Technology (ITs)

* Institutes of technology provide certificates, diplomas, degrees (including master's and doctorates).
* They are located at 14 sites around the country, including Tralee, Cork, Waterford, Athlone, Blanchardstown, Dundalk and Sligo.
* DIT is Ireland's largest third-level institute.
* ITs provide education and training in a range of occupations in areas such as business, engineering, journalism, science, catering and music.
* The Department of Education and Science has responsibility for all institutes of technology.

Colleges of Education/Teacher Training Colleges

Primary Teachers:
* Trainee teachers study a degree programme in one of five colleges:
  * St Patrick's, Dublin.
  * Church of Ireland College.
  * St Mary's, Marino.
  * Froebal College of Education.
  * Mary Immaculate College, Limerick.

> A key requirement for gaining a place at a primary-school college is a keen understanding of Irish.

Second-Level Teachers:
* Most second-level teachers complete a three-year degree programme and then choose to study for the higher diploma in education.
* Home Economics teachers must train for four years in St Angela's, Sligo.
* Teachers of Art train in the National College of Art and Design (NCAD), Dublin.
* Teachers of PE train in Thomond College, Limerick.

Further and Adult Education

* Adult education helps to promote the idea of lifelong learning.

- AONTAS is the Irish National Association of Adult Education, a voluntary membership organisation. It exists to promote the development of a learning society which is accessible to and inclusive of all.
- Adult education is available in full-time or part-time courses.

Fig 2.2: Adults at an IT evening class.

- Sources of adult education courses include:
  - Universities and institutes of technology.
  - Distance learning, e.g. Open University courses.
  - Vocational Educational Committees (VECs).
  - Post-Leaving Certificate courses.
  - FÁS provides a range of education and training for the employed and the unemployed.
  - Adult Literacy Community Education Scheme (ALCES) provides basic literacy courses for the disadvantaged.
  - Agencies such as Teagasc and Coillte provide training in specific areas.
  - Vocational Training Opportunity Scheme (VTOS) is a programme that offers second-chance education for the unemployed.
- A feature of further education is its diversity and its links with employment, training, partnership and welfare.
- Adult education co-ordinators in schools and colleges organise the adult education courses on offer in their school.

Advantages of Adult Education:
- Following a particular interest or hobby.
- Keeping up with technological advances, e.g. in information technology.
- Improving personal qualifications.
- Meeting new people.
- Improving a person's chances of employment.

Special Needs Education

- Special needs refers to physical, intellectual or emotional needs.
- Special needs education provides for individuals with ADHD (attention-deficit hyperactivity disorder), dyslexia, Down syndrome, autism, and visual and hearing impairments.
- Special needs education is provided in:
  - Mainstream schools.
  - Special schools.

Mainstream Schools:

- A resource teacher/special needs assistants support students.
- Visiting teachers advise and assist class teachers of:
  - Visually impaired children.
  - Pupils with Down syndrome.
  - Children from Traveller families.

These teachers also advise parents.

Fig 2.3: A student with Down syndrome in class.

- Special needs pupils go into smaller classes with a low pupil-teacher ratio.
- Students with specific learning disabilities may be able to get an exemption from some of the usual educational requirements. For example, children with dyslexia may be

exempt from the requirement to study Irish and/or a European language.

* The National Council for Curriculum and Assessment (NCCA) is a statutory body. One of its functions is to advise the Minister for Education and Science on the curriculum and syllabus requirements of students with disabilities or with special educational needs. The council has published Guidelines for Teachers of Students with General Learning Disabilities. The NCCA is also currently developing guidelines for teachers of exceptionally able students.

* The National Educational Psychological Service (NEPS) is an executive agency of the Department of Education and Science. NEPS provides psychological services to both state and private primary and second-level schools.

* NEPS processes applications for 'reasonable accommodation' in the state examination arrangements for children with disabilities.

Special Schools:

* Special needs can range from mild, moderate or severe to profound.

* There are 107 special schools in Ireland catering for particular types of disability and special needs.

* Cope is a school which provides for students with mild to severe learning disabilities.

* Visually and hearing impaired students can be enrolled in special schools, e.g. St Mary's School for Deaf Girls, Dublin.

* Members of the Travelling community can be accommodated in special schools.

* Special needs education is provided for children in detention centres, e.g. Trinity House School, Lusk, County Dublin.

> **Note:** The Education for Persons with Special Educational Needs Act, 2004 provides that children are to be educated in an inclusive setting unless this would not be in the best interests of the child or the effective provision of education for other children in mainstream education.

Education Plans:

Under the Education for Persons with Special Educational Needs Act, 2004 each child assessed with a special educational need should have a personal education plan. This system is not yet in place but its implementation is being co-ordinated by the National Council for Special Education (NCSE), which has published guidelines.

Equality of Educational Opportunity

Since the 1960s, the Department of Education and Science has tried to secure equality of educational opportunity and it has aimed to achieve this through policies and systems.

* Inequalities in education exist because of:
  * Socio-economic status.
  * Gender inequalities.
  * Disadvantaged students.
  * Early school leavers.

Socio-Economic Status

* The socio-economic status of a child's parents may determine whether or not they do well at school.

* Research shows that students who come from families in higher socio-economic groups are more likely to complete second-level education and go on to third level.

* The cost of books, uniforms and extracurricular activities, such as school trips, can be a financial strain for families in the lower socio-economic groups.

* Children in poverty may not avail of extra grinds and revision courses or participate in school excursions.

* Children of families from a low socio-economic group:
  * Are more likely to begin school without being able to read.
  * Are more likely to be in lower streams.
  * Tend to get poorer results.
  * Are more likely to leave school at the minimum leaving age.

* Parents from lower socio-economic groups may not value education and therefore may not instil the importance of education in their children.

* Parents from higher socio-economic groups tend to have an appreciation of education and provide encouragement and support for educational achievement.

* Lower socio-economic groups tend to have lower educational and occupational aspirations than middle and higher socio-economic groups.

* There are two distinct forms of language. Public, or restricted, code, used by lower to middle socio-economic groups; and formal, or elaborate, code, used by middle to higher socio-economic groups. Education often incorporates both forms, thereby hindering students from lower socio-economic groups as they may not understand what the teacher is saying.

Kathleen Lynch (1999) carried out a study entitled *Equality in Education*. This study found that socio-economic status had a major influence on education.

Learning Links Learning Links Learning Links

Gender Inequalities

* There are noticeable differences between the sexes in terms of educational attainment.

* Girls show higher levels of achievement than boys, even though the same number of girls and boys go on to study in university.

* There have been changes in female attitudes because more mothers are working, therefore girls have positive role models.

* In the 1960s, women realised their potential to fulfil roles in society other than being a mother and housewife.

* Girls tend to mature earlier than boys.

* Studies show that girls' schools tend to place greater emphasis on self-control, gentleness and refinement. Boys tend to be more disruptive and lack motivation.

* Positive peer pressure is often found among girls, whereas boys tend to get more credit from their peers for poor application to studies.

* Gender-specific subjects can be found in single-sex schools, e.g. Home Economics is generally

Fig 2.4: A Home Economics class.

not offered in an all-boys school.

* Much of the curriculum had a patriarchal bias. Gender stereotyping can be found in texts, though more recent textbooks have a good gender balance.

Disadvantaged Students

* There are 311 primary schools and 203 second-level schools in Ireland that have been designated as disadvantaged.

* Schools seeking disadvantaged status were assessed and prioritised on the basis of socio-economic and educational indicators such as:
  * Unemployment levels.
  * Housing.
  * Number of medical card holders.
  * Information on basic literacy and numeracy.

* In addition, in assessing the relative levels of disadvantage among applicant schools, account was taken of pupil–teacher ratios. This means that they receive a greater level of support in terms of pupil–teacher ratios, special

grants and extra support for pupils.

* Schools are generally middle socio-economic institutions and therefore highlight such values as hard work, studying and making sacrifices. For some students, such values are unfamiliar.
* Schools in deprived areas are more likely to have discipline problems.
* Schools in low socio-economic areas found that staff expectations of students were not high.

Early School Leavers

* It is estimated that as many as 750 children fail to transfer every year from primary to second-level school.
* The number of students who leave education with no qualifications is 3.2 per cent, while another 15.3 per cent leave with only a Junior Certificate qualification.

* Early school leavers are at particular risk in the labour market.
* Of those who enter the labour market after school, the unemployment rate is 47.5 per cent for those with no qualifications, compared with 9.6 per cent for those with the Leaving Certificate.
* Research also shows that both the levels of education and the grades achieved have a marked influence on gaining employment and, in general, that higher qualifications and grades:
  * Increase the chances of gaining employment.
  * Reduce the length of time spent seeking work.
  * Reduce the risk of unemployment.
  * Promote higher earnings levels.

Contemporary Initiatives to Improve Educational Accessibility

Pre-Primary Initiatives	Primary School Iniatives	Second-Level Initiatives	Post-School/Second Chance Initiatives
• The Early Start project. • Pre-school for Travellers.	• Home–School–Community Liaison Scheme. • Early School Leaver initiative. • Travellers' education needs.	• The Stay in School retention initiative.	• Youthreach. • VTOS (Vocational Training and Opportunities Scheme).

Pre-Primary Initiatives

The Early Start project

* This project is offered to children aged three to four from disadvantaged areas.
* It is a one-year programme.
* It runs for two hours per week.
* Each Early Start centre, set up in vacant classrooms in existing schools, caters for approximately sixty children.
* It is operated by a qualified primary teacher assisted by childcare assistants.

* It is crucial that parents are involved in the programme.
* The aim is to expose children to a programme that will enhance their overall development and provide a solid foundation for successful educational attainment.
* The Early Start Pre-School Programme was introduced in October 1994 in eight schools in disadvantaged areas. It was expanded the following year, and currently caters for approximately 1,700 pupils in 40 schools throughout the country.

Pre-school for Travellers

* The aim of this initiative is to prevent inequality of educational access.
* There are 45 pre-schools for Travellers located throughout the country.
* Most of these were established through voluntary local development and later received support from the Department of Education and Science, the Department of Health and Children and various voluntary and charitable groups.
* Funding covers costs of childcare assistant and health and hygiene facilities.

Primary School Initiatives

Home-School-Community Liaison Scheme

* The Home-School-Community Liaison Scheme was established in Ireland in 1990.
* It is targeted at students who are at risk of not reaching their potential in the educational system because of economic or social disadvantage.
* The scheme encourages active participation of disadvantaged students in school while promoting co-operation between home, community and school.
* A co-ordinator is assigned; this is generally a teacher from the school.
* The home–school liaison co-ordinator has access to specific funding and this is provided by the Department of Education and Science.
* The work of the co-ordinator includes home visits, organisation of in-school activities for parents, and advising and supporting parents.

Early School Leaver initiative

* This scheme aims to develop and implement policies aimed at tackling the problem of early school leavers.
* It focuses at the integration of in- and out-of-school programmes to offer maximum participation from the age of eight to fifteen years.
* Attention is also given to students transferring from primary to secondary schools.

Travellers' education needs

* The provision of primary education for Traveller children takes the place in three forms:
  * Special schools.
  * Special classes.
  * Mainstream schools.
* The pupil–teacher ratio is 14:1.
* Most Traveller students are given extra assistance when they are in mainstream classes.

Second-Level Initiatives

Stay in School retention initiative:

* This initiative is a continuation of the Early School Leaver initiative at primary-school level.
* The aim is to reduce the number of students who drop out of senior cycle before completing the programme.
* Each school involved in this scheme must develop a retention plan specific to its needs.
* Monitoring of absences, extra teaching hours, and an induction plan for first years are all key parts of this initiative.

Post-School/Second-Chance Initiatives

Youthreach

* Youthreach is a joint programme between the Department of Education and Science and the Department of Enterprise, Trade and Employment.
* It is for people between the ages of 15 and 20.
* The Youthreach programme provides opportunities for basic education, personal development, vocational training and work experience.
* English, Maths and Life Skills are generally covered by all trainees.
* The course generally lasts from one to two years.
* A Foundation Certification from the Further Education and Training Awards Council (FETAC) or the Junior Certificate is attainable. Students may continue to a Progression Programme.

* This gives the opportunity to progress to the Leaving Certificate Applied course or a higher-level FETAC award or to continue other training, e.g. an apprenticeship course.
* The courses take place in Youthreach Centres managed by Vocational Education Committees (VECs) and FÁS Community Training Centres.
* The Youthreach programme is widely available in Ireland with over 120 centres and 6,000 places available for trainees.

Vocational Training and Opportunities Scheme (VTOS)

* This provides courses of up to two years for long-term unemployed over 21 years of age.
* The scheme provides courses from basic education in literacy, numeracy and personal development at Junior and Leaving Certificate level and FETAC awards at Level 3, 4, and 5 on the National Framework of Qualifications.
* The Department of Education and Science draws up the guidelines and the scheme is managed and provided at local level by Vocational Education Committees.

National Education Welfare Board

* The National Educational Welfare Board (NEWB) is the national agency established to ensure that every child attends school regularly, or otherwise receives an appropriate minimum education.
* It also advises the Government on school attendance and education provision.
* It employs educational welfare officers at local level throughout the country to provide support and advice to parents and schools and to follow up on absences from school.
* It monitors school attendance and takes a range of measures where children do not attend school.
* A child must not miss more than 20 days in a school year.
* The NEWB maintains a register of young persons of 16 and 17 years of age who leave school early to progress their education or go into employment.

Sample Exam Questions
Higher Level (2008)

Questions

1. Discuss the purpose of education in relation to the physical, emotional, moral and intellectual development of the child. (24)
2. Comment on how socio-economic status impacts on equality of opportunity in education. (15)
3. Name and give an account of one national initiative that improves access to education. (11)

Sample Answers

1. Discuss the purpose of education in relation to the physical, emotional, moral and intellectual development of the child. (24)

   4 headings x 6 marks = 24.

Physical Needs	Emotional Needs	Intellectual Needs	Moral Needs
• Encourages the development of dexterity and hand-eye co-ordination. • Physical skills are developed in subjects such as Home Economics, Art and PE (Physical Education).	• Children develop emotionally to become mature in their feelings towards them-selves and others. • Emotional skills are developed in subjects such as SPHE and RSE (Relationships and Sexuality Education).	• Schooling promotes intellectual development by the wide range of subjects it offers. • Continuous assessments, class tests and exams motivate pupils to achieve academically.	• The school's ethos sets out the values and thinking of the school. • Each student is expected to behave according to the ethos of the school. • Moral develop-ment is explored in subjects such as Religion, SPHE, CSPE (Civic, Social and Political Education) and Home Economics.

2. Comment on how socio-economic status impacts on equality of opportunity in education. (15)

   3 points x 5 marks each = 15.

   • The socio-economic status of a child's parents will determine whether or not they do well at school. Research shows that students who come from families in higer socio-economic groups are more likely to complete second-level education and go on to third level.

     The cost of books, uniforms and extracur-ricular activities, such as school trips, can be a financial strain for families from lower socio-economic groups. Children in poverty may not avail of extra grinds and revision courses or participate in school excursions.
   • Children of families from a low socio-economic group:
     – Are more likely to begin school without being able to read.
     – Are more likely to be in lower streams.
     – Tend to get poorer results.
     – Are more likely to leave school at the minimum leaving age.
   • Parents from families in lower socio-eco-nomic groups may not value education and therefore may not instil the importance of education in their children. Parents from higher socio-economic groups tend to have an appreciation of education and provide encouragement and support for educational achievement. Lower socio-economic groups tend to have lower educational and occupa-tional aspirations than middle and higher socio-economic groups.

3. Name and give an account of one national initiative that improves access to education. (11)

   naming the initiative = 2.
   3 points x 3 marks each = 9.

Youthreach

- Youthreach is a joint programme between the Department of Education and Science and the Department of Enterprise, Trade and Employment. It is for people between the ages of 15 and 20.

  The Youthreach programme provides opportunities for basic education, personal development, vocational training and work experience. English, Maths and Life Skills, are generally covered by all trainees.

- The course generally lasts from one to two years. A Foundation Certification from the Further Education and Training Awards Council (FETAC) or the Junior Certificate is attainable. Students may continue to a progression programme. This gives the opportunity to progress to the Leaving Certificate Applied course or a higher-level FETAC award or to continue other training, e.g. an apprenticeship course.

- The courses take place in Youthreach Centres managed by Vocational Education Committees (VECs) and FÁS Community Training Centres. The Youthreach programme is widely available in Ireland with over 120 centres and 6,000 places available for trainees.

Work **3**

Types of Work

Work can be categorised into three distinct groups:

* Paid work.
* Unpaid work.
* Voluntary work.

Paid Work	Unpaid Work	Voluntary Work
• Paid work can be subdivided according to whether it is temporary work, permanent work, or full-time, part-time or contract based. • There is financial gain from this form of work. This offers security. • Generally done for an employer in exchange for payment; or a person may be self-employed. • Time spent at work is very distinct and separated from non-work activity. • Not necessarily done for pleasure. • Work is often carried out in a designated area, however this is changing as more people working from home.	• Unpaid work is usually work within the home or home-related activities. • Individuals who do unpaid work rarely get credit for work they carry out. • This type of work is repetitive, unrewarding and low status by nature. • Examples of this work include: cooking, cleaning, and care of children, elderly or disabled people.	• In the past, voluntary work was based on charity. • Today, voluntary work places a strong emphasis on empowering people to help themselves by providing people with the skills and knowledge to carry out tasks. • Examples of this type of work include working for the St Vincent de Paul or in the local community centre.

Fig 3.1: Collecting for the Simon Community.

Attitudes to Work and Work Attainment

An individual's attitude to and experience of work is important to their personal happiness because a lot of time is spent in work or carrying out work-related activities.

Attitudes to Work

Attitudes to work can be affected by:
* Social class.
* Family background.
* Education.
* Self-esteem.
* Working conditions.
* Interaction with others.
* Work ethic.

Social Class:

* The aspirations an individual has towards work can reflect their socio-economic status.
* People from the lower socio-economic groups tend to have low job expectations and this occurs due to high level of unemployment, low levels of education and little, if any, job satisfaction.

Family Background:

* How parents perceive work can have a huge bearing on how their children perceive work.
* When parents have a negative attitude towards their chosen profession, their children tend to have similar, if not the same attitudes.

Education:

* People who drop out of school before completing their formal education generally find it difficult to obtain a full-time job.
* People from the middle to upper socio-economic groups get better educational opportunities and are more likely to have a rewarding career.

Self-Esteem:

* When an individual has had a good home experience and a good school experience, this gives them a high level of self-esteem.
* Individuals with good self-esteem and confidence tend to excel in work and put themselves forward for promotion.

Working Conditions:

* A clean, safe, warm, well-maintained work environment provides workers with the encouragement and motivation needed to get the job done.
* A negative environment will have the opposite effect.

Interaction with Others:

* Work provides people with the opportunity to meet new people and form new friendships.
* When people are isolated from others, their attitude to work becomes worse and therefore their performance deteriorates.

Work Ethic:

* A person's work ethic affects factors such as:
  * Level of interest in the job.
  * Setting personal targets.
  * Pride and belief in oneself.
  * Degree of commitment.
  * Punctuality.
  * Absenteeism.

Job Satisfaction

* Job satisfaction refers to the degree of pleasure individuals get from their area of work.
* Job satisfaction falls into two categories: intrinsic satisfaction and extrinsic satisfaction.

Intrinsic Satisfaction	Extrinsic Satisfaction
• This is the most important feature of a job. • It is the amount of pleasure and fulfilment that a job offers an individual. • The individual gets a sense of pride in the work they do. • Often the work can be viewed as positively challenging. • High pay is not viewed as the most important reason for engaging in this type of work. • This attitude is generally associated with professional vocations, e.g. nursing and teaching.	• In this type of satisfaction, the most important aspect of the job is the wage given. • This is generally found in individuals who find the work they do to be uninteresting, boring and repetitive. • People in this type of work try to earn as much as possible, usually by doing shift work or overtime. • Luxury items are purchased with wages received.

Alienation

Alienation is the term that is applied to the situation where workers have no job satisfaction and are not fulfilled by their chosen area of work.

The Downside of Alienation

* Workers taking extended or unofficial breaks.
* Workers are absent from work on a regular basis.
* Workers produce poor-quality merchandise.
* There are conflicts with management.
* Workers cause damage to the workplace or equipment in some way.
* Workers quit the job because they do not find it stimulating.

Combating Alienation

* Job rotation offers individuals the opportunity to change the type of job they carry out.
* Develop teamwork strategies.
* Introduction of flexitime, which gives the worker more independence.
* Profit-sharing schemes enable the worker to have a stake in the company.
* Give workers a greater participation in management decision-making.

Changes in Patterns of Work and Work Availability

* Increased automation due to technological advances.
* Increased educational requirements.
* Increased participation of women in employment.
* Decline in primary and secondary industries and increase in service industry.
* Improved working conditions and hours of employment.
* Casualisation of the workforce.

Automation

This applies to machines and computers doing jobs traditionally carried out by workers.

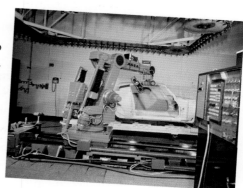

Fig 3.2: Machines on a production line.

Advantages of Automation	Disadvantages of Automation
<ul><li>There is now an increased requirement for well-educated workers.</li><li>Eliminates boring repetitive jobs.</li><li>Increases the number of quality goods produced.</li><li>Reduces running costs for the employer.</li><li>Provides a safer, healthier work environment by eliminating dangerous jobs.</li><li>Increases the amount of leisure time available.</li><li>New more interesting jobs are created.</li></ul>	<ul><li>Decreases wages as work becomes less skilled.</li><li>Workers lose their skills to machines: this is known as deskilling.</li><li>Loss of pride in craftsmanship.</li><li>There is an increase in boring, supervisory work, e.g. watching machines.</li><li>Less interaction with other workers.</li><li>Increase in the levels of unemployment.</li></ul>

Increased Educational Requirements

✱ The Leaving Certificate is often the minimum requirement sought by employers.

✱ In the past, a primary degree was seen as a great achievement, but today students continue their education to achieve master's and doctorates.

✱ This level of education provides an increase in the number of quality employees.

Increased Participation of Women in Employment

Women were often seen – and are still seen – as 'home-makers'. This idea is changing with the number of women entering the job market.

Reasons why more Women are in the Workforce:

✱ A higher number of women today have received a third-level education, which provides the qualifications needed to pursue a career.

✱ Attitudes towards women in the workplace have changed greatly with a huge acceptance of their participation.

✱ Women today are postponing marriage and child bearing until they have become established in their career.

✱ Women choose to work to gain a better standard of living.

✱ Today there is an increase in more flexible working patterns (job-sharing and part-time work) which give mothers the opportunity to work and have sufficient time with their children.

✱ Employment now offers women the opportunity to progress in their field through promotion.

✱ Women seek employment as a means to interact with others and form friendships.

Women in Work Still Experience Inequalities:

✱ Women are over-represented in jobs in clerical and secretarial sectors.

✱ Women tend to work in lower-paid jobs.

✱ Fewer women hold managerial positions at the top of many professions.

✱ A lot of women work in service industries.

✱ Women's wages in Ireland are lower than those earned by men in comparable jobs.

✱ Few companies provide childcare facilities, therefore families are forced to pay large fees for childcare. This is not always suitable for working women.

Irish Industry

Irish industry is divided into three sectors:
- Primary. ● Secondary. ● Tertiary.

Primary Sector	Secondary Sector	Tertiary Sector
• Farming. • Forestry. • Fishing. • Mining.	• Building. • Factory jobs. • Food manufacture.	• Tourism. • Media. • Transport. • Education.

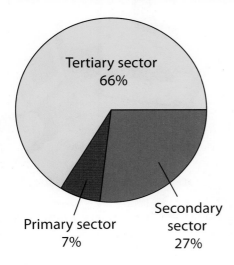

Fig 3.3: Percentage of workers in primary, secondary and tertiary industries.

Reasons for Decline in Primary and Secondary Industries:

✻ Work patterns altered during the twentieth century as Ireland changed from an agricultural economy to a manufacturing one.

✻ Due to technological advances, the primary sector now requires less manual labour as machinery can do the work faster and more efficiently.

✻ In the secondary sector, automation has brought a reduction in the number of workers needed.

✻ A decline in manufacturing, as a large percentage of the workforce is now working in the service sector.

Reasons for an Increase in the Service Sector:

✻ Because of the expansion and growth of the world economy, Ireland is now forced to compete with other industrialised nations.

✻ People today have more disposable income, which provides them with the money to indulge in personal interests, whether it be shopping or going to the gym.

✻ Technology has brought with it a development in secondary industry, changing it into a tertiary sector.

✻ Multinational companies opt for a cheaper labour force. Ireland responds by offering grants to these companies to establish in Ireland.

✻ Tourism has increased in Ireland and this has caused a growth in the employment in the service sector.

Improved Working Conditions and Hours

Regulations relating to health and safety at work have resulted in a number of improvements in working conditions.

✻ The Health and Safety Authority is responsible for encouraging health and safety in the workplace.

✻ The Safety, Health and Welfare at Work Act, 2005 stipulates that employers must care for the health, safety and welfare of employees correctly.

- Improvements in technology now enable people to work from home.
- The National Minimum Wage Act, 2000 ensures that every experienced adult worker is entitled to a minimum wage.
- Other legislation that provides good working conditions includes:
  - Equality Act, 2004.
  - Employment Equality Act, 1998.
  - Maternity Protection Amendment Act, 2004.
  - Protection of Young Persons (Employment) Act, 1996.
- The average working week is now thirty-nine hours and any hours worked over this time are considered overtime.
- Stringent working hours have become less apparent with the introduction of flexitime. (This involves working in a time range instead of at set times.)
- In some jobs, e.g. nursing, people can choose to job share. (This includes a reduction in working hours to spend more time on family life.)
- Part-time work involves a reduction in working hours and the opportunity to avail of seasonal work.

Casualisation of the Workforce

- This occurs where companies employ individuals as they are required, on temporary or part-time contracts, to carry out specific tasks over a short time span.
- This means that individuals will face many changes in their working life.
- Casualisation offers little job security.
- People will be offered periods of temporary work.
- However, in some situations people may find themselves with no work at all.

The Protection of Young Persons (Employment) Act, 1996

- This act aims to protect the health of young workers by ensuring that any work they are involved in does not interfere with their educational opportunities.

- The act relates to all people under the age of 18.
- It prevents employers from employing any people under the age of 16 in full-time jobs.
- The employment of 14- and 15-year-olds in light work is permitted, i.e. work during holidays or work experience.
- Anyone employed under the age of 16 is entitled to half an hour's rest break after every four hours worked.

Fig 3.4: Young person in a part-time job.

- The act states that employers must:
  - See a copy of a birth certificate before hiring someone under 16.
  - Get written permission from the parents of the individual.
  - Keep a record of hours worked, wages paid and the total amount paid.

Voluntary Organisations and Voluntary Work

A voluntary organisation is a non-profit-making organisation which is not controlled by the government.

The Role of Voluntary Organisations

* To supply a wide range of services in areas that are insufficiently provided by the state.
* Voluntary organisations save the state money, as workers choose to volunteer and services tend to be free.
* These groups can focus media attention on social problems.
* These organisations work closely with problem areas and can offer government bodies detailed information and possible solutions.
* Voluntary organisations act as **pressure groups**.

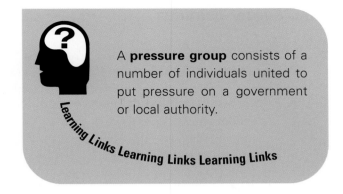

A **pressure group** consists of a number of individuals united to put pressure on a government or local authority.

Learning Links Learning Links Learning Links

The Benefits of Voluntary Work:

To a Volunteer	To the Community
• The work is very rewarding. • It can improve the personal development of the volunteer through improved communication and organisational skills. • Provides volunteers with the opportunity to see first-hand the difficulties faced by others, therefore volunteers develop empathy. • Volunteers develop expertise in particular areas.	• Friendships are formed. • Voluntary work empowers communities. • Voluntary work can foster a sense of community. • Voluntary work is immediate and therefore resolves situations more quickly.

Reconciling Employment and Family Responsibilities

In recent years, there has been a change in the patterns of gender roles within families.

* The increase of women entering full-time employment has brought about a move away from the traditional segregation of roles.
* An egalitarian approach has been adopted whereby family decisions are made by both spouses.
* Housework is more equally divided between couples.
* Parents are now more aware of gender issues and adopt a more open approach within the home, e.g. a young boy might get a play kitchen for his birthday.
* Family finances are divided between both partners.

Dual-Earner Families

Advantages of Dual-Earner Families	Disadvantages of Dual-Earner Families

• **Improved standard of living:** As both partners are working, there is more money coming into the family.
 	
• **The role of the father:** The father has become more actively involved in childcare in recent years. Fathers also participate in household tasks, cooking, cleaning, etc.
 	
• **Children's attitude:** Children are more ambitious in areas of education and work as they adapt a positive attitude from their parents healthy approach to work.
 	
• **Increased security:** This is provided financially when both partners work.
 	
• **Equality for women:** Women are more involved in decision-making in the home.
	• **Family size:** There is a reduction in family size as both partners work. In particular, women who have a career tend to focus on a career and decide at a later stage to have children. These women are also choosing to have fewer children.
	
	• **Vulnerable members:** In dual-earner families, there is no one to care for vulnerable family members, e.g. elderly family members are often put into institutionalised care.
	
	• **Childcare:** Childcare can be expensive and sometimes this responsibility falls on older siblings or relatives.
	
	• **Marital breakdown:** One of the factors that can lead to marital breakdown is the increasing financial independence of women who work.
	
	• **Extra responsibilities on children:** This occurs when older children of dual-earner families are responsible for themselves when they come home from school. This can have one of two effects :
	  – Children become more independent.
	  – Children seek attention from parents, which can lead to problems.
	
	• **Role overload:** Women tend to suffer most from role overload as housework and childcare falls primarily on the shoulders of mothers.
	
	• **Less leisure time:** As women suffer the effects of role overload.
	
	• **Role conflict:** Conflict balancing work and home activities. This conflict often occurs for women, who must prioritise work versus home – a choice where someone will always lose out.

Childcare Facilities

✳ Childcare can refer to:
- Daycare facilities.
- Provisions for pre-school children.
- After-school services.

✳ Childcare therefore covers a range of services and facilities, including:
- Education.
- Care.
- Socialisation.

Fig 3.5: Daycare facility for pre-school children.

Requirements for Childcare

Requirement	
Cost	• The funds available to the family will often be a major factor when deciding on a childcare option.
Availability	• The forms of childcare available must be considered. Often in rural areas there may be a limited range of childcare options.
Age of Child	• The age of the child will affect the type of childcare options available. • In some crèches, there is a minimum age requirement of 12 months: this may not be suitable for parents with a child under this age.
Needs of Child	• The needs of a baby differ greatly from those of a toddler. • If a child has special needs, a suitable childcare option which caters for these needs is essential.
Qualifications/Experience	• The qualifications of the carer are of utmost importance to parents. • Often parents seek minders who have specialised training and an up-to-date first aid certificate.
Environment	• The facilities should be clean, hygienic, warm and safe. • If care is taking place in the parent's home, the same requirements are necessary.
Convenience	• The location of the facilities is important for ease of access. • Parents often choose facilities close to work or home. In some cases, children are cared for in their own home.
Knowing the Minder	• Some parents would prefer to know the childminder; this provides them with peace of mind.

Types of Childcare

✻ Childcare facilities include:
  - Daycare facilities (nurseries and crèches). (See p.414 and p.437.)
  - Playgroups. (See p.414.)
  - Nursery schools (Montessori or Froebel). (See p.414.)
  - Naíonraí
  - After-school groups.
  - Childminders.

Naíonraí

This type of school offers children the opportunity to socialise with other children, while encouraging the use of the Irish language.

After-School Groups:

✻ These are often provided by crèches.
✻ These are an important facility for working parents.
✻ After formal school, children attend these groups where they are provided with a setting in which to complete homework.
✻ Help is offered by an assistant.

Childminders:

(See below.)

Evaluating Childcare Options

Childminder Versus Daycare Facilities

Childminders:

✻ Childminders provide care for children in a comfortable, hygienic, safe, home-like environment where a child can achieve personal development needs.
✻ They provide a childminding service either in their home or in the home of the child.
✻ Childminders tend to be relatives, friends, recognised childminders, au pairs or nannies.

Fig 3.6: Childminder with children.

✻ When a childminder cares for more than four children, they have a duty to be registered with the local health service executive.
✻ A childminder has a responsibility of duty of care to the children.
✻ In relation to cost, childminders tend to be less expensive than other childcare options.

The responsibilities of a childminder:

✻ The home of the childminder should be safe and hygienic.
✻ Trustworthiness and honesty should be the characteristic traits of any childminder.
✻ They should have the necessary training.
✻ Back-up arrangements should be made for when the minder is ill.
✻ All personal details of children should be recorded and easily accessible in case of emergency, e.g. parents' phone numbers.
✻ Regular contact with parents is an essential requirement to monitor a child's progression.
✻ Childminders must comply with statutory regulations.
✻ It is the responsibility of the minder to have adequate insurance.

Advantages of Childminders:

- Childminders are often recommended by friends of the parents.
- In some cases, childminders can look after children in their own home.
- Children tend to see their childminder's home as an extension of their own.
- Childminders are flexible about pick-up and drop-off times.
- Children have more attention as there are few children to look after.
- Childminders get to know children's traits and can read the signs of a child's mood.
- A childminder is often the only option for care after school.
- Childminders provide more time for children with special or specific needs.

Disadvantages of Childminders:

- Childminders may not have adequate insurance.
- Some childminders lack the correct training.
- Childminders may not have a first-aid certificate.
- The home of the childminder may not meet statutory guidelines.
- Parents can experience feelings of jealousy about the closeness that can develop between a child and the minder.
- A childminder's style of child rearing may differ from that required by parents.
- Parents may be left without a childminder if the childminder becomes sick.
- It is difficult for parents to monitor the level of care given by a childminder.

Daycare Facilities

Daycare facilities provide care and activities, which helps the development of the child.

The Responsibilities of Daycare Facilities:

* The daycare provider must ensure that there are enough staff to cater for the children.

* The premises should be well ventilated and adequately heated. They must be self-contained and provide safe areas for rest and play.
* An outdoor area for play must be provided.
* The premises and facilities must meet regulations.

Advantages of Daycare Facilities:

- Staff are trained and are qualified in first aid.
- The services are reliable, with set opening and closing hours.
- Children can socialise with other children.
- A variety of activities provide stimulation.
- Some crèches/nurseries are attached to workplaces, which is convenient for working parents.
- Premises that are subject to inspection must adhere to regulations.

Disadvantages of Daycare Facilities:

- Most do not cater for babies and toddlers.
- They may not offer care when children are sick.
- Rigid pick-up and drop-off times are set.
- Staff must focus their attention on more than one child.
- Children may find it difficult adapting to a unfamiliar environment.
- Children tend to get more infections.
- Daycare facilities tend to be an expensive childcare option.

Exam Questions 2008

Requirements for childcare vary depending on family circumstances.

1. Summarise the factors that can affect a family's requirement for childcare. (12)

1. Summarise the factors that can affect a family's requirement for childcare. (12)
2. Evaluate two types of childcare options. (18)

4 points x 3 marks each = 12.

Cost	• The funds available to the family will often be a major factor when deciding on a childcare option.
Availability	• The forms of childcare available must be considered. Often in rural areas there may be a limited range of childcare options.
Age of Child	• The age of the child will affect the type of childcare options available. • In some crèches, there is a minimum age requirement of 12 months; this may not be suitable for parents with a child under this age.
Needs of Child	• The needs of a baby will differ greatly from those of a toddler. • If a child has special needs, a suitable childcare option which caters for these needs is essential.

2. Evaluate two types of childcare options. (18)

9 points x 2 marks each = 18.

Childminder versus daycare facility
Childminder

- The childminder provides care for children in a comfortable, hygienic, safe, home-like environment where a child can achieve personal development needs. They provide a childminding service either in their home or the home of the child. Childminders tend to be relatives, friends, recognised childminders, au pairs or nannies.

When a childminder cares for more than four children, they have a duty to be registered with the local health service executives. A childminder has a duty of care to the children.

The responsibilities of a childminder:

- The home of the childminder should be safe and hygienic. Trustworthiness and honesty should be the characteristic traits of any childminder.
- They should have the necessary training. Back-up arrangements should be made for when the minder is ill.

- All personal details of children should be recorded and easily accessible in case of emergency, e.g. parents phone numbers. Regular contact with parents is an essential requirement to monitor a child's progression.
- Childminders must comply with statutory regulations. It is the responsibility of the minder to provide adequate insurance.

Advantages:
- Childminders are often recommended by friends of the parents.
- In some cases, childminders can look after children in their own home.
- Children tend to see their childminder's home as an extension of their own.
- Childminders are more flexible about pick-up and drop-off times.

Disadvantages:
- Childminders may not have adequate insurance.
- Some childminders lack the correct training.
- Childminders may not have a first-aid certificate.
- The home of the childminder may not meet statutory guidelines.

Daycare

Daycare facilities provide care for a child, incorporating activities throughout the day to help the development of the child.

The responsibilities of daycare facilities:
- The daycare provider must ensure that there are enough staff to cater for the number of children enrolled.
- The premises should be well ventilated and adequately heated.
- The premises must be self-contained and provide areas for rest and play in safety.
- An outdoor area for play must be provided.

Advantages:
- Staff will be qualified in first aid; children are supervised by qualified individuals.
- The facilities have set opening and closing hours.
- Daycare facilities enable a child to socialise with other children.
- A variety of activities are provided for the children; this offers stimulation.

Disadvantages:
- A majority of crèches/nurseries do not cater for babies and toddlers.
- Rigid pick-up and drop-off times are set. In some cases, a fee is charged if parents are regularly late collecting children.
- Staff must focus their attention on more than one child.
- Children may find it difficult adapting to an unfamiliar environment.

4 Unemployment

The economy affects employment levels. When a country's economy is very strong, unemployment figures tend to be low.

What is Unemployment?

✳ Unemployment is defined as a situation that exists when people in a labour force wish to work for a wage but have difficulty in getting a job. This is known as **involuntary unemployment**.

✳ **Voluntary unemployment** is when an individual makes a conscious decision to not work or to stay at home, e.g. a housewife.

Fig 4.1: People queuing at a social welfare office.

Types of Unemployment

There are two types of unemployment:

✳ **Short-term unemployment:** This type last for less than six months.

✳ **Long-term unemployment:** This type lasts for longer than six months. When long-term unemployment is prevalent, this is an indication that an economy is in trouble.

The Extent of Unemployment in Ireland

✳ Experts have dramatically revised their predictions for 2009 and now estimate that 400,000 people may join the dole queues before the end of the year.

✳ The record rise in unemployment in 2008 meant an average of 10,000 people lost their jobs every month.

✳ Unemployment now stands at a ten-year high of 8.3 per cent of the workforce.

✳ The rate of unemployment has been driven by the slowdown in construction activity. Layoffs in the sector rose by almost 250 per cent in 2008 compared to 2007.

✳ Detailed charts that accompany the CSO figures reveal the number of men without work in December 2008 rose by 83 per cent, while the number of women unemployed was up by 50 per cent compared with December 2007.

The Causes of Unemployment

There are many causes of unemployment.
✳ New technology/automation.
✳ Foreign competition.
✳ Lack of skills.
✳ Low wages.
✳ Seasonal factors.
✳ Geographical location.
✳ Level of the demand for goods and services.
✳ Economic recession.

New Technology/Automation:

✳ The group most at risk from this development tends to be the unskilled workforce.

* Work that was once carried out manually has now been automated.
* This means that fewer workers are needed.

Foreign Competition:

* Manufacturing companies based in Ireland may decide to:
  * Terminate the employment of some of their workers to reduce costs.
  * Move to a country with cheaper labour costs.
* Foreign competition can also lead to downsizing when companies cut staff numbers due to takeovers and competition.

Lack of Skills:

* When workers lack skills in the area of technology and computerisation, this reduces their chances of employment.
* At present, most employers seek the minimum educational qualification of the Leaving Certificate. With this qualification, most individuals have had some level of computer training.

Low Wages:

* In some incidences, social welfare payments can be more financially rewarding than wages from a low-paid job.
* Families can claim unemployment benefit and allowances which supply them with a higher income than the earnings they would get from low wages and paying taxes.

Seasonal Factors:

* Types of work that are seasonal, e.g. tourism, result in many workers being let go when the season is over.
* Students can affect the unemployment figures as some students will sign on for social welfare during the holidays and sign off when they return to college.

Geographical Location:

* Unemployment levels can be affected by location.
* The highest risk of unemployment is found in villages and small towns, large social housing areas and inner cities.
* Rural areas are of particular concern as few industries are situated there.

Fig 4.2: Flats in inner-city Dublin.

Level of Demand for Goods and Services:

In sparsely populated areas, there is less demand for products and services. This will affect the employment level in the area.

Economic Recession:

* A fall in the economy can cause severe redundancies/job losses, which can lead to a reduction in the amount of disposable income spent.
* For the first time since 1983, the economy experienced a recession in 2008.
* The ESRI projected that the outflow of people from the country will reach 20,000 in 2009, a level of emigration not seen since 1990.

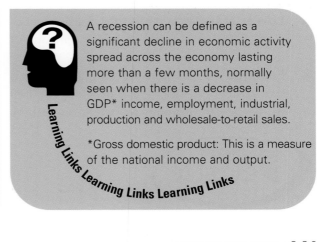

A recession can be defined as a significant decline in economic activity spread across the economy lasting more than a few months, normally seen when there is a decrease in GDP* income, employment, industrial, production and wholesale-to-retail sales.

*Gross domestic product: This is a measure of the national income and output.

Learning Links Learning Links Learning Links

Consequences of Unemployment

Unemployment has a number of effects on the individual, the family and society.

Consequences for Individuals

* **Depression:** Those in long-term unemployment can often suffer from overwhelming feelings of depression. In order to get relief from this, some individuals turn to drink or drugs as an escape.
* **Poverty:** When individuals are not working, they become completely dependant on social welfare; in some instances they fall into poverty.
* **Stress and anxiety:** When an individual is unable to get a job, money issues become a worry. This leads to feelings of stress and anxiety. This too instils feelings of low self-esteem.
* **Loss of identity and status:** With work comes status and identity. When an individual fails to work, they lose a sense of worth.
* **Isolation:** When people are working, they have an opportunity to interact with their peers or get involved in similar interests. An individual becomes very isolated when they are unemployed.
* **Feelings of failure:** An unemployed person may feel a sense of failure towards their family if they are unable to support them. This brings with it feelings of guilt.

Consequences for Families

* **Lower standards of living:** With a reduction of income comes a lower standard of living.
* **Feelings of insecurity:** Family members start to feel insecure. This can affect children in particular, leading to attention-seeking behaviour (e.g. bullying). In some cases children inadvertently show their insecurity through bed-wetting.
* **Education:** Children's school work may be affected when they are worried about income. Children may be deprived of certain educational opportunities, e.g. class trips or extra help.
* **Relationship problems:** Relationships can become strained if a couple are constantly arguing over finances. In some cases, this can lead to marital breakdown.
* **Role confusion:** This occurs if the woman becomes the sole earner, a role which was traditionally the man's.
* **Loss of home:** When an individual suffers from long-term unemployment, bills and debt mount up. If these bills are not paid, goods may be repossessed. Families may also lose their home.

Consequences for Society

* **Taxes increase:** Unemployment costs the state as there is an increase in the number of people claiming social welfare payments. The government responds to this increase by increasing taxes in order to cover costs.
* **Poverty cycle:** This occurs when there is long-term unemployment. In families where there is long-term unemployment, studies show that this pattern continues throughout the generations.
* **Social problems:** Unemployment can cause problems such as poverty, homelessness, crime and drug abuse.
* **Emigration:** When unemployment levels are high, people are forced to look abroad in search of work. This is known as emigration.
* **A growth in the black economy:** This involves people carrying out odd jobs for cash while also claiming benefits from the state.

Leisure **5**

Leisure time generally involves the following:
- Time that is free from work and study.
- Time to spend on freely chosen activities.
- Being involved in activities that are viewed as enjoyable.

The Functions and Values of Leisure

Fig 5.1: People at a hip-hop dance class.

Leisure is a very important part of people's lives for the following reasons:

✳ **Form of relaxation:** Leisure relieves the stresses of everyday life.

✳ **Relieves boredom:** Leisure takes up time, thereby reducing feelings of boredom. An individual is kept busy by their leisure activity.

✳ **Allows new skills to be developed:** For example, taking up cookery courses, introductory lessons on art, taking up a musical instrument. Cognitive, psycho-motor and social skills can all be developed.

✳ **Satisfies the senses:** For example, visiting an art gallery, going to an opera. The senses of sight, sound, smell, taste and touch can be heightened.

✳ **Provides a challenge:** People are stimulated both physically and intellectually.

✳ **Physical well-being:** Sporting activities enable the individual to maintain or improve their physical health.

✳ **Promotes personal development:** Leisure encourages social interaction, gives an individual a feeling of self-confidence and improves self-esteem.

Choosing a Leisure Activity

There are four factors that influence the choice of leisure activity.

✳ Social and cultural influences.
✳ Occupation.
✳ Age.
✳ Gender.

Social and Cultural Influences

Social Influences	Cultural Influences
• The type of socio-economic group that a person belongs to will have an impact on the type of leisure activity they choose.	• Culture can influence one's choice of leisure activity.

Social Influences	Cultural Influences
• Middle and lower socio-economic groups will have different leisure pursuits due to differences in income, educational qualifications, work hours and availability of facilities. • Golf club membership and gym membership may be out of financial reach for those in lower socio-economic groups. • Trends in leisure activities can change quite quickly, e.g. ice skating and all types of dancing have become very popular due to reality TV shows such as *Dancing on Ice* and *Dancing with the Stars*. • The local amenities in an area may influence the chosen leisure activities that an individual pursues, e.g. access to GAA pitches, swimming pools, night classes.	• Certain sports and games are associated with specific countries, e.g. hurling in Ireland, baseball in the USA. • Music and dance are also influenced by the culture of an area, e.g. Irish dancing, salsa dancing in Latin America, reggae in the Caribbean.  • The way an individual is raised may impact on leisure activity, e.g. if all family members played traditional musical instruments.

Occupation

✱ An individual's occupation may influence the leisure activity they choose.

✱ The number of hours an individual works, shift work, overtime are all factors that influence the time available for leisure pursuits.

✱ Sociologists suggest there are three types of occupational leisure:

- **Neutrality:** When an individual's job is viewed as uninteresting, the chosen leisure activities usually involve relaxing at home with family.

- **Oppositional:** This occurs when leisure activities completely contrast with a person's occupation. For example, a physically active occupation may enjoy a non-taxing leisure pursuit.

- **Extension:** This is where leisure pursuits enjoyed often involve people's work, e.g. dinners with clients, business golf outings.

Age

✱ Young people are more leisure-centred as they generally have more time. Part-time jobs offer them disposable income.

✱ People who are middle-aged with grown-up children and whose mortgage payments are lower have the most time and money to spend on leisure pursuits.

✱ Leisure activities for older people tend to be home-based due to a change in health status or limited finances.

✱ Leisure activities often enjoyed by older people include playing cards, bingo, reading and listening to music.

✱ Young couples with a family have the least amount of time and money for leisure pursuits.

✱ People's leisure interests may change as they get older. For example, a young girl may enjoy ballet classes but as she gets older may prefer going to the gym.

Gender

* The term 'gender' refers to being a man or woman.
* Men and women may have different leisure interests.
* A stereotype is a fixed way of looking at something and there can often be stereotyping when it comes to leisure activities. For example, girls can't box, boys don't dance.
* Stereotyping is becoming less frequent, with both genders enjoying a wide range of leisure interests.
* Some activities however, are still very much gender-dominated. For example, women are more likely to pursue activities such as dancing, aerobics and keeping fit. Men are more inclined to choose activities such as boxing, motor racing and car maintenance.

Fig 5.2: Girls playing rugby.

The Role of Leisure

Leisure can help a person's physical, social, intellectual and emotional development.

Physical Development	Social Development	Intellectual Development	Emotional Development
<ul><li>Physical fitness.</li><li>Muscle toning.</li><li>Weight control.</li><li>Good health and well-being.</li></ul>	<ul><li>Meeting new people, e.g. bingo, playing cards, book clubs.</li><li>Communication skills, e.g. team sports such as hurling and football, quiz teams.</li><li>Listening skills in activities such as drama, debating.</li></ul>	<ul><li>Powers of concentration, e.g. playing bridge.</li><li>Decision-making skills are improved, e.g. quizzes.</li><li>Analysis of situations, e.g. card games and debating.</li></ul>	<ul><li>Personal development is enhanced as a person's confidence and self-esteem are boosted.</li><li>Inner-space activities, e.g. yoga, provide the opportunity for relaxation.</li><li>A sense of belonging, e.g. by joining teams and having a sense of identity.</li></ul>

Leisure Pursuits Explored

Outdoor Activities	Indoor Activities	Indoor/Outdoor Activities
• Fishing. • Football. • Golf.	• Aerobics. • Badminton. • Boxing. • Choirs. • Drama. • Art and craft classes.	• Basketball. • Swimming. • Hockey.

Being a Volunteer

Communities encourage the participation of members in a variety of voluntary organisations, including:

✱ ICA (Irish Countrywomen's Association).
✱ Macra Na Feirme.
✱ Local political organisations.
✱ Voluntary organisations, e.g. St Vincent de Paul.

Leisure Facilities Available in the Community

Below is a cost and value comparison of two facilities:

✱ A leisure centre
✱ A book club.

Type of Facility	Leisure Centre	Book Club
Membership Fee	• €500 + per year	• Cost of the books to be read.
Physical Benefits	• Improves fitness. • Strengthens muscle. • Builds stamina. • Leads to a healthy heart.	• Limited physical benefit as the reader is generally sitting or lying down.
Emotional Benefits	• Relaxes and leads to stress relief. • Enables people to switch off from work. • Provides a sense of achievement.	• Relaxes and leads to stress relief. • Allows people to switch off from work. • Provides a sense of achievement.

Type of Facility	Leisure Centre	Book Club
Intellectual Benefits	• Learning how to operate physical machines. • Development of hand-eye co-ordination.	• Powers of concentration. • Analysis of situations. • Forming opinions and ideas.
Social Benefits	• Opportunity to meet friends. • Opportunity to meet new people. • Sets up social contacts for future leisure opportunities.	• Opportunity to meet friends. • Opportunity to meet new people.
Value for Money	• Many activities in one environment. • Provides for physical, mental and social needs. • Should be used regularly to be financially viable.	• Good value for money as books, once read, can be resold if desired.
Time Required	• Varies depending on chosen activity: one hour or more for workout.	• Varies depending on the type and length of book.
Value to the Community	• Increases employment in the community. • Only suitable for those who can afford it.	• Generates social interaction in rural areas. • Suitable for the majority of people in the community.

Sample Exam Questions
Higher Level (2007)

Questions

1. Discuss the function and value of leisure in today's society. (15)
2. Outline how social and cultural influences impact on our choice of leisure activities. (15)

Sample Answers

1. Discuss the function and value of leisure in today's society. (15)

   3 points x 5 marks each = 15.

Leisure is a very important part of people's lives for the following reasons:

• **Form of relaxation:** Leisure relieves the stresses of everyday life. It enables people to unwind and it relieves boredom. Leisure takes up time, thereby reducing any time for boredom. An individual is kept busy by the leisure activity. It also gratifies the senses e.g. visiting an art gallery, going to an opera. The senses of sight, sound, smell, taste and touch can be heightened.

- **Allows new skills to be developed**: For example, taking up cookery courses, introductory lessons on art and taking up a musical instrument. Cognitive, psycho-motor and social skills can all be developed. It provides a challenge – both physical and intellectual.

- **Physical well-being**: Sporting activities enable the individual to improve or maintain their physical health. It promotes personal development. Leisure encourages social interaction, gives an individual a feeling of self-confidence and improves self-esteem.

2. Outline how social and cultural influences impact on our choice of leisure activities. (15)

    3 points x 5 marks each = 15.

Social Influences

- The type of **socio-economic group** that a person belongs to will have an impact on the type of leisure activity chosen. Middle and lower socio-economic groups will have different leisure pursuits due to differences in income, educational qualifications, work hours and availability of facilities. Golf club membership, gym membership may be out of financial reach for those in lower socio-economic groups.

- Trends in leisure activities can change quite quickly, e.g. ice skating, all types of dancing have become very popular due to reality TV shows such as *Dancing on Ice* and *Dancing with the Stars*. The local amenities in an area may influence the chosen leisure activities that an individual pursues, e.g. access to GAA pitches, swimming pools and night classes.

Cultural Influences

- Culture can influence a person's choice of leisure activity. Certain sports and games are associated with specific countries, e.g. hurling in Ireland and baseball in the USA. Music and dance is also influenced by the culture of an area, e.g. Irish dancing, salsa dancing in Latin America, reggae in the Caribbean. The way an individual is raised may impact on leisure activities, e.g. if all family members played traditional musical instruments.

Poverty 6

Types of Poverty

There are two types of poverty:
* Absolute poverty.
* Relative poverty.

Absolute Poverty

* Absolute poverty is when individuals completely lack the basic needs of food, clothing and shelter.

Fig 6.1: Homeless person sleeping on the streets.

* This form of poverty is prevalent in under-developed countries.
* In Ireland, absolute poverty is seen among the homeless.

Relative Poverty

* Relative poverty can be defined as a standard of living below an acceptable level within a society.
* A low standard of living prevents an individual's participation in various activities which are considered the norm within society.
* There are two key aspects which make up relative poverty:
  * **Income poverty:** This occurs when individuals are living below the poverty line.
  * **Deprivation:** This relates to an individual's lack of provisions. It occurs when individuals fail to own something or carry out a task which is deemed as the norm within a society, e.g. owning a new pair of jeans, going to the cinema. The cause of this deprivation is lack of income.

Poverty Line
* This is a minimum income to maintain a basic standard of living.
* People living below the poverty line will have a poor standard of living.
* The poverty line will vary from country to country.

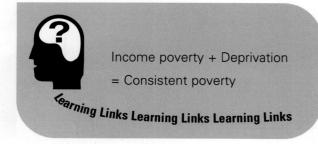
Groups at Risk

✳ **Unemployed and low wage earners:** Being unemployed or in a low-paid job makes people more likely to be poor.

✳ **Lone-parent families:** One-parent families are more likely to be poor than two-parent families.

✳ **Disabled:** People with long-term illnesses or who are disabled are at greater risk of poverty.

✳ **Women, children, members of large families:** Many older people and children whose parents are poor are at greater risk of poverty.

✳ **Lack of education:** People who left school early or without qualifications are more likely to experience poverty.

Distribution of Poverty in Ireland

✳ The number of people living below the poverty line has fluctuated over the past fifty years.

✳ In the 1960s and into the 1970s, there was a decrease in the number of people living below the poverty line.

✳ In the 1980s, the economy dropped into a recession and the number of people living below the poverty line increased.

✳ At the beginning of the 1990s, the 'Celtic Tiger' brought low unemployment levels, which caused fewer people to be below the poverty line.

✳ In the mid-2000s, there was an increase in the number of people living below the poverty line. This change has been brought about due to extremely high house prices and the high cost of living.

✳ Some social groups have higher poverty levels than the rest of the population: lone-parent families, the unemployed, people with disabilities or long-term illnesses and immigrants.

Causes of Poverty

Lack of Education:

Education is the key to job success. Those who lack a basic level of education also lack the basic skills required for most jobs. This can lead to long-term unemployment.

Low-Paid Jobs:

People who lack education are often forced to apply for low-paid jobs. The wage may be insufficient if the family is large.

Geographical Location:

Poverty is a problem that has no one particular geographical location. However, core areas linked with poverty are:

✳ Inner cities.

✳ Large social housing estates located on the outskirts of towns/cities.

✳ Isolated rural areas.

Poverty Cycle:

✳ This suggests that children born into poverty inherit the values and behaviour of their parents. These include:
  ● Having a poor level of education.
  ● Having few, if any, educational opportunity.
  ● Living in poor housing.
  ● Living in a poor neighbourhood.
  ● Eating a poor diet.
  ● Having poor health facilities.
  ● Marrying young.
  ● Having children at a young age.
  ● Being dependent on social welfare.

✳ These individuals drop out of school. The lack of education offers them little scope in the workforce. This cycle continues on from generation to generation.

Social Problems:

Drug abuse and alcoholism can cause poverty as the focus is not on family, life and work but on the next fix.

Economic Recession:

An economic recession can lead to an increase in unemployment levels. People can fall victim to poverty and have little hope of employment.

Cycle of Deprivation in Families:

The cycle of deprivation involves factors in an individual's life that can lead to further poverty. These factors are difficult if not impossible to overcome. This cycle often affects the next generation.

Social Policy:

People who are dependant on social welfare benefits often believe that these benefits are equal to if not better than the wages they could receive from working. Therefore, our social policies in relation to unemployment and work can be a hindrance to those who are unemployed. Individuals who have minimum wage jobs automatically lose out on benefits and therefore are unable to get out of the poverty trap.

The National Anti-Poverty Strategy(NAPS)

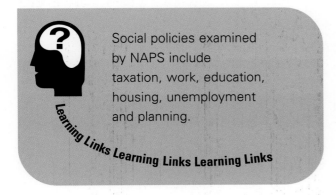

Social policies examined by NAPS include taxation, work, education, housing, unemployment and planning.

Learning Links Learning Links Learning Links

The National Anti-Poverty Strategy (NAPS) aims to focus government attention on the growing causes of poverty and on government policies that can be altered to minimise the numbers suffering from poverty.

* **Improvements in education:** To ensure a highly trained workforce.
* **Training for the unemployed:** When people are trained, they are more employable.
* **Financial assistance through state benefits:** The Family Income Supplement is an example of such a benefit.
* **Creation of jobs:** The government encourages companies to establish operations in Ireland by offering incentives such as grants.

The Poverty Trap

* The poverty trap affects the unemployed whose main source of income is state benefits.
* When individuals in this group seek employment, their only option tends to be low-paid jobs.
* However, their income is not increased by returning to work because returning to work often means that state benefits cease. Therefore, no financial gain is achieved by working, causing them to become trapped in poverty.

The Effects of Poverty

* **Stress:** This occurs when finances become a worry and individuals and their families struggle to meet regular bills. All members become affected by the stress and uncertainty of what will happen.
* **Health issues:** People living below the poverty line in poor housing conditions can become prone to infection, which is not easily cured as the high cost of visiting the doctor prevents people seeking medical attention.
* **Poor diet:** A nutritionally poor diet can lead to many deficiencies. These deficiencies, if untreated, can become very serious problems. Often people in poverty lack the nutritional education to provide a balanced meal. These individuals rely solely on convenience foods, which tend to be more expensive and less nutritious.

* **Psychological problems:** Poverty can lead to depression, low self-esteem and isolation, all of which have a negative psychological affect on individuals.
* **Unemployment:** Those who are classed as long-term unemployed are often living in poverty.
* **Poor housing:** People living in poverty are unable to afford some basic needs, such as heating. Housing conditions tend to be poor.

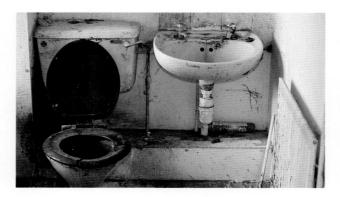

Fig 6.2: Poor housing conditions.

Statutory and Community Responses to Creating Employment and Eliminating Poverty

Creating Employment		Eliminating Poverty	
Statutory	**Community**	**Statutory**	**Community**
• **Social welfare assistance and benefits:** – Back to Work Allowance. • **Initiatives encouraging foreign investment:** – Enterprise Ireland. • **Initiatives encouraging employment:** – County Enterprise Board. – FÁS. – Forfás. – Industrial Development Agency (IDA). – Foreign investment.	• **Community-based educational training and employment initiatives.** – Adult and second-chance education (see p. 418–19, 423) – VTOS (see p. 424) – Co-operatives (see p. 454) – Cottage industries.	• **Social welfare assistance and benefits:** – Child Benefit. – One-Income Family Benefit. – Disability Allowance. – Family Income Supplement. • **State Agencies and Projects:** – MABS. – The National Anti-Poverty Strategy. – The Community Development Programme. – CLÁR. – Local Development Social Inclusion Programme. • **Scheme to reduce expenditure for low-income families:** – Local authority housing and schemes (see p.258-9). – Medical cards. – Back to school clothing and footwear allowance.	• **The work of voluntary organisations:** – Society of St Vincent de Paul. – FOCUS Ireland. – Simon Community.

Creating Employment

Statutory Responses

Social Welfare Assistance and Benefits

Back to Work Allowance:
* This scheme encourages people to take up employment.
* People participating in this scheme retain a percentage of their social welfare payment along with secondary benefits for a period of up to three years.

Initiatives Encouraging Foreign Investment

Enterprise Ireland:
* Enterprise Ireland is the government agency responsible for the development and promotion of the indigenous (Irish-owned companies) business sector.
* Its aim is to achieve a strong position in global markets resulting in increased national and regional prosperity.

Initiatives Encouraging Employment

County Enterprise Board:
* This agency give individuals advice on:
  * The steps involved in setting up a business.
  * Grants for feasibility studies.
  * Financial support for the establishment of new businesses or expansion of existing businesses.
  * Training and mentoring.

FÁS:
* FÁS provides expert guidance and resources, with access to job vacancies.
* The Jobseeker Directory offers invaluable aids, such as an A-Z of careers.
* There are also job clubs where people can actively develop skills for job-hunting.

Foras Áiseanna Saothair
Training & Employment Authority

* FÁS aims to encourage education in the workplace and the improvement of skills for work, or upskilling, through its One Step Up initiative.
* Training for apprentices enables men and women to become craftspeople.
* FÁS offers social inclusion programmes, such as Women Returning to Work.

Forfás:
* Established in 1994, Forfás is the national policy and advisory board for enterprise, trade, science, technology and innovation in Ireland.

Industrial Development Agency (IDA):
* This is an Irish government agency with responsibility for securing new investment from overseas in manufacturing and service sectors.
* It encourages existing investors to expand and develop their businesses.

Foreign investment:
* Ireland obtains investments from global corporations because:
  * The Irish workforce is viewed as highly qualified.
  * It has one of the best educated populations.
  * It has low corporation tax.
  * It is an English-speaking country in the EU.
* Today, Ireland is home to companies such as Intel, Yahoo, Adobe, Microsoft, HP, Apple, Google, Amazon.com, to name just a few.

Microsoft®

* Almost a thousand overseas companies have chosen to invest in Ireland as their European base and are involved in a wide range of activities in sectors as diverse as engineering, information and communications technologies, pharmaceuticals, medical technologies, financial and international services.

Community Responses

Community-based Educational Training and Employment Initiatives

* Adult and second-chance education (see pp. 418–19).
* VTOS (see p. 424).

Emergence of Co-operatives and Cottage Industries

Co-operatives:

* Co-operatives can take many forms; for example, a group of single parents may decide to band together to provide a childcare facility so they will have reliable daycare for their children.
* A credit union is also a type of co-operative. The purpose of a credit union is not to make a profit for itself, but to help each member be more financially secure.
* Co-operatives are most commonly found in agricultural areas. Agricultural co-operatives enable members to save money on materials needed to produce and market their product, which means a larger profit margin for all members. For example, Ocean Spray Cranberries, Inc. is a co-operative of several hundred cranberry and citrus growers.

Cottage Industries:

Fig 6.3: A cottage industry: hand-made chocolates being made in the home.

* The production of goods takes place at the home of the producer rather than in a factory.
* Cheeses, jams, chutneys and hand-made chocolates are examples of cottage industries in Ireland.
* Speciality foods have emerged as a growing area.
* Hand embroidery, sewing, crochet, knitting and other highly specialised activities still operate as cottage industries today.

Eliminating Poverty

Statutory Responses

Social Welfare Assistance and Benefits

Child Benefit:
This is payable to the parents or guardians of children under 16 years of age, or under 19 years of age if the child is in full-time education, FÁS, Youthreach training or has a disability.

One-Income Family Benefit:
This is made up of a personal rate and extra amounts for your dependent children. The amount you receive depends on your weekly means.

Disability Allowance:
People are entitled to a disability allowance if they have an injury, disease or physical or mental disability that has continued or may be expected to continue for at least one year. As a result of this condition, a person is substantially restricted in undertaking work that would otherwise be suitable for a person between 16 and 65.

Family Income Supplement:
See p. 245.

MABS (Money Advice and Budgeting Service)
This is a free, independent, confidential service. It offers money advice to people through a network of 52 local offices nationwide. MABS is funded by the Department of Social and Family Affairs. It works with people who are having difficulties with

debt or who are seeking advice on money management and budgeting. MABS staff also work with local groups to provide programmes and presentations on money issues. The MABS National Helpline provides callers with advice and guidance on handling debt problems. The MABS website – www.mabs.ie – supports people in managing debt problems for themselves.

The National Anti-Poverty Strategy (NAPS):

* NAPS aims to reduce poverty in Ireland.
* The Office for Social Inclusion, established in December 2002, took over the functions of the NAPS unit.
* The office has the overall responsibility for developing, co-ordinating and driving Ireland's National Action Plan for Social Inclusion.
* The new plan was published on 21 February 2007 and covers the ten-year period from 2007 to 2016.

The Community Development Programme:

* There are currently 180 Community Development Projects (CDPs) and ten support agencies funded under the Community Development Programme. There were just 15 CDPs in 1990.
* The projects in the Community Development Programme are based in disadvantaged communities in:
  * Inner-city areas.
  * Rural areas.
  * Small towns.
* Projects are concerned with Travellers, the homeless, unemployed and children.
* Its function is to create a sense of ownership in the community and to develop community decision-making and participation.

CLÁR:

* The CLÁR programme (Ceantair Laga Árd-Riachtanais), launched in October 2001, is a targeted investment programme for rural areas.
* It helps to provide access to basic services such as sewerage, water supply, broadband communication.

Local Development Social Inclusion Programme:

* The Social Inclusion Programme places great importance on ensuring that the most disadvantaged individuals and groups within our society are supported.
* The groups and individuals supported under this programme include:
  * Unemployed people.
  * Members of the Travelling community.
  * Low-income households.
  * Lone parents.
  * Disabled people.
  * Disadvantaged children and young people, etc.

Schemes to Reduce Expenditure for Low-income Families:

* **Local authority housing and schemes:** See p. 258–9.
* **Medical cards:** Medical cards issued by the Health Service Executive (HSE) in Ireland enable the bearer to receive certain health services free of charge, e.g. free GP (family doctor) services, in-patient public hospital services, out-patient services, and dental, optical and aural services.
* **Back-to-School Clothing and Footwear Allowance:** This helps meet the cost of uniforms and footwear. Certain conditions apply, e.g. a person must be receiving certain social welfare payments or payments for training, employment schemes or adult education and the total household income must be below a certain amount.

Community Responses

The Work of Voluntary Organisations

Society of St Vincent de Paul
* The Society of St Vincent de Paul is a voluntary Christian organisation.
* It was established in Ireland in 1844.
* It has a network of over 8,000 volunteers.

* Funding is raised by corporate and public contributions, internal collections and government support for projects tackling social exclusion.
* It is strongly committed to working for social justice and advocates the creation of a more just and caring society.
* It is involved in a number of projects:
  * Family visits.
  * Hostels for people who are homeless.
  * Social housing.
  * Breakfast clubs.
  * Community resource centres.
  * Education grants.
  * Holiday breaks.
  * Pre-schools/crèches.

Focus Ireland

* Focus Ireland aims to advance the right of those without homes to live in a place they can call home through services, creating awareness and research.

* Some examples of some services they provide include:
  * Coffee shop and housing advice centre.
  * The AIB Better Ireland Programme Schoolmate Project. This project works to ensure that children of homeless families do not miss out on their education. Children are supported to stay in school despite the disruption of homelessness. Help is given with homework and tutors are provided.

* The Outreach Team works with people who are sleeping rough, helping them to move away from the streets by encouraging them to use other services that will help them out of homelessness.
* Off-the-Streets provides short-term accommodation and support to young people between sixteen and eighteen years of age. The young people are encouraged to address the issues that led to them becoming homeless and help them move on with their lives
* The Young Women's Aftercare Project is a residential programme offering support to young women both during their time in the project and after they move on.
* Focus Ireland launched a national campaign in November 2007 that aimed to raise awareness and help break down stereotypes around homelessness. This campaign featured on TV and radio during 2008.

Simon Community

* This is an organisation based between the eight independent communities in Cork, Dublin, Dundalk, Galway, the Midlands, the Mid West, the North West and the South East.
* It has over 800 volunteers.
* The Simon Community works with people who experience homelessness and housing exclusion in Ireland by:
  * Providing emergency accommodation for homeless people.
  * Lobbying the government for policy changes for people who have no homes.
  * Provides projects and services for homeless people, e.g. detox programmes, Simon shops, transitional, long-term and move-on accommodation.

Sample Exam Questions (2006)

While Ireland has become increasingly wealthy in recent years, it still has one of the highest levels of income inequalities in the EU.

1. Define each of the following:
   - Relative poverty.
   - Absolute poverty. (10)
2. Discuss the reasons why poverty continues to be a feature of modern society. In your answer, include reference to the cycle of poverty and the influence of social policy on poverty. (24)
3. Give an account of two statutory initiatives aimed specifically at eliminating poverty in Ireland. (16)

1. Define each of the following:
   - Relative poverty.
   - Absolute poverty.

   2 definitions x 5 marks each = 10.

Relative Poverty

- Relative poverty is defined as a standard of living below an acceptable level within a society.
- A low standard of living prevents an individual's participation in various activities which are considered the norm within society.
- There are two key aspects which make up relative poverty:
  - Income Poverty.
  - Deprivation.

Absolute Poverty

Absolute poverty is when individuals completely lack the basic needs of food, clothing and shelter.

- This form of poverty is prevalent in under-developed countries.
- Here in Ireland absolute poverty is seen in the case of the homeless.

2. Discuss the reasons why poverty continues to be a feature of modern society. In your answer, include reference to the cycle of poverty and the influence of social policy on poverty. (24)

   4 points x 6 marks each = 24.

Lack of education:

Education is the key to job success. Those who lack a basic level of education also lack the basic skills required for most jobs. This can lead to long-term unemployment.

Geographical location:

Poverty is a problem that has no single particular geographical location. However, core areas linked with poverty are:

- Inner cities.
- Large social housing estates located on the outskirts of towns/cities.
- Isolated rural areas.

Poverty cycle:

Children born into poverty inherit the values and behaviour of their parents. These include:

- Having a poor level of education.
- Having few, if any, educational opportunities.
- Living in poor housing.
- Living in a poor neighbourhood.
- Eating a poor diet.

- Having poor health facilities.
- Marrying young.
- Having children at a young age.
- Being dependent on social welfare.

These individuals drop out of school. Their lack of education offers them little scope in the workforce. And this cycle continues on from generation to generation.

Social policy:

People who are dependant on social welfare benefits often believe that these benefits are equal to if not better than the wages they could receive from working. Therefore, our social policies in relation to unemployment and work can be a hindrance to those who are unemployed. Individuals who have minimum wage jobs automatically lose out on benefits and therefore are unable to get out of the poverty trap.

3. Give an account of two statutory initiatives aimed specifically at eliminating poverty in Ireland. (16)

   2 initiatives x 8 marks each = 16.
   Name = 4 marks.
   Explanation = 4 marks (x2).

MABS (Money Advice and Budgeting Service)

- This is a free, independent, confidential service.
- It offers money advice to people through a network of 52 local offices nationwide.
- MABS is funded by the Department of Social and Family Affairs.
- It works with people who are having difficulties with debt or who are seeking advice on money management and budgeting.
- MABS staff also work with local groups to provide programmes and presentations on money issues.
- The MABS National Helpline provides callers with advice and guidance on handling debt problems.
- The MABS website – www.mabs.ie – supports people in managing debt problems for themselves.

The National Anti-Poverty Strategy

- NAPS aims to reduce poverty in Ireland.
- The Office for Social Inclusion, established in December 2002, took over the functions of the NAPS unit.
- The office has the overall responsibility for developing, co-ordinating and driving Ireland's National Action Plan for Social Inclusion.
- The new plan was published on 21 February 2007 and covers the ten-year period from 2007 to 2016.

1 Cottage Pie

2 Lasagne

3 Chilli Chicken and Pasta

4 Chicken and Vegetable Stir Fry with Brown Rice

5 Vegetable Soup

6 Bacon and Leek Quiche

7 Vegetable and Potato Pie

8 Creamy Cod Bake

9 Mixed Vegetable Curry

10 Pineapple Upside Down Cake

11 Strawberry Cheesecake

12 Profiteroles/Éclairs

13 Chocolate Soufflé

14 Vanilla Ice Cream

15 Raspberry/Passion Fruit/Mixed Berry Meringue Roulade

16 Country Kitchen Carrot Cake

17 Home-Made Brown Bread

18 Barm Brack

Recipes

Cottage Pie

Ingredients

4 large potatoes
1 onion
1 large carrot
1 vegetable stock cube
500g lean minced beef
2 tablespoons frozen peas
1 tablespoon tomato purée
1 teaspoon mixed herbs
25g butter
Milk to combine (approx 75–100ml)
Salt and pepper

Method

1. Wash and peel the potatoes.
2. Cover with water and boil until soft.
3. Prepare the vegetables: peel and dice the onion and wash, peel, top, tail and grate the carrot.
4. Make the stock: dissolve stock cube in 125ml of water.
5. Dry fry the mince until brown.
6. Add in the vegetables (onion, carrots and frozen peas) and sauté for three minutes.
7. Add in the stock, tomato purée and mixed herbs.
8. Bring to the boil and allow to simmer for twenty minutes.
9. Strain and mash the potatoes. Add in butter and milk as desired.
10. Place the meat sauce in a Pyrex dish and cover with mashed potato. Score the top with a fork.
11. Cook in a preheated oven 190°C/180°C fan/gas mark 6 for twenty minutes until golden brown.
12. Serve with steamed green beans and buttered carrot batons.

Lasagne

Ingredients

1 onion	500g lean minced meat
1 carrot	2 tablespoons peas (frozen)
½ red pepper	1 tin tomatoes
½ green pepper	1 tablespoon tomato purée
4 mushrooms	1 teaspoon oregano
2 cloves garlic	Salt and pepper
2 rashers	9 sheets of lasagne

Cheese sauce:

25g margarine

25g flour

500ml milk

75–100g cheddar cheese

Method

1. Prepare all the vegetables: dice the onion, grate the carrot, slice and dice the peppers and mushrooms, crush the garlic, etc.
2. Chop the rashers.
3. Dry fry the mince.
4. Add in the rashers and cook right through.
5. When the meat is brown, add in the vegetables, including the frozen peas. Cook for approximately five minutes.
6. Add in the tomatoes, tomato purée, herbs and seasoning.
7. Allow the mixture to come to the boil and simmer for fifteen to twenty minutes.
8. Meanwhile, make the cheese sauce.

Cheese sauce:

Method 1

If asked to demonstrate a roux sauce:
1. Melt the margarine.
2. Tip in the flour and cook through.
3. Gradually add in the milk, stirring all the time to prevent lumps.
4. Add in three-quarters of the cheese and allow to melt.

Method 2

This is a quick, no skill method:
1. Combine all the ingredients except the cheese in a saucepan.
2. Allow the mixture to thicken on the heat by stirring all the time.
3. Add in three-quarters of the cheese and allow to melt.

Assemble the lasagne in a lasagne dish as follows:
1. Layer of meat sauce.
2. Layer of lasagne sheets.
3. Layer of cheese sauce.
4. Continue this layering process, finishing off with a layer of cheese sauce.
5. Sprinkle on the remainder of the cheese.
6. Cook in a preheated oven 190°C/180°C fan/gas mark 6 for approximately thirty minutes.
7. Serve with a baked potato and a side salad.

Chilli Chicken and Pasta

Ingredients

1 onion	2 tomatoes
2 cloves garlic	2 fillets of chicken
½ red pepper	1 tablespoon vegetable oil
½ green pepper	100g small pasta shapes
½ red chilli	200ml chicken stock
½ green chilli	½ teaspoon of tumeric, onion, ginger and chilli powder
	2 tablespoon jalapeno relish
	Fresh parsley to garnish

Method

1. Peel and chop the onion.
2. Crush the garlic.
3. Slice and dice the peppers.
4. Slice the fresh chillies.
5. Halve and quarter the tomatoes.
6. Cut the chicken into bite-sized pieces.
7. Heat the oil in a pan.
8. Add the chicken and cook right through.
9. Lift the chicken out onto a plate.
10. Fry the vegetables and toss in the hot oil for two to three minutes.
11. Return the chicken pieces to the pan.
12. Add in the pasta shapes, stock and spices.
13. Bring the mixture to the boil and allow to simmer.
14. Simmer for fifteen to twenty minutes.
15. Stir in the jalapeno relish.
16. Serve and garnish with fresh parsley.

Chicken and Vegetable Stir Fry with Brown Rice

Ingredients

4 chicken fillets

1 red onion

1 red pepper

1 carrot

6 mushrooms

2 cloves of garlic

300g brown rice

2 tablespoons vegetable oil

50g baby sweetcorn

50g mangetout

2 tablespoons soya sauce

2 tablespoons balsamic vinegar

Salt and pepper

Method

1. Cut the chicken into strips.
2. Prepare the vegetables. Cut the onion and pepper and cut into strips. Cut the carrot into julienne strips. Wash and slice the mushrooms. Crush the garlic.
3. Put the rice in a saucepan of boiling water.
4. Add 1 tablespoon oil to the wok. Add the chicken and cook for five minutes until completely cooked. Remove the chicken from wok. Put the chicken on a plate and cover with tinfoil.
5. Add 1 tablespoon of oil to wok: add the carrot and stir fry for two minutes. Continue by adding sweetcorn, pepper, onion, garlic and mushrooms, allowing one to two minute intervals.
6. Return the chicken to the wok. Add the soya sauce and vinegar. Season with salt and pepper.
7. Strain the rice.
8. To serve, place the rice on a plate and put the stir fry in the centre.

Vegetable Soup

Ingredients
1 onion
1 carrot
3 potatoes
1 leek
2 sticks of celery
1 tablespoon oil
400ml vegetable stock
1 bouquet garni
Salt and pepper
Cream and chopped parsley, to serve

Method
1. Wash, peel and chop the vegetables.
2. Heat the oil in a medium-sized saucepan.
3. Add vegetables and sauté for five minutes.
4. Cover vegetables with damp greaseproof paper and allow to sweat for five minutes.
5. Make stock. Remove greaseproof paper and add stock to the saucepan together with bouquet garni and seasoning.
6. Bring to the boil and then simmer gently for twenty-five to thirty minutes.
7. When vegetables are soft, remove bouquet garni and liquidise soup.
8. Serve soup with a swirl of fresh cream and freshly chopped parsley.

Bacon and Leek Quiche

Ingredients

100g plain flour

50g margarine

3 back rashers

1 leek

1 tablespoon oil

3 eggs

150ml milk

75g grated cheddar cheese

Method

1. Weigh 100g flour and 50g margarine.
2. Sieve the flour into a bowl and cut in the margarine with a butter knife.
3. Rub in the margarine until the mixture resembles breadcrumbs.
4. Make a well in the centre of the mixture and add approximately three to four tablespoons of cold water.
5. Combine the ingredients using a butter knife.
6. Knead lightly. Wrap in cling film. Place in the refrigerator until ready to use.
7. Remove the rind from the rashers: cut the rashers into small pieces.
8. Using a vegetable chopping board, cut up the leek.
9. Add oil to the frying pan: add rashers and lightly cook. Add the leek (and watch it reduce in size).
10. Remove from the heat. Crack eggs into bowl. Add milk and whisk lightly.
11. Roll out pastry and line a quiche dish with the pastry. Add bacon and leek.
12. Pour over the egg/milk mixture. Add cheese.
13. Bake in oven 180°C/gas mark 5 for twenty-five to thirty minutes.
14. Serve with summer salad.

Vegetable and Potato Pie

Ingredients

3 large potatoes
1 carrot
½ red pepper
½ green pepper
1 clove garlic
1 onion
½ tablespoon oil
½ tin tomatoes
50g grated cheddar cheese
Salt and pepper
Knob of butter

Method

1. Wash and peel potatoes.
2. Place in a saucepan, cover with water and bring to the boil.
3. Peel and grate the carrot.
4. Chop the peppers, crush garlic, dice onion.
5. Put oil into a saucepan. Add onion and garlic.
6. Add peppers and carrot to saucepan.
7. Once softened, add the tin of tomatoes and season well.
8. Strain potatoes when soft and mash.
9. Add butter and seasoning to potatoes. Mix the cheese with the potatoes.
10. Place the vegetable mixture in a Pyrex dish and add the potato mixture on top.
11. Cook for twenty minutes in oven 180°C/fan 170°C/gas mark 5.
12. Serve with green beans.

Creamy Cod Bake

Ingredients

400g cod

3 rashers (optional)

3–4 potatoes

1 onion

1 clove garlic

100g mushrooms

1 tin tomatoes

125ml cream

2 bay leaves

1 teaspoon oregano

25g butter

A little milk

Method

1. Preheat oven to 190°C/180°C fan/gas mark 6.
2. Grease a round Pyrex dish with a little butter.
3. Wash, skin and chop the cod.
4. Slice up the rashers and place both in the Pyrex dish.
5. Wash, peel and chop the potatoes.
6. Put the potatoes on to boil.
7. Prepare the vegetables: peel, dice the onion, crush the garlic, slice the mushrooms.
8. Heat a little oil in a pan and fry the vegetables until soft.
9. Add tomatoes, cream and herbs. Season well.
10. Allow to cook for fifteen minutes.
11. Strain the potatoes and mash with butter and milk.
12. Remove the bay leaves from the sauce.
13. Pour the sauce over the fish and rashers.
14. Add the mashed potato to the top and score with a fork.
15. Place in the preheated oven and cook for twenty-five to thirty minutes.
16. Garnish with some chopped parsley and serve with garlic bread.

Note: Prawns can be used instead of or in addition to the cod.

Mixed Vegetable Curry

Ingredients

250ml vegetable stock

1 onion

1 leek

2 medium potatoes

2 cloves garlic

1 red pepper

2 carrots

2 sticks celery

100g mangetout

1 tablespoon vegetable oil

1 tablespoon curry powder

1 tablespoon flour

25g peanuts

1 tablespoon mango chutney

Method

1. Prepare the stock: dissolve a stock cube in boiling water.
2. Prepare vegetables: wash, peel, slice the onion, leek and potatoes. Crush the garlic, slice the red pepper, cut the carrots into julienne strips or batons, slice the celery, wash the mangetout.
3. Heat the oil in a pot.
4. Add the vegetables gradually (beginning with the hardest vegetable first e.g. carrots, potatoes, celery etc.).
5. Allow the vegetables to toss in the hot fat for ten minutes.
6. Add in the curry powder and flour and cook for one minute.
7. Gradually add in the stock until it has reached the desired consistency.
8. Add the peanuts, bring the mixture to the boil and allow to simmer.
9. Serve with the mango chutney.

Pineapple Upside Down Cake

Ingredients

Madeira mixture:
100g butter/margarine
100g caster sugar
2 eggs
150g self-raising flour
1 tablespoon pineapple juice

50g butter/margarine
50g demerara sugar
1 small can pineapple rings
A few glacé cherries, halved

Method
1. Grease a loaf tin.
2. Mix the 50g butter/margarine with 50g demerara sugar. Spread this mixture on the base of the tin.
3. Arrange pineapple rings in the base of the tin. Place cherries in the centre of the pineapple rings with the round side down.
4. Make the Madeira mixture – place all ingredients for the Madeira mixture into a large bowl and beat vigorously until smooth.
5. Spread Madeira mixture over pineapples and cherries (take care to cover the fruit).
6. Bake in an oven 180°C/fan 170°C/gas mark 5 for thirty to forty minutes until cooked.
7. Remove from the oven and turn upside down to remove cake.
8. Serve with warm custard.

Strawberry Cheesecake

Ingredients

150g digestive biscuits
75g butter
1 packet strawberry jelly
200g Philadelphia cheese
1 small carton strawberry yoghurt
1 tin strawberries
1 tablespoon caster sugar
150ml cream, whipped

Method

1. Prepare the base: crush biscuits by placing them in cling film and crush with a rolling pin.
2. Melt the butter, add the biscuits to the butter and press the biscuit base into the tin.
3. Make jelly by dissolving it in a measuring jug with 150ml of water.
4. Beat the Philadelphia cheese in a bowl using an electric beater. Add the yoghurt and gently mix in.
5. Add the strawberries and caster sugar, mix, and add cooled jelly.
6. Fold in whipped cream.
7. Pour the filling onto the biscuit base. Allow to set in the refrigerator.
8. To serve, cut a slice, put it on a plate and add some fresh strawberries and a small dollop of whipped cream.

Profiteroles/Éclairs

Ingredients
125g plain flour
100g margarine
300ml water
4 eggs

To fill:
500ml cream
Chocolate sauce: 2 Mars bars
2 tablespoons milk

Method
1. Sieve the flour onto a large plate.
2. Melt the margarine in the water and allow to boil rapidly for three to four minutes.
3. Take the melted mixture off the heat and tip in all of the sieved flour. Beat.
4. Allow mixture to cool slightly.
5. Gently beat the eggs in a separate bowl or measuring jug.
6. Add the egg mixture gradually and beat vigorously after each addition. (Note: each time it must look the same as it did at the beginning.)
7. The mixture should stand in peaks.
8. The mixture can either be piped through a piping bag or spooned onto a dampened baking tray.
9. Cook in a preheated oven 200°C/210°C fan/gas mark 8 for twenty to twenty-five minutes.
10. Allow to cool on a wire tray and slit a hole in each profiterole.
11. Fill with whipped cream.
12. Melt the Mars bar in a microwave for thirty seconds. Stir. Add the milk and microwave on high for a further thirty seconds.
13. Pour the melted chocolate sauce over the profiteroles.

Chocolate Soufflé

Ingredients

2 teaspoons cocoa powder
370ml milk
35g cornflour
150g dark chocolate
75g caster sugar
6 eggs
Pinch salt
1 teaspoon lemon juice

Method

1. Place 1½ teaspoons cocoa powder and all the milk, cornflour and chocolate in a saucepan. Heat gently.
2. When melted, place in a bowl and allow to cool slightly.
3. Grease six ramekin dishes.
4. Mix a teaspoon of cocoa powder with a teaspoon of caster sugar. Place in each ramekin.
5. Separate the eggs. Whisk the egg whites with salt and lemon juice. Continue whisking until the mixture is stiff. Add sugar and continue mixing.
6. Add the egg yolks and the rest of the sugar to the chocolate sauce.
7. Gently fold the egg white mixture into the chocolate mixture.
8. Divide the mixture equally between the ramekins. Place ramekins in a baking tin with hot water (a bain-marie).
9. Bake for fifteen minutes in oven 180°C/fan 170°C/gas mark 5.
10. Sieve icing sugar over each and serve with whipped cream.

Vanilla Ice Cream

Ingredients
4 eggs
200g icing sugar
1 teaspoon vanilla essence
200ml cream

Method
1. Turn the freezer to -25°C.
2. Separate the eggs. Whisk the egg whites until stiff.
3. Sieve the icing sugar. Add the icing sugar to the whisked egg whites, a little at a time.
4. Whisk after each addition.
5. Beat the egg yolks together with the vanilla essence. Add to the egg white mixture.
6. Whip the cream until stiff.
7. Fold the cream into the egg mixture.
8. Place in a freezer container, cover and freeze for five to six hours.
9. Stir after every hour.
10. Home-made ice cream can stored for up to three months.

Raspberry/Passion Fruit/Mixed Berry Meringue Roulade

Ingredients
5 large egg whites
250g caster sugar
50g flaked almonds

To fill:
250ml cream
200g raspberries/3-4 passion fruit or fruit of choice

Method
1. Line a Swiss roll tin with baking parchment.
2. Put the egg whites in a spotlessly clean bowl and whisk them until soft.
3. Add the sugar, beating all the time.
4. Spread the meringue mixture in the lined Swiss roll tin.
5. Sprinkle with the flaked almonds.
6. Cook in a preheated oven 200°C/190°C fan/gas mark 7 for five minutes and reduce heat to 160°C/150°C fan/gas mark 3 for a further twelve minutes.
7. Turn out the meringue with flaked almond side down.
8. Spread with whipped cream and fruit e.g. passion fruit or raspberries.
9. Roll up into a Swiss roll shape.
10. Cut into slices to serve.

Country Kitchen Carrot Cake

Ingredients

200g plain flour

1 teaspoon baking powder

2 teaspoons ground allspice

4 eggs

200g finely grated carrot

400g caster sugar

220ml vegetable oil

To decorate:

50g butter

200g cream cheese

200g icing sugar

100g chopped walnuts

Method

1. Sieve the flour into a mixing bowl.
2. Add the baking powder and allspice.
3. In a separate bowl, combine the eggs, carrot, caster sugar and oil. Beat with an electric mixer for three minutes.
4. Add the dry ingredients to the wet ingredients and beat after each addition.
5. Divide the mixture into two round cake tins.
6. Cook in a preheated oven 180°C/170°C fan/gas mark 5 for approximately thirty to thirty-five minutes.
7. Allow to cool and remove from the tins.
8. Make icing by mixing the butter, cream cheese and icing sugar together.
9. Spread half the icing on one of the cakes, sandwich the cakes together and spread the rest of the icing on top.
10. Sprinkle with the chopped walnuts.

Home-Made Brown Bread

Ingredients

350g stoneground wholemeal flour

75g plain flour

1 teaspoon bread soda

1 tablespoon bran

1 tablespoon wheatgerm

1 tablespoon porridge oats

1 tablespoon demerara sugar

400ml buttermilk

1 egg

2 tablespoons olive oil

Method

1. Preheat oven to 170°C/160°C fan/gas mark 4.
2. Line a loaf tin with baking parchment.
3. Combine all the dry ingredients in a bowl (wholemeal flour, plain flour, bread soda, bran, wheatgerm, oats, sugar).
4. In a separate bowl or measuring jug combine the milk, egg and oil. Whisk gently.
5. Add the wet mixture to the dry ingredients and mix together (it should be a wet dough).
6. Pour the dough into the loaf tin.
7. Cook in the oven for approximately one hour. Test to see if it is done by tapping the base (you should hear a hollow sound).
8. Allow to cool on a wire tray.
9. Serve in its own or as an accompaniment to vegetable soup.

Barm Brack

Ingredients
400g strong plain flour
½ teaspoon nutmeg
½ teaspoon cinnamon
Pinch salt
1 sachet of fast action dried yeast
40g caster sugar
40g butter/margarine
1 egg
270ml tepid milk
220g sultanas
40g mixed peel (chopped)

For the syrup:
2 tablespoons sugar
4 tablespoons water

Method
1. Sieve the flour, spices (nutmeg and cinnamon) and a pinch of salt into a bowl.
2. Add the yeast to the mixture. Add one teaspoon of sugar and stir in.
3. Rub the butter or margarine into the flour mixture.
4. Make a well in the centre and add sugar, egg and milk to the dry mixture.
5. Mix well with a wooden spoon.
6. Add the sultanas and mixed peel. Place in a greased loaf tin.
7. Allow to prove (double in size).
8. Bake at fan 200°C/190°C/gas mark 7 for ten minutes. Reduce heat to fan 190°C/180°C/gas mark 6 for thirty to thirty-five minutes.
9. To make the syrup, dissolve the sugar in the water in a saucepan.
10. When the brack is ready remove from oven and glaze with syrup.

Index

ABS (acrylonitrile-butadiene styrene), 368
abuse, 320
accelerated freeze drying, 220
ACCORD, 309–10
acid in food preservation, 207, 221
acid rain, 376
acrylic, 357, 369
actin, 9
additives in food, 186–92
adipose tissue, 33
adolescents, 313, 315
    dietary guidelines, 61–2
adult education, 418–19
advertising, 3, 279, 282, 293
Advertising Standards Authority, 293
aeration, 20, 93
aesthetics, 340
    food, 161–2
    interior design, 349
affordable housing, 259, 334
aflatoxins, 207
Agriculture and Food, Dept of, 170, 229
agri-food industry, 170–4
airbricks, 397
air composition, 395
air pollution, 289
alarm systems, 262, 302, 329
albumin, 8
alcohol, 155–6
alienation, 429
aluminium, 367
aluminium cans, 180, 182–3
amenities, 335
amino acids, 5–6, 12, 13, 48
amperage (amps), 383
amylase, 24
anaemia, 70
angina, 66
annulment of marriage, 310–11
anorexia nervosa, 70–1
antibiotics, 192
antibodies, 11

anti-caking agents, 189
anti-oxidants, 188, 191, 221
AONTAS, 419
apartments, 326, 331
apples
    apple and raisin chutney, 217
    sensory analysis, 164
appliances, 262–72
    energy efficiency, 263, 378
    safety, 159, 385
architects, 339
aroma of food, 161, 162
ascomycetes, 197
ascorbic acid, 39
aspergillus, 197, 207
asymmetrical balance, 348, 349
attic insulation, 393
autism, 318
automation, 429–30, 440–1

babies, 60–1
bacillus, 202
Back-to-School Allowance, 455
Back-to-Work Allowance, 453
bacon and leek quiche, 466
bacteria, 200–4, 207
    food poisoning, 208–10
bakelite, 368
baking, 145
    baking blind, 153
    pastry, 151–5
    recipes, 466, 470–3, 475–8
baking powder, 154
balance in design, 348
bananas, ripening, 206
bank giro, 247
banking, 246–51
bar codes, 185
barbecuing, 145
barley, 134
barm brack, 478
barring order, 320

basal metabolic rate (BMR), 55
bathroom safety, 385
beans, 128
    soya, 115–16
bedroom safety, 385
beds, 363
    bed linen, 364–5
beriberi, 40
betacarotene, 37, 125
bile, 33
Bill Pay, 248
bills, electricity, 383–4
binary fission, 201
biomass and bio energy, 290, 376
black economy, 442
blanching, 207, 214
bleach, 274
blended family, 301
blinds, 364–5
blood clotting, 39, 47
blood pressure, 63, 67
BMR (basal metabolic rate), 55
bogs, 373
boiling, 144
book clubs, 446–7
Bord Bia, 170
Bord Iascaigh Mhara, 170
borrowing, 249–50
    mortgages, 256–9
bottled food, 176–7, 219
    glass containers, 180, 182–3
bowel disorders, 69–70
braising, 144
bran, 23, 131
brand names, 262
bread, 153–5
    recipe, 477
bread mould, 196
bread soda, 154
breakfast cereals, 133, 134
breast-feeding, 60, 63
browning, enzymic, 206
browning, non-enzymic, 10, 20, 22
BSE (Bovine Spongiform Encephalopathy), 81
budgeting, 246
    advice, 454–5
buffers, 189
builders, 340
building a house, 337–42
Building Energy Certificate, 328
building societies, 251
building standards, 328, 332, 342
bulimia nervosa, 71
butter, 106–7
buttermilk, 101

CAD (computer aided design), 341
cadmium, 192
cake recipes, 470–3, 475–6, 478
calcium, 47–8

Irish eating habits, 169
calories, 54, 56, 58–9
cancer, 70
canned food, 124, 176–7, 219
    containers, 180, 182–3
    fish, 88
    meat, 80
    peas, 222–3
Capital Assistance Scheme, 334
car insurance, 254
caramelisation, 20, 142
carbohydrates, 16–26, 58–9
carbon dioxide, 376
care labels, 275
carotene, 119
carotenoids, 37
carpets, 356–8
carrots
    carrot cake, 476
    freezing, 214
casein, 7, 8
caseinogen, 9, 10, 12, 13
cash, 247
cast iron, 367
casual workers, 432
catalyst, 31
cavity wall insulation, 393–4
CE symbol, 286
cellulose, 19, 21, 23, 131
central heating, 390–2
ceramic tiles, 354, 361
cereals, 129–34
    breakfast, 133, 134
    composition tables, 59
CFC gases, 376
CFL lightbulbs, 401–2
cheese, 112–14
    cheese sauce, 462
cheesecake, strawberry, 471
chemical formula, 4
chemical preservatives, 187, 220–1
cheques, 247
chicken, 82–3
    chicken and vegetable stir fry, 464
    chilli chicken and pasta, 463
Child Benefit, 245, 454
childcare, 435–7
Child Care Act, 321
childminders, 436–7
children
    child-parent relationship, 315
    development and needs, 412–13
    dietary guidelines, 61
    rights of, 315
chilli chicken and pasta, 463
chipboard, 366
chlorination, 387
chlorophyll, 16
chocolate soufflé, 473
cholecalciferol, 37

cholesterol, 67, 73–4
choux pastry, 152
chutney, 217
circuit breakers, 384
Citizen Information Centres, 292–3
CJD (Creutzfeldt-Jakob Disease), 81
Clár programme, 455
climate change, 377
Clostridium botulinum, 208
clothes, 273
       washing, 274–8
coagulation, 10, 92
coal, 374
cobalamin, 43, 65
coccus, 202
cod bake, 468
coeliac disease, 3, 65, 130
cohabitation, 303
coir flooring, 358
collagen, 8, 9, 10–11
colleges of education, 418
colon cancer, 70
colour, 343–7
colouring in food, 187
colour washing, 360
Comhairle, 292–3
communication, 237, 316
communications technology, 302
community centres, 335
Community Development Programme (CDP), 455
community schools, 416
comparison tests, 163
comprehensive schools, 416
computer aided design (CAD), 341
condensation, 396
condensed milk, 103
conditioners (laundry), 275
conditioning agents in food, 189
conduction of heat, 142–3
consommé, 149
constipation, 69–70
Constitution of Ireland, 300
consumer, 279–95
Consumer Affairs, Director of, 230, 292
Consumer Association of Ireland (CAI), 293
Consumer Credit Act, 250
consumer research, 283
contaminants in food, 191–2
convalescents, dietary guidelines, 63
convection of heat, 142–3, 391
convenience foods, 176–7
       in Ireland, 167, 169
cook-chill food, 176–7
cooker hoods, 398
cooking, 141–58
cooking equipment, 146–8, 262–72
       metals used, 367
       safety, 159, 385
co-operative housing, 334
co-operatives, 454

copper, 367
coronary heart disease, 66–7, 77
cottage cheese, 113
cottage industries, 454
cottage pie, 460
cottages, 324
cotton, 276
council houses, 258, 334
counselling, marriage, 309–10
County Enterprise Board, 453
cream, 108–9
crèches, 414, 437
credit, 249–50
credit cards, 249
credit history, 256
credit transfer, 247
credit unions, 250, 454
crème fraîche, 109
critical control point (CCP), 225
crystallisation, 21
culture, 298
      family differences, 234, 239, 241
      food choices, 2, 64, 140
      leisure, 443–4
      marriage variations, 307–8
curdling, 10
curing meat, 80
current, electric, 383
curry, vegetable, 469
curtains, 364–5
custard, 150
cutlery, 367

dairy spreads, 137–8, 178
damask, 369
deamination, 12
debit cards, 247
decision-making, 237
decorating, 358–61
deep frying, 146
      smoke point, 31
degumming, 136
denaturation, 10
dental caries, 68–9
department stores, 280
deprivation, 449, 451
design, interior, 343–70
design of house, 340–2
detergents, 274
dextrinisation, 21, 142
diabetes, 65–6
diet, 2–4
      Irish, 167–9
      modified, 63–5
dietary disorders, 70–1
dietary fibre, 23, 63, 70
      Irish eating habits, 169
dietary guidelines, 57–9
Dietary Reference Values (DRVs), 58
dietary requirements, 60–74

guidelines, 57–9
    sample menu, 72–3
dietetic value, 4
digestion, 12–13, 24–5, 33
dioxins, 191
direct debit, 248
Disability Allowance, 454
disabled people, 316–17
    housing, 329
disaccharides, 17–18, 19
discount stores, 281
disulphide link, 6–7
diverticulitis, 70
divorce, 311
domestic violence, 320
doors, insulation, 395
double glazing, 394–5
Down syndrome, 317, 419
draught excluders, 395
dried foods, 124, 176–7, 219–20
    home drying, 217
dried milk, 103, 219
drinks industry, 171
dual role, 238, 434
duodenum, 12–13, 24
durum wheat, 133–4
duvets, 364–5

E. coli, 210
E numbers, 186–92
early school leavers, 422, 423
Early Start Pre-School Programme, 414, 422
eating disorders, 70–1
eating guidelines, 57–9
eating patterns, 2–3
    adolescents, 62
    in Ireland, 167–9
éclairs, 472
Eco-Label symbol, 288
ecological footprint, 287
economic changes, 301–3, 314, 408
economic recession, 441
education, 409, 412–26
eggs, 90–8
    bacon and leek quiche, 466
    egg sauces, 150
    whisked egg whites, 10
elastin, 9
elderly people, 238, 316
    dietary guidelines, 62–3
    family role, 313
    housing, 328–9
electricity, 371–2
    in houses, 382–6, 389, 392
electricity bills, 383–4
electrolytes, 45
Electronic Commerce Act, 291
elemental composition, 3
emigration, 442
emotional development, 445

emphasis in interior design, 349
employment, 427–39
    employment initiatives, 452–4
    equality, 241, 411, 430
    family and work, 241, 409, 433–4
    income and tax, 241–4, 410
    minimum wage, 410
    unpaid and voluntary, 427, 432–3
emulsifying, 32, 94
    food additives, 189
endosperm, 131
endospores, 201
endotoxins, 203–4, 208
endowment assurance, 253
endowment mortgage, 257
energy, 289–90, 371–81
    efficiency in the home, 263, 378–80, 392–5, 401
energy, in the body, 54–6, 58–9
engineers (building), 339
Enterprise Ireland, 171, 453
entertainment technology, 262, 302
environment, 286–90
    energy, 289–90, 371–81
Environment, Heritage and Local Government, Dept of, 230
environmental health officers, 230
enzymes, 4, 8
    food spoilage, 206–7
enzymic browning, 206
equality, 238, 241, 411, 430
    education, 420, 421
ergocalciferol, 37
ergonomics, 341, 349
ESB (Electricity Supply Board), 382
essential fatty acids, 29
European Communities Regulations (food), 231–2
European Consumer Centres, 293
evaporated milk, 102–3
exotoxins, 204, 208
expenditure, 246
export of food, 171–2
extended family, 300–1
extractor fans, 397–8

fabric finishes, 276, 277
fabrics, 273–8, 369
family, 300–22
    conflict in, 315–16
    financial management, 241–55
    management of resources, 234–40
    roles, 238, 303, 313–14, 410, 433–4
    social change and, 301–3, 314, 408–11
    types of, 300–1
    unemployment and, 442
Family Income Supplement, 245
family mediation, 311
fans, extractor, 397–8
farming, organic, 120
FÁS, 453
fat, composition tables, 58–9
fats, 135–9

animal fats, 77, 82
    lipids, 27–35
fatty acids, 27–35, 85
fermentation, 155–6
fibre (dietary), 23, 63, 70
    Irish eating habits, 169
fibre (textiles), 276, 369
fibreboard, 366
fibre optics, 404
filo pastry, 152
filtration, 387
finance for housing, 256–61
finance management, 241–55
Financial Regulator, 293
fire-resistant textiles, 276–8
fish, 84–9
    buying and storing, 86–7
    preserving and processing, 88–9
    recipe, 468
flame-retardant finishes, 277
flats, 326, 331
flavour, 161, 162
flavourings, 188
flexitime, 432
Floor Area Compliance Certificate (FACC), 342
floor plans, 351
floors, 352–5, 395
flour, 131–3
fluorescent lighting, 400–1
fluorescents, 274
fluoridation, 387
fluorocarbons, 368
foam formation, 10
Focus Ireland, 456
folic acid, 42, 50
food, 2–4
food additives, 186–92
food advertising, 3
food aesthetics, 161–2
food choices, 2–3
    Irish diet, 167–9
food composition tables, 58–9
food, dietary guidelines, 57–9
food, eating disorders, 70–1
food, eating patterns, 2–3
    adolescents, 62
    in Ireland, 167–9
food hygiene, 224–30
    regulations, 231
food industry in Ireland, 170–4
food labelling, 184–5, 231
food laws, 231–2
food packaging, 180–4
food poisoning, 207–10, 224
food preparation, 141, 159
food presentation, 161–2
food preservation, 212–23
food processing, 176–9
    fish, 88
    meat, 79–80

food processors, 264–5
food pyramid, 57
food regulations, 231–2
food requirements, 60–74
food safety, 224–30
food safety agencies, 229–30
Food Safety Authority of Ireland, 171, 230
food, sensory analysis, 161–6
food spoilage, 206–11
foreign investment, 453
Forfás, 453
fossil fuels, 371, 376
freeze drying, 220
freezing, 213–14
    blanching before, 207, 214
    commercial, 218, 222–3
    fish, 88
    meat, 79
    peas, 222–3
fridges, 266–8
frozen foods, 176–7
fructose, 16, 19
fruit, 118–20
    composition tables, 58–9
    preserves, 215–17
    recipes, 470–1, 475
    ripening, 206
    sauces, 150, 151
frying, 146
    smoke point, 31
fuel, 289–90
functional foods, 178
fungi, 194–9
furnishings, 364–5, 369
furniture, 362–4
    fire safety, 277–8
fuses, 384

Gaeltacht area house grant, 342
galactose, 16, 19
gallstones, 68
game, 76
garnishes, 150
gas, 373
    thermostats, 389
gelatinisation, 10–11, 21, 22
gender, 445
    equality, 241, 411, 421
    roles, 238, 314, 410–11, 433–4
generation conflict, 316
genetically modified food, 178–9
Georgian-style houses, 324–5
geothermal energy, 290
giro, 247
glass, 367–8
    containers, 180, 182–3
glazing, 93
gliadin, 8
global warming, 377
globulin, 9

glucose, 16, 19, 25
gluten, 8
    special diets, 3, 65, 130
glycerol, 27
glycogen, 18, 19, 22
GM food, 178–9
goitre, 49
Gothic-style houses, 325
gram staining test, 202–3
green areas, 327, 335
Green Dot symbol, 288
greenhouse effect, 377
grilling, 145
grills, 143
Guaranteed Irish symbol, 285
guarantees, 291

HACCP (hazard analysis and critical control point), 224–8
haemoglobin, 8, 45
haemorrhoids (piles), 70
halogen lamps, 400
hardboard, 366
hazard analysis, 224–8
hazard symbols, 286
HBV (high biological value) protein, 9, 64, 82, 85, 91
Health Acts, 232
Health and Children, Dept of, 229
Health and Safety Authority, 431
health insurance, 253
health levy, 244
health officers, 230
Health Regulation, 231
heart attack, 66
heart disease, 66–7, 77
heating, 388–92
    energy efficiency, 378
hedonic ranking tests, 163
hire purchase, 250
histogram, 164
Hollandaise sauce, 94
Homebond Certificate, 342
homelessness, 329, 449, 456
home ownership, 331
    compared to renting, 332–3
    schemes, 359, 334
Home-School-Community Liaison Scheme, 423
homogenisation, 102
hormones, 11
hot water cylinders, 382
    lagging jackets, 394
house building and design, 337–42
    room plans, 350–1
house insurance, 254
house prices, 333
house systems and services, 382–405
household appliances, 262–72
    energy efficiency, 263, 378
    safety, 159, 385
household finances, 241–55
housing, 324–42

choice of house, 259–60, 327–9, 340–1
energy efficiency, 263, 378–80
housing schemes, 258–9, 334
provision in Ireland, 258–60, 331–4
renting/buying comparison, 332–3
housing finance, 256–61
humectants, 189
humidity, 396
hydrochloric acid, 47
hydro-electric power, 374–5
hydrogen bonds, 6–7
hydrogenation, 31
hydrolysis, 6, 20, 21
hygiene, 224–30
hygroscopic property, 21
hyperglycaemia, 66
hypermarkets, 280
hypertension, 21
hypervitaminosis, 39
hypoglycaemia, 66

ice cream, vanilla, 474
IDA (Industrial Development Authority), 453
imported food, 172
impulse buying, 282
income, 241–6
industry, 431–2
inheritance, 321–2
inputs, 235–6
instant foods, 176–7
institutes of technology (ITs), 418
insulation, 379, 392–5
insulin, 66
insurance, 252–4
intellectual ability, 413
intellectual development, 445
interest rates
    loans, 249–50
    mortgages, 256, 257
    savings, 251–2
interior decorating, 358–61
interior design, 343–70
intestine, small, 12–13, 24, 33
iodine, 49
Irish diet, 167–9
Irish food industry, 170–4
Irish food safety agencies, 229–30
Irish industry, 431–2
Irish Standards Mark, 285
iron, 45–7
    Irish eating habits, 169
ironware, 367
irradiation, 124, 221–2
irritable bowel syndrome, 70
ISO standards, 227
isolation, 442
ITs (institutes of technology), 418

jam-making, 215–17
job satisfaction, 428

joules, 54, 56, 58–9
judicial separation, 311, 320–1
jute flooring, 358

kettles, 265–6
kilocalories and kilojoules, 54, 56, 58–9
kilowatts, 383
kinship, 298
kitchen appliances, 146–8, 262–72
    metals used, 367
    safety, 159, 385
kitchen design, 341
kitchen hygiene, 224–30
Kitemark, 285
kwashiorkor, 9, 12

labelling
    energy efficiency, 263
    fire-resistant fabrics, 277–8
    food, 184–5, 231
    quality and safety symbols, 285–6
    recycling symbols, 288
    textile care, 275
lactalbumin, 9
lactic acid, 99
lactoglobulin, 9
lactose, 17–18, 19, 20, 99
lagging jackets, 394
laminated floors, 354–5
landlords, 332
lasagne, 461–2
laundry, 274–6
    energy efficiency, 263, 378
law
    building standards, 342
    consumer protection, 290–1
    education and special needs, 420
    employment, 431–2
    equality, 411
    family, 320–2
    food, 231–2
    marriage, 308–11
    rented accommodation, 332
LBV (low biological value) protein, 9
lead, 192
Leaving Certificate, 416–17, 430
lecithin, 8, 94
lecithinlipase, 33
leek and bacon quiche, 466
legumes, 128
leisure, 409, 443–8
leisure centres, 446–7
lentils, 128
letting agency, 332
life assurance, 253
life cycle, 238
light, 403
lightbulbs, 399–402
lighting, 398–404
    energy efficiency, 379, 401

street lighting, 335
linoleum, 355
lipids, 27–35
lipoprotein, 8, 67
Listeria monocytogenes, 209
liver, and digestion, 13, 25, 33
livetin, 9
loans, 249–50
local authority housing, 258–9, 334
lone parents, 238, 301, 450, 454
low-fat spreads, 137–8, 178
loyalty schemes, 282

MABS (Monetary Advice and Budgeting Service), 246, 454–5
macronutrients, 3
'mad cow disease', 81
Maillard reaction, 10, 20, 22
maintenance charges (housing), 333
maize, 134, 179
malnutrition, 4
    in Ireland, 169
    mineral deficiency, 45–9
    protein deficiency, 12
    vitamin deficiency, 36–43
maltase, 24
maltose, 17–18, 19, 24
management systems, 234–40
marasmus, 12
marble, 354
margarine, 137, 178
marketing, 279, 282
marriage, 307–12, 410
Marriage and Relationship Counselling Service, 309–10
mattresses, 363
mayonnaise, 94
MDF fibreboard, 366
meal planning, 140
    modifying recipes, 160
    sample daily menu, 72–3
meat, 76–81
    processed, 79–80
    recipes, 460–4, 466
medical cards, 455
melamine, 368
meringues, 10
    fruit meringue roulade, 475
metabolic rate, 4
metabolism, 4
metals, 367
microbiology, 193–205
micronutrients, 3
micro-organisms, 193–4, 207
microwave ovens, 147–8, 269–71
milk, 99–105
    dried, 103, 219
    substitutes, 101, 116
    types of milk, 101–3
minced meat recipes, 460–2
minerals, 45–51
miso, 116

money management, 241–55
    advice, 454–5
monogamy, 307
monosaccharides, 16–17, 19, 25
monosodium glutamate, 188
Montessori schools, 414
mores, 298
mortgages, 256–9
motor insurance, 254
moulds, 194–7, 199, 207
mucor, 196
multiple chain shops, 281
mushrooms, 198
mycelium, 195
mycoprotein, 117
mycotoxins, 194, 204
myoglobin, 46
myosin, 9

naíonraí, 436
napthoquinones, 38–9
National Anti-Poverty Strategy (NAPS), 451, 455
National Council for Curriculum and Assessment (NCCA), 415, 420
National Disability Authority, 317
National Educational Psychological Service (NEPS), 420
National Education Welfare Board, 424
National Housing Policy, 260
National Standards Authority of Ireland (NSAI), 285, 292
natural floor coverings, 358
needs of children, 412–13
negative equity, 333
niacin, 41, 131
nitrates, 221
nitrogen oxide, 376
noise pollution, 289
Nolan's, 173
non-renewable energy, 289, 371–4
norms, 298
NSP (non-starch polysaccharide), 19, 21–2
nuclear family, 300
nullity of marriage, 310
nurseries, 414, 437
nurturing, 304
nutrition, 3–4
    guidelines and requirements, 57–74
    Irish survey, 167–9
nutritional labelling, 184–5
nutritional supplements in food, 178, 190
nuts, 127
    composition tables, 59
nvCJD, 81
nylon, 276, 357, 369

oats, 134
obesity, 68
offal, 80
Office of the Director of Consumer Affairs, 230, 292
oil, 372
oil, cooking, 135–9

olive oil, 135
Ombudsman, 292
Omega-3 fatty acids, 29, 85
one-parent families, 238, 301, 450, 454
One-Parent Family Payment, 454
online banking, 248
online shopping, 291
organic fruit and vegetables, 120
osteomalacia, 38, 47
osteoporosis, 69
outdoor lighting, 404
outputs, 237
Outreach Team, 456
ovalbumin, 9
ovens, 143
overdrafts, 249
oxalic acid, 47, 48
oxidase, 124, 206
ozone layer, 377

packaging, 180–4
paint, 359–60
paired preference tests, 163
pancreas, 13, 24, 33
paper packaging, 180, 182–3
parasites, 193, 200
parathormone, 48
parenting, 313, 315, 410
passion fruit meringue roulade, 475
pasta, 133–4
    recipes, 461–3
pasteurisation, 102, 219
pastry, 151–5
pattern, interior design, 346–7
PAYE, 242–4
paying for goods and services, 246–50
peas, freezing and canning, 222–3
peat, 373
pectin, 18, 120
    jam-making, 215–16
    testing for, 216
peers, 414
pellagra, 41
penicillium, 197
pensions, 245
pepsin, 12, 13
peptidase, 12, 13
peptide links, 6
peptides, 12
peptones, 13
peristalsis, 19
pesticides, 192
PET label, 288
phenolase, 123
phenolics, 368
phosphorus, 48
photosynthesis, 16
photovoltaic technology, 375
phycomycetes, 196
phytic acid, 47, 48

pickles and chutneys, 217
pie chart, 164
piles (haemorrhoids), 70
pillows, 365
pineapple upside down cake, 470
planning permission, 338–9
plaque, 68
plastic, 368
        food packaging, 182–3
plasticity, 30
playschools, 414
PLC (Post-Leaving Certificate), 416
plugs, wiring, 385
plywood, 366
poaching, 144
pollution, 289
polyandry, 308
polyester, 357, 369
polyethylene, 368
polygamy, 307–8
polygyny, 308
polyphosphates, 189
polysaccharides, 18–19, 21–2
polystyrene, 182, 368
polyunsaturated fat, 135
Post, An, saving with, 251–2
Post-Leaving Certificate (PLC), 416
potassium, 48
potato and vegetable pie, 467
pot-roasting, 145
poultry, 82–3, 224
poverty, 449–58
        poverty cycle, 442, 450
        poverty line, 449
        poverty trap, 451
preference tests, 163
pregnancy, and diet, 63
pre-school education, 414, 422–3, 436
        childcare, 435–7
presentation of food, 161–2
preservation of food, 212–23
preservatives in food, 187, 220–1
preserves, 215–17
pressure cooking, 146–7
pressure group, 433
primary schools, 415, 423
Proban, 277
probiotics, 178
profiteroles, 472
prolamines, 8
property insurance, 254
proportion in interior design, 349
protection order, 320
protein, 5–15, 58–9
        alternative protein foods, 115–17
        HBV protein, 9, 64, 82, 85, 91
PRSI (pay-related social insurance), 244
public analyst laboratories, 230
puff pastry, 152
pulses, 121, 122

pyrex, 368
pyridoxine, 41

quality standards (ISO), 227
quality symbols, 81, 95, 285–6
quartz lamps, 400
quiche, bacon and leek, 466
quorn, 117

radiation of food (irradiation), 124, 221–2
radiation of heat, 142–3, 391
radiators, 390
radioactive residues, 191
rag rolling, 360
raising agents, 153–5
rancidity, 31
ranking and rating tests, 163
rapeseed, 376
raspberry meringue roulade, 475
recession, 441
recipes, 459–78
        modifying, 160
reconstituted family, 301
recycling, 183, 287–8
Reference Nutrient Intake (RNI), 58
refrigerators, 266–8
refuse collection, 335
regulations, food, 231–2
Rehab, 317
religion, and food, 2, 64, 140
renewable energy, 289–90, 374–6
rennin, 7
Rental Subsidy Scheme, 334
rented accommodation, 258, 332–3
        compared to buying, 332–3
research, consumer, 283
residual current devices (RCDs), 384
resource management, 234–40
responsibilities of consumer, 284, 286–90
retail outlets, 280–1
retail psychology, 281–2
retinol, 36
rhizopus, 196
rhythm in interior design, 349
riboflavin, 40, 65
rice, 134
rickets, 38, 47
rights of children, 315
rights of consumer, 283–4, 290–4
ripening, 206
roasting, 145
role, 298, 313
        conflict, 313, 434
        confusion, 442
        dual role, 238, 434
        family roles, 313–14
        gender roles, 238, 314, 410–11, 433–4
        overload, 434
roulade, 475
roux sauces, 150

recipe, 462
rural depopulation, 408
rural unemployment, 441

saccharin, 190
safety
electricity, 384–6, 402
flame-retardant fabrics, 276–8
food, 224–30
food agencies, 229–30
kitchen equipment, 159, 385
lighting, 402
smoke point, 31
symbols, 286
workplace, 431
safety order, 320
St Vincent de Paul (SVP), 455–6
Sale of Food and Drugs Acts, 231
Sale of Goods and Supply of Services Act, 290–1
sales techniques, 281–2
Salmonella, 209
salt, 49, 63
saprophytes, 193, 200
saturated fat, 135
Irish eating habits, 169
in meat, 77, 82
saucepans, 367
sauces, 150–1
cheese sauce, 462
saving, 250–2
schools and education, 409, 412–26
scurvy, 39
seafood, 84–5
secondary schools, 415–16
seitin, 117
self-esteem, 428
sensory analysis of food, 161–6
separation, marriage, 311, 320–1
service industry, 431
services in houses, 382–405
shared ownership scheme, 259
shellfish, 84–5
shepherd's pie (hygiene and safety), 226–7
shopping, 279–95
shops, types of, 280–1
shortcrust pastry, 151
showers, electric, 384
silk, 369
Simon Community, 456
single parents, 238, 301, 450, 454
sisal flooring, 358
sites for building, 337, 338
SLÁN Survey, 167–9
Small Claims Court, 293–4
smell of food, 161, 162
smog, 376
smoke point, 31
smoking, 62, 67
smoking fish, 88
social change, 298, 301–3, 314, 408–11

social class, 241 *see also* socio-economic status
social development, 445
social housing, 334
Social Inclusion Programme, 455
social mobility, 299
social welfare, 244–5, 409–10, 454
initiatives creating employment, 453
poverty trap and, 451
socialisation, 298, 412
society, 299
Society of St Vincent de Paul (SVP), 455–6
socio-economic status, 239, 241, 299
education, 420–3
leisure, 443–4
work, 428
sociology, 298–9
sodium, 49
soft furnishings, 364–5, 369
solar energy, 290, 375
solicitors, 340
sorbic acid, 187
soufflé, chocolate, 473
soup, 148–50
recipe, 465
sour cream, 109
soya beans, 115–16
soya milk, 101, 116
soya protein, 64, 116
soya sauce, 116
special needs, 316–18
Disability Allowance, 454
education, 409, 419–20
housing, 329
special offers, 282
special schools, 420
spoilage of food, 206–11
sponging, 360
spores, 194–6, 201
sport, 446
spreads, dairy, 137–8, 178
stabilisers, 32, 189
stamp duty, 333
standing orders, 248
Staphylococcus aureus, 209
star diagrams, 164
starch, 19, 21, 23
status, 299
Stay in School Retention Initiative, 423
steaming, 144
steel, stainless, 367
stencilling, 360
stereotyping, 314, 445
sterilisation, 219
sterilised milk, 102
stewing, 144
stir frying, 146
chicken and vegetable stir fry, 464
stock, 148–9
stomach, 12–13
stopcock, 387

storage, 363
storage heaters, 392
strawberry cheesecake, 471
strawberry jam, 216
street lighting, 335
suburbs, 331
Succession Act, 321
sucrose, 17–18, 19
suet crust pastry, 152
sugar, 19–21, 23
sugar levels in blood, 66
sulphur dioxide, 221, 376
sun drying, 220
supermarkets, 280
Supplementary Welfare Allowance, 245
surveyors, 339
sustainability, 287
sweeteners, 190
sweet sauces, 150
symbiosis, 194
symmetrical balance, 348
syrup, 20, 22

takeaways, 176–7
    in Ireland, 167, 169
tannin, 47
tartrazine, 187
taste, 161, 162
tax, 242–4, 258
teacher training colleges, 418
Teagasc, 170
technological changes, 301–2
teenagers, 313, 315
    dietary guidelines, 61–2
teeth, 47, 68–9
telephone banking, 248
tenderising, 141
term loans, 250
terracotta tiles, 354
textiles, 273–8, 369
texture, 348
texture of food, 161, 162
textured vegetable protein (TVP), 116
thermo expansion, 391
thermogenesis, 55
thermoplastics, 368
thermostats, 389
thiamine, 40
third-level education, 418
throughputs, 236
tiles, 354, 361
tin, 367
tinned food *see* canned food
tints, 344
tocopherol, 38
tofu, 116
tones, 344
tower blocks, 326
towns, growth of, 331
toxins, 203–4

aflatoxins, 207
    food poisoning, 208–10
    mycotoxins, 194, 204
trace elements, 45
transition year, 416
transport systems, 335
Travellers, 423
triglycerides, 27
truffles, 198
trypsin, 12, 13
Tudor-style houses, 325
tungsten bulbs, 399–400
turf, 373
TVP (textured vegetable protein), 116

UHT cream, 109
UHT milk, 102
under-floor heating, 392
undernutrition, 4 *see also* malnutrition
unemployment, 411, 440–2
universities, 418
unsaturated fat, 135
upholstery, 364
upside down cake, 470
urban growth, 331, 408
urine, 12

vacuum packing, 80
values, 238, 299
    consumers, 279, 282
vanilla ice cream, 474
vegans, 64
vegetable oils, 135–9
vegetables, 121–6
    canning, 222–3
    freezing, 214, 222–3
    organic, 120
    vegetable and potato pie, 467
    vegetable curry, 469
    vegetable soup, 465
vegetarians, 63–5, 115–17
    recipes, 465, 467, 469
ventilation, house, 395–8
vinaigrette, 94
vinegar, 221
vinyl floor coverings, 355
violence, domestic, 320
viruses, 204
viscose, 276, 369
vitamins, 36–44
    A, 36–7, 119
    B group, 40–3, 50, 65, 131
    C, 39, 47, 119, 125, 141
    D, 37–8, 48
    E, 38
    K, 38–9, 50
    relationship with minerals, 50
vitellin, 9
vocational schools, 416, 424
Vocational Training Opportunities Scheme (VTOS), 419, 424

voltage, 383
voluntary housing, 334
voluntary organisations, 432–3, 455–6
voluntary work, 427, 432–3, 446

wage, minimum, 410
wall finishes, 358–61
wall insulation, 393–4
wallpaper, 360–1
wall tiles, 361
washing (laundry), 274–6
    energy efficiency, 263, 378
waste, 183, 287–8, 335
water, 52, 386–8
    energy efficiency, 379
    energy from, 374–5
    house supply, 386–8
    pollution, 289
    treatment, 386–7
wattage, 383
weaning, 61
wells, 387
wheat, 131
    durum wheat, 133–4
wheat protein (seitan), 117
whisking, 10
wills, 321–2
wind energy, 289, 290, 374

windows and heat loss, 394–5
women, changing roles, 238, 241, 314, 410–11, 430, 433–4
wood, 366
    floors, 354–5
wool, 276, 369
    carpets, 357
work, 427–39
    creating employment initiatives, 452–4
    equality, 241, 411, 430
    family and work, 241, 409, 433–4
    income and tax, 241–4, 410
    minimum wage, 410
    unpaid and voluntary, 427, 432–3
    work ethic, 428

yeast, 193, 198–9
    in baking, 154–5
yoghurt, 110–11, 221
yoghurt drinks, 178
Young Woman's Aftercare Project, 456
Young Person's Employment Act, 432
Youthreach, 423–4

zinc, 49, 65
zone heating, 390
zygospore, 195–6

For permission to reproduce photographs the author and publisher gratefully acknowledge the following:

ALAMY: 2, 21T, 49, 54T, 61, 62, 67, 68, 69B, 78, 108, 110, 112, 118, 121, 133, 149L, 152C, 152B, 154, 172, 179, 185R, 196, 197, 220, 225, 234, 246, 249, 260, 263, 267, 271, 273, 274, 289, 290, 301R, 304, 307B, 314, 324, 325TL, 325BL, 325TR, 326, 328, 329, 332, 338, 348, 350, 354, 358, 359, 360, 361, 362, 363, 366, 367, 372, 374, 375R, 401, 404L, 404C, 409, 412, 414, 415, 419L, 432, 435, 436, 440, 441, 443, 444, 449, 452, 454; AN POST: 252; ANTHONY BLAKE: 84TR, 180; AVONMORE: 101; BROWN THOMAS: 280B; CONSUMER CHOICE: 293; CORBIS: 114, 303L, 325BR, 344, 344, 344, 344, 346B, 347, 355, 358, 365, 410, 419R, 473; DAIRYGOLD: 178B; FLORA: 106, 138; FRESH FOOD IMAGES: 469; GETTY: 8L, 21B, 29R, 38, 79, 84BR, 149R, 206, 215, 216, 238, 300, 301L, 303R, 321, 349, 358, 364, 365, 375L, 398, 411, 446R; HOVIS: 155; IMAGEFILE: 8R, 36, 42, 46L, 54B, 55, 60, 69T, 80L, 84L, 84C, 116, 117, 152T, 214, 241, 256, 313, 315, 317, 404R, 429, 446L, 460, 468, 471, 476; LUAS: 335; NEIL RYAN: 92, 278, 280T; NOLANS SEAFOOD: 173; ODLUMS: 132; PA Photos: 307TL, 307TC, 307TR; PANOS: 308; REPORT DIGITAL: 421; SCIENCE PHOTO LIBRARY: 9, 39, 40, 41, 47, 70, 71, 376, 377, 384; SIMON COMMUNITY: 427; SPORTSFILE: 298, 445; STOCKFOOD: 3, 20, 46R, 80R; TOPFOTO: 29L; TRINITY COLLEGE: 418; YAKULT: 178T.

The author and publisher have made every effort to trace all copyright holders, but if any has been inadvertently overlooked we would be pleased to make the necessary arrangement at the first opportunity.